Developmental Mathematics:

A Modular Curriculum for North Carolina
Second Printing

PROPORTION, RATIO, RATE AND PERCENTAGE
DMA 030

ALAN S. TUSSY
CITRUS COLLEGE

R. DAVID GUSTAFSON
ROCK VALLEY COLLEGE

DIANE R. KOENIG
ROCK VALLEY COLLEGE

BROOKS/COLE
CENGAGE Learning

Brazil • Japan • Korea • Mexico • Singapore • Spain • United Kingdom • United States

Developmental Mathematics: A Modular Curriculum for North Carolina, Second Printing: Proportion, Ratio, Rate and Percentage
Alan S. Tussy, R. David Gustafson, Diane R. Koenig

Publisher: Charlie Van Wagner

Senior Developmental Editor: Danielle Derbenti

Senior Development Editor for Market Strategies: Rita Lombard

Assistant Editor: Stefanie Beeck

Editorial Assistant: Jennifer Cordoba

Media Editor: Heleny Wong

Marketing Manager: Gordon Lee

Marketing Assistant: Angela Kim

Marketing Communications Manager: Katy Malatesta

Content Project Manager: Jennifer Risden

Creative Director: Rob Hugel

Art Director: Vernon Boes

Print Buyer: Linda Hsu

Rights Acquisitions Account Manager, Text: Mardell Glinksi-Schultz

Rights Acquisitions Account Manager, Image: Don Schlotman

Text Designer: Diane Beasley

Photo Researcher: Bill Smith Group

Illustrators: Lori Heckelman; Graphic World Inc; Integra Software Services

Cover Designers: Ryan and Susan Stranz

Cover Image: Background: © Hemera/Thinkstock. © iStockphoto/Thinkstock.

Compositor: Integra Software Services

ISBN-13: 978-1-285-14054-4

ISBN-10: 1-285-14054-0

Brooks/Cole
20 Davis Drive
Belmont, CA 94002-3098
USA

Cengage Learning is a leading provider of customized learning solutions with office locations around the globe, including Singapore, the United Kingdom, Australia, Mexico, Brazil, and Japan. Locate your local office at **www.cengage.com/global**

Cengage Learning products are represented in Canada by Nelson Education, Ltd.

To learn more about Brooks/Cole, visit **www.cengage.com/brookscole**

Purchase any of our products at your local college store or at our preferred online store **www.CengageBrain.com**

Printed in the United States of America
1 2 3 4 5 6 7 14 13

To my lovely wife, Liz,

thank you for your insight and encouragement

ALAN S. TUSSY

■

To my grandchildren:

Daniel, Tyler, Spencer, Skyler, Garrett, and Jake Gustafson

R. DAVID GUSTAFSON

■

To my husband and my best friend, Brian Koenig

DIANE R. KOENIG

■

PREFACE

Developmental Mathematics: A Modular Curriculum for North Carolina is a fully integrated learning system that has been aligned to the redesigned curriculum established by the North Carolina Developmental Math Redesign Task Force. With the helpful input from instructors across the state, we have put together a program that presents problems in a meaningful context and explains the "why" behind problem solving in order to promote conceptual and sound mathematical learning. This is one of eight modules for the DMA curriculum, and is supported by a highly customizable online homework system that includes assessment tools, personalized study plans, and algorithmically generated problems to reinforce learning.

One central goal of the North Carolina Redesign Task Force was to create a curriculum with streamlined content in a modular format that could be completed in one academic year. Students can purchase only the modules needed for their developmental math requirements, and can work at a pace that is appropriate for their needs. Instructors can easily use this content with different classroom delivery methods, including self-paced Emporium labs, seated courses, and online or hybrid settings.

Another principle of the new curriculum is to develop students' conceptual understanding of mathematics through the use of contextually based problems. To that end, we have added the following features:

- New **Applied Introductions** have been written to introduce sections that are more applications-driven.
- Within the *Study Sets*, **Applications** problems and examples have been added and written to align with the NCCCS learning outcomes.
- **Concept Extensions** have been written and added to the *Study Sets* to ensure that key concepts meet the NCCCS curriculum.

In addition to new conceptual features that we have written specifically for North Carolina, we have added the following features to help guide students toward mastery of each module:

- **Course Information Sheets** start each module. These offer an explanation of the NCCCS process and ask questions that guide students to the practical knowledge that they will need in order to complete the program.
- **Are You Ready?** quizzes have been added to the beginning of each section to test students on the basic skills they will need in order to be successful with that section.
- **Module Tests**, appearing at the end of each module, have been carefully constructed to include the NCCCS learning outcomes required to pass the mastery test.

All content in these modules is supported by a corresponding prebuilt course in Enhanced WebAssign®, Cengage Learning's powerful online homework solution. Enhanced WebAssign® (EWA) engages students with immediate feedback on algorithmically generated versions of problems for unlimited practice. The *Show My Work* feature allows students to upload a file with the problem worked out, or to use a simple math palette to show their steps–helping you assess whether they understand the steps to solving a problem. The North Carolina EWA course has been prebuilt with a Personalized Study Plan, assignments, homework, and a Pre and Post Test for every module. Instructors can use the prebuilt course as is, or can customize or add material with ease.

A corresponding and fully interactive eBook, the Cengage YouBook, is integrated into the Enhanced WebAssign® course, and offers students convenient access to all module content. This powerful eBook lets you tailor the content to fit your course and provide your students with the ultimate learning experience with note-taking, highlighting, book-marking and search capabilities. Link students to your lecture notes, audio summaries, and engage them through conceptual tutorial videos as well as YouTube clips.

Cengage Learning is committed to providing unparallel service and training for faculty.

- **TeamUP Faculty Programs** help you reach and engage students by offering peer-to-peer consulting on curriculum and assessment, workshops, and professional development conferences.

TeamUP Faculty Program Consultants are a team of educators who understand your challenges whether your classroom is on-ground, online, or both.

Cengage Learning's team of **Faculty Advisors** are full-time educators and expert teachers in a diverse range of subject areas. They are available to share their experience on using Cengage Learning solutions and instructional best practices developed in their own classroom.

Explore all the ways TeamUP Faculty Programs can help you launch a new program or support your continuous improvement efforts. http://www.cengage.com/teamup/programs/ offers service and support from a dedicated team of experts to ensure your success using Enhanced WebAssign, including help with course set up, and more. http://www.cengage.com/coursecare/

TRUSTED FEATURES

- **Study Sets** found in each section offer a multifaceted approach to practicing and reinforcing the concepts taught in each section. They are designed for students to methodically build their knowledge of the section concepts, from basic recall to increasingly complex problem solving, through reading, writing, and thinking mathematically.

  Vocabulary—Each *Study Set* begins with the important *Vocabulary* discussed in that section. The fill-in-the-blank vocabulary problems emphasize the main concepts taught in the chapter and provide the foundation for learning and communicating the language of algebra.

  Concepts—In *Concepts,* students are asked about the specific subskills and procedures necessary to successfully complete the *Guided Practice* and *Try It Yourself* problems that follow.

  Notation—In *Notation,* the students review the new symbols introduced in a section. Often, they are asked to fill in steps of a sample solution. This strengthens their ability to read and write mathematics and prepares them for the *Guided Practice* problems by modeling solution formats.

  Guided Practice—The problems in *Guided Practice* are linked to an associated worked example or objective from that section. This feature promotes student success by referring them to the proper examples if they encounter difficulties solving homework problems.

  Try It Yourself—To promote problem recognition, the *Try It Yourself* problems are thoroughly mixed and are *not* linked to worked examples, giving students an opportunity to practice decision-making and strategy selection as they would when taking a test or quiz.

Applications—The *Applications* provide students the opportunity to apply their newly acquired algebraic skills to relevant and interesting real-life situations.

Writing—The *Writing* problems help students build mathematical communication skills.

Review—The *Review* problems consist of randomly selected problems from previous chapters. These problems are designed to keep students' successfully mastered skills up-to-date before they move on to the next section.

- **Detailed Author Notes** that guide students along in a step-by-step process appear in the solutions to every worked example.
- **Think It Through** features make the connection between mathematics and student life. These relevant topics often require algebra skills from the chapter to be applied to a real-life situation. Topics include tuition costs, student enrollment, job opportunities, credit cards, and many more.
- **Using Your Calculator** is an optional feature that is designed for instructors who wish to use calculators as part of the instruction in this course. This feature introduces keystrokes and shows how scientific and graphing calculators can be used to solve problems. In the *Study Sets,* icons are used to denote problems that may be solved using a calculator.

ACKNOWLEDGMENTS

We want to express our gratitude to all those who helped with this project: Steve Odrich, Mary Lou Wogan, Paul McCombs, Maria H. Andersen, Sheila Pisa, Laurie McManus, Alexander Lee, Ed Kavanaugh, Karl Hunsicker, Cathy Gong, Dave Ryba, Terry Damron, Marion Hammond, Lin Humphrey, Doug Keebaugh, Robin Carter, Tanja Rinkel, Bob Billups, Jeff Cleveland, Jo Morrison, Sheila White, Jim McClain, Paul Swatzel, Matt Stevenson, Carole Carney, Joyce Low, Rob Everest, David Casey, Heddy Paek, Ralph Tippins, Mo Trad, Eagle Zhuang, and the Citrus College library staff (including Barbara Rugeley) for their help with this project. Your encouragement, suggestions, and insight have been invaluable to us.

We would also like to express our thanks to the Cengage Learning editorial, marketing, production, and design staff for helping us craft this new edition: Danielle Derbenti, Michael Stranz, Kim Fry, Heleny Wong, Charlie Van Wagner, Jill Staut, Liz Kendall, Marc Bove, Gordon Lee, Rita Lombard, Angela Hodge, Angela Kim, Maureen Ross, Jennifer Risden, Vernon Boes, Diane Beasley, Carol O'Connell, Graphic World and Integra Software Services.

Additionally, we would like to say that authoring a textbook is a tremendous undertaking. Producing a product of this scale that is customized to match a brand new curriculum would not have been possible without the thoughtful feedback and support from the following colleagues from throughout North Carolina listed below. Their contributions to this edition have shaped the creation of this book in countless ways.

A special acknowledgment is due to Lisa Key Brown, of Central Carolina Community College. Lisa's experience in the Developmental Math classroom, detailed knowledge of the new North Carolina curriculum, and expertise in using Enhanced WebAssign has been invaluable to us as we have prepared this developmental math program.

Alan S. Tussy
R. David Gustafson
Diane R. Koenig

North Carolina Developmental Mathematics Advisory Board

Kochi Angar, *Nash Community College*
Tim Beaver, *Isothermal Community College*
Lisa Key Brown, *Central Carolina Community College*
Ann DeBoever, *Catawba Valley Community College*
Robin Hendrix, *Surry Community College*
Brenda C. Keller, *Central Carolina Community College*
Susan Lauer, *South Piedmont Community College*
Judy McInerney, *Sandhills Community College*
Nancy Paxton, *Sandhills Community College*
Molly Jane Ray, *Vance-Granville Community College*
Karen H. Sanders, *Piedmont Community College*
Calvin Stansbury, *Halifax Community College*
Elaine Tucker, *Sandhills Community College*
Solomon L. Willis, *Cleveland Community College*
Susan Worth, *Surry Community College*
Sue Zimmerman, *Vance-Granville Community College*

Content Reviewers

Darla Aguilar, *Pima Community College*
Sheila Anderson, *Housatonic Community College*
David Behrman, *Somerset Community College*
Michael Branstetter, *Hartnell College*
Joseph A. Bruno, Jr., *Community College of Allegheny County*
Eric Compton, *Brookdale Community College*
Joy Conner, *Tidewater Community College*
Ruth Dalrymple, *Saint Philip's College*
Nathalie Darden, *Brookdale Community College*
John D. Driscoll, *Middlesex Community College*
LaTonya Ellis, *Bishop State Community College*
Steven Felzer, *Lenoir Community College*
Rhoderick Fleming, *Wake Technical Community College*
Heather Gallacher, *Cleveland State University*
Kathirave Giritharan, *John A. Logan College*
Marilyn Green, *Merritt College and Diablo Valley College*
Joseph W. Giuciardi, *Community College of Allegheny County*
Geoff Hagopian, *College of the Desert*
Deborah Hanus, *Brookhaven College*
A.T. Hayashi, *Oxnard College*
Cheryl Hobneck, *Illinois Valley Community College*
Todd J. Hoff, *Wisconsin Indianhead Technical College*
Susan Kautz, *Cy-Fair College*
Jack Keating, *Massasoit Community College*
Russ Alan Killingsworth, *Seattle Pacific University*
Sandy Lofstock, *Saint Petersburg College–Tarpon Springs*
Lynn Marecek, *Santa Ana College*
Lois Martin, *Massasoit Community College*
Mikal McDowell, *Cedar Valley College*
Chris Mirbaha, *The Community College of Baltimore County*
K. Maggie Pasqua, *Brookdale Community College*
Gregory Perkins, *Hartnell College*
Euguenia Peterson, *City Colleges of Chicago–Richard Daley*
Carol Ann Poore, *Hinds Community College*
Christopher Quarles, *Shoreline Community College*
George Reed, *Angelina College*

Patricia C. Rome, *Delgado Community College*
Patricia B. Roux, *Delgado Community College*
Rebecca Rozario, *Brookdale Community College*
John Squires, *Cleveland State Community College*
Sharon Testone, *Onondaga Community College*
Bill Thompson, *Red Rocks Community College*
Barbara Tozzi, *Brookdale Community College*
Donna Tupper, *Community College of Baltimore County–Essex*
Andreana Walker, *Calhoun Community College*
Jane Wampler, *Housatonic Community College*
Arminda Wey, *Brookdale Community College*
Mary Lou Wogan, *Klamath Community College*
Valerie Wright, *Central Piedmont Community College*
Kevin Yokoyama, *College of the Redwoods*
Mary Young, *Brookdale Community College*

ABOUT THE AUTHORS

Alan S. Tussy

Alan Tussy teaches all levels of developmental mathematics at Citrus College in Glendora, California. He has written nine math books—a paperback series and a hardcover series. A meticulous, creative, and visionary teacher who maintains a keen focus on his students' greatest challenges, Alan Tussy is an extraordinary author, dedicated to his students' success. Alan received his Bachelor of Science degree in Mathematics from the University of Redlands and his Master of Science degree in Applied Mathematics from California State University, Los Angeles. He has taught up and down the curriculum from Prealgebra to Differential Equations. He is currently focusing on the developmental math courses. Professor Tussy is a member of the American Mathematical Association of Two-Year Colleges.

R. David Gustafson

R. David Gustafson is Professor Emeritus of Mathematics at Rock Valley College in Illinois and coauthor of several best-selling math texts, including Gustafson/Frisk's *Beginning Algebra, Intermediate Algebra, Beginning and Intermediate Algebra: A Combined Approach, College Algebra,* and the Tussy/Gustafson developmental mathematics series. His numerous professional honors include Rock Valley Teacher of the Year and Rockford's Outstanding Educator of the Year. He earned a Master of Arts from Rockford College in Illinois, as well as a Master of Science from Northern Illinois University.

Diane R. Koenig

Diane Koenig received a Bachelor of Science degree in Secondary Math Education from Illinois State University in 1980. She began her career at Rock Valley College in 1981, when she became the Math Supervisor for the newly formed Personalized Learning Center. Earning her Master's Degree in Applied Mathematics from Northern Illinois University, Ms. Koenig in 1984 had the distinction of becoming the first full-time woman mathematics faculty member at Rock Valley College. In addition to being nominated for AMATYC's Excellence in Teaching Award, Diane Koenig was chosen as the Rock Valley College Faculty of the Year by her peers in 2005, and, in 2006, she was awarded the NISOD Teaching Excellence Award as well as the Illinois Mathematics Association of Community Colleges Award for Teaching Excellence. In addition to her teaching, Ms. Koenig has been an active member of the Illinois Mathematics Association of Community Colleges (IMACC). As a member, she has served on the board of directors, on a state-level task force rewriting the course outlines for the developmental mathematics courses, and as the association's newsletter editor.

Module 3: Ratios, Rates, Proportions, and Percents

DMA 030

Nick White/Getty Images

from *Campus to Careers*

Chef

Chefs prepare and cook a wide range of foods—from soups, snacks, and salads to main dishes, side dishes, and desserts. They work in a variety of restaurants and food service kitchens. They measure, mix, and cook ingredients according to recipes, using a variety of equipment and tools. They are also responsible for directing the tasks of other kitchen workers, estimating food requirements, and ordering food supplies.

In **Problem 104** of **Study Set 3.2,** you will see how a chef can use proportions to determine the correct amounts of each ingredient needed to make a large batch of brownies.

JOB TITLE:
Chef
EDUCATION: Training programs are available through culinary schools, 2- or 4-year college degree programs, and the armed forces.
JOB OUTLOOK: Job openings are expected to be plentiful through 2016.
ANNUAL EARNINGS: The average (median) salary in 2008 was $55,976.
FOR MORE INFORMATION:
www.searchbydegree.com/chef-cook-career.html

Course Information Sheet

Overview

Module 3: Ratios, Rates, Proportions, and Percents is one of the eight modules that make up the North Carolina Community College System Developmental Math Program. This program is for students who want to meet the prerequisites for the math requirements for their two year degree, or for those who are planning to transfer to a college or university. It is designed to allow you to complete the required developmental math courses at a pace that is appropriate to your needs and knowledge.

Placement

The diagnostic test that you took to enter the NCCCS Developmental Math Program has indentified your mathematical strengths and weaknesses. The test results that you received indicate which of the eight modules you are required to complete before you can enroll in more advanced mathematics courses, such as Precalculus and Statistics. It is important to note that any modules you are required to take must be taken in numerical order. For example, if the diagnostic test indicated that you need to take Modules 3 and 4, you must successfully complete Module 3 before you can register for Module 4.

Mastery

A core principle of the NCCCS Developmental Math Program is the concept of mastery of the material. To show mastery, students need to successfully complete all coursework in a module, as well as pass a final assessment exam.

Getting started

Starting a new course can be exciting, but it might also make you a bit nervous. In order to be successful, you need a plan. Here are some suggestions: Make time for the course, know what is expected, build a support system. You can begin to form your personal plan for success by answering questions on the next page.

1. What is your instructor's name? What is his/her phone number and email address?

2. When and where does your class meet?

3. What are the days and times of your instructor's office hours? Where does he/she hold office hours?

4. Does your campus have a math tutoring center? If so, where is it located and what are its hours of operation? Is the tutoring free? Do you need your instructor to sign a form before you begin at the tutoring center?

5. What other ways are there for you to receive additional help with this module?

6. What are the names, phone numbers, and email addresses of three students in your class that you can contact for help if you have missed class, want to form a study group, or have questions regarding a homework assignment?

7. How many hours does your instructor feel you should expect to spend on this course each week?

8. Did you write down your WebAssign user id and password in a safe place where you can find it should you forget?

9. On what day and at what time is the *final module assessment exam*?

10. What percent correct is needed to pass the *final module assessment exam*? How many times can the *final module assessment exam* be taken?

SECTION 3.1

Applications Introduction: Mathematical Comparisons

We make comparisons all the time in our daily lives. For example, when deciding on which college to attend, students compare the educational programs that are offered. Television viewers compare the performances of contestants on shows like *American Idol* and *America's Got Talent.* As consumers, we compare foods, automobiles, and places to vacation. The examples are endless.

Comparions can be quite useful. They help us see situations more clearly and they enable us to make informed decisions about our future.

Ratios

In Module 3, we will discuss several ways to make mathematical comparisons. These comparisons of numerical quantities can take several forms. The first form that we will study is called a **ratio**.

Ratios

A **ratio** is the quotient of two numbers or the quotient of two quantities that have the same units.

To introduce the concept of *ratio*, refer to the illustration below which displays the ratio of the number of left-handed to right-handed people in the United States. (Source: *Scientific American*)

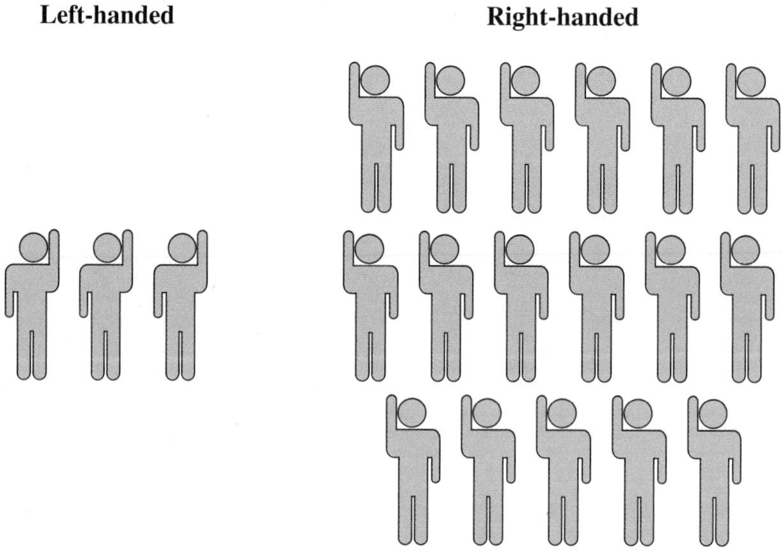

If we count the number of figures in each category, we see that the ratio of left-handed to right-handed people in the U.S. is 3 to 17.

The most common way of expressing a *ratio* is using a fraction. Ratios can also be written as two numbers separated by the word *to*, or as two numbers separated by a colon. For the illustration above, we can write the ratio as:

$\frac{3}{17}$ 3 to 17   3:17   Each is read as "the ratio of 3 to 17."

1. Refer to the illustration on the previous page. Write each answer in three ways.

a. What is the ratio of the number of right-handed to left-handed people in the U.S.?

b. What is the ratio of the number of left-handed people to the *sum* of left-handed and right-handed people in the U.S.?

c. What is the ratio of the number of right-handed people to the *sum* of left-handed and right-handed people in the U.S.?

Proportions

If we were working with a large group of people, it would be interesting to determine if the group had the same ratio of left-handed to right-handed people as the general population. To do that, we would need to compare ratios.

As an example, suppose a class of 1,000 Army recruits were surveyed, and the following results were obtained:

Left-handed: 150 Right-handed: 850

The left-handed to right-handed ratio for the group would be $\frac{150}{850}$. To see if this is the same ratio as the general population, we could simplify the fraction.

$$\frac{150}{850} = \frac{2 \cdot 3 \cdot 5 \cdot 5}{2 \cdot 5 \cdot 5 \cdot 17}$$ Prime factor 150 and 850.

$$= \frac{\cancel{2}^1 \cdot 3 \cdot \cancel{5}^1 \cdot \cancel{5}^1}{\cancel{2}_1 \cdot \cancel{5}_1 \cdot \cancel{5}_1 \cdot 17}$$ Remove the common factors of the numerator and denominator.

$$= \frac{3}{17}$$

We see that the ratio $\frac{150}{850}$ is, indeed, the same as $\frac{3}{17}$. We say that the ratios (fractions) are **equivalent.**

Equivalent ratios (fractions)

Two ratios (fractions) are **equivalent** if they represent the same number.

Since the ratios are equivalent, we can write:

$$\frac{3}{17} = \frac{150}{850}$$

The equation shown above, that compares equal ratios, is called a **proportion.**

Proportion

A **proportion** is a mathematical statement that two ratios are equal.

It is interesting to note that we could also show the ratios are equal by *building* the first ratio to obtain the second.

$$\frac{3}{17} = \frac{3}{17} \cdot \frac{50}{50}$$ Multiply numerator and denominator by a form of 1.

$$= \frac{150}{850}$$ Use the rule for multiplying fractions. Multiply the numerators and multiply the denominators.

2. Match each ratio in the first column with its equivalent ratio in the second column. Then write the corresponding proportion.

a. Ratio of owned cats to owned dogs: $\frac{43}{39}$ **i.** $\frac{64}{36}$

b. Ratio of salt to water for seawater: $\frac{5}{132}$ **ii.** $\frac{315}{735}$

c. Ratio of picture length to width of HD TV: $\frac{16}{9}$ **iii.** $\frac{86}{78}$

d. North Carolina public school student-to-teacher ratio: $\frac{15}{1}$ **iv.** $\frac{25}{660}$

e. Orange to blue M&M's color ratio: $\frac{5}{6}$ **v.** $\frac{450}{30}$

f. Ratio of nonrecycled to recycled aluminum cans: $\frac{21}{29}$ **vi.** $\frac{125}{150}$

Percent

Another way to make a mathematical comparison is to base the comparison on the number 100. Such a comparison is called a **percent.** You may think of a percent as the *numerator* of a ratio that has a denominator of 100.The word *percent* can be written using the symbol **%.**

Percent

Percent means parts per one hundred.

The Language of Algebra The word *percent* is formed from the prefix *per*, which means ratio, and the suffix *cent*, which comes from the Latin word *centum*, meaning 100.

per · cent

ratio → per; cent ← 100

In problem 1b, we saw that the ratio of left-handed people to the *sum* of left-handed and right-handed people in the U.S. is $\frac{3}{20}$. To determine what percent of the U.S. population is left-handed, we need to express $\frac{3}{20}$ as an equivalent ratio (fraction) with denominator 100. This can be accomplished by multiplying it by the correct form of 1.

$$\frac{3}{20} = \frac{3}{20} \cdot \frac{5}{5}$$
$$= \frac{15}{100}$$

Ask: "What number times 20 produces 100?" The answer is 5. It follows that $\frac{5}{5}$ should be the form of 1 that is used to build an equivalent fraction. Use the rule for multiplying fractions. Multiply the numerators and multiply the denominators.

Since percent is the numerator of a fraction with denominator 100, we can conclude that 15 percent, written 15%, of the U.S. population is left handed.

Numerator

$\frac{15}{100}$ 15%

3. In problem 1c, we saw that the ratio of right-handed people to the *sum* of left-handed and right-handed people in the U.S. is $\frac{17}{20}$. Build an equivalent fraction with denominator 100 to find the percent of the U.S. population that is right-handed.

4. a. Shade $\frac{17}{20}$ of the figure shown below

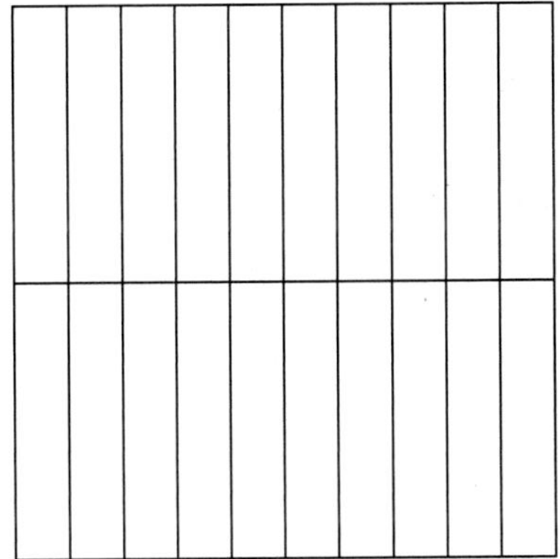

b. Shade $\frac{85}{100}$ = 85% of the figure shown below.

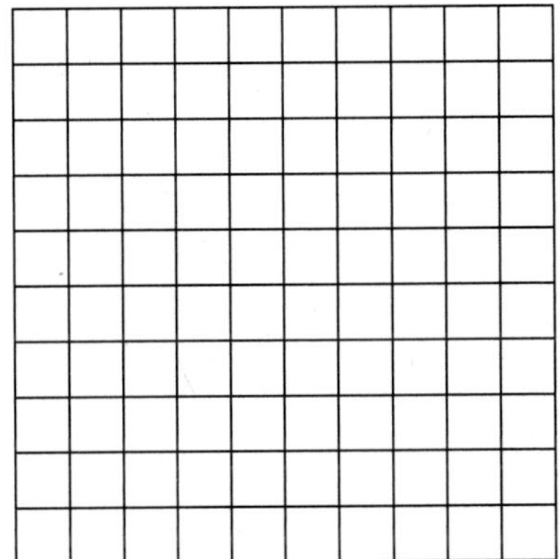

c. What do you notice about your answers to parts a and b?

d. What percent of the figure in part b is not shaded? What does the unshaded portion of the figure represent?

Objectives

1. Write ratios as fractions.
2. Simplify ratios involving decimals and mixed numbers.
3. Convert units to write ratios.
4. Write rates as fractions.
5. Find unit rates.
6. Find the best buy based on unit price.

SECTION 3.1
Ratios and Rates

ARE YOU READY?

The following problems review some basic skills that are needed when working with ratios and rates.

1. Simplify: $\frac{42}{54}$

2. Multiply: $2.09 \cdot 100$

3. Divide: $6\overline{)28.5}$

4. Divide: $6\frac{1}{4} \div 3\frac{3}{4}$

Ratios are often used to describe important relationships between two quantities. Here are three examples:

To prepare fuel for an outboard marine engine, gasoline must be mixed with oil in the ratio of 50 to 1.

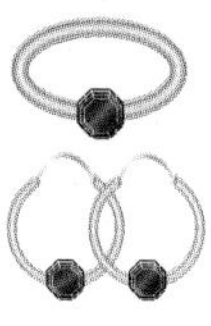

To make 14-karat jewelry, gold is combined with other metals in the ratio of 14 to 10.

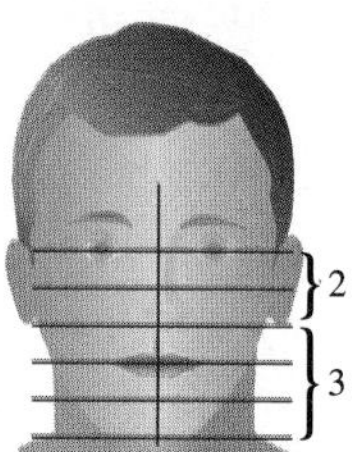

In this drawing, the eyes-to-nose distance and the nose-to-chin distance are drawn using a ratio of 2 to 3.

1 Write ratios as fractions.

Ratios give us a way to compare two numbers or two quantities measured in the same units.

Ratios

A **ratio** is the quotient of two numbers or the quotient of two quantities that have the same units.

There are three ways to write a ratio. The most common way is as a fraction. Ratios can also be written as two numbers separated by the word *to,* or as two numbers separated by a colon. For example, the ratios described in the illustrations above can be expressed as:

$\frac{50}{1}$, 14 to 10, and 2:3

- The fraction $\frac{50}{1}$ is read as "the ratio of 50 to 1." — A fraction bar separates the numbers being compared.
- 14 **to** 10 is read as "the ratio of 14 to 10." — The word "to" separates the numbers being compared.
- 2**:**3 is read as "the ratio of 2 to 3." — A colon separates the numbers being compared.

Writing a Ratio as a Fraction

To **write a ratio as a fraction,** write the first number (or quantity) mentioned as the numerator and the second number (or quantity) mentioned as the denominator. Then simplify the fraction, if possible.

EXAMPLE 1 Write each ratio as a fraction: **a.** 3 to 7 **b.** 10:11

Strategy We will identify the numbers before and after the word *to* and the numbers before and after the colon.

WHY The word *to* and the colon separate the numbers to be compared in a ratio.

Solution

To write the ratio as a fraction, the first number mentioned is the numerator and the second number mentioned is the denominator.

a. The ratio 3 **to** 7 can be written as $\frac{3}{7}$. The fraction $\frac{3}{7}$ is in simplest form.

b. The ratio 10 **:** 11 can be written as $\frac{10}{11}$. The fraction $\frac{10}{11}$ is in simplest form.

Self Check 1

Write each ratio as a fraction:

a. 4 to 9 **b.** 8:15

Now Try **Problem 13**

> ***Caution!*** When a ratio is written as a fraction, the fraction should be in simplest form. (Recall that a fraction is in **simplest form,** or **lowest terms,** when the numerator and denominator have no common factors other than 1.)

EXAMPLE 2 Write the ratio 35 to 10 as a fraction in simplest form.

Strategy We will translate the ratio from its given form in words to fractional form. Then we will look for any factors common to the numerator and denominator and remove them.

WHY We need to make sure that the numerator and denominator have no common factors other than 1. If that is the case, the ratio will be in *simplest form.*

Solution

The ratio 35 **to** 10 can be written as $\frac{35}{10}$. The fraction $\frac{35}{10}$ is not in simplest form.

Now, we simplify the fraction.

$$\frac{35}{10} = \frac{\overset{1}{\cancel{5}} \cdot 7}{2 \cdot \underset{1}{\cancel{5}}}$$ Factor 35 as 5 · 7 and 10 as 2 · 5. Then remove the common factor of 5 in the numerator and denominator.

$$= \frac{7}{2}$$

The ratio 35 to 10 can be written as the fraction $\frac{35}{10}$, which simplifies to $\frac{7}{2}$ (read as "7 to 2"). Because the fractions $\frac{35}{10}$ and $\frac{7}{2}$ represent equal numbers, they are called **equal ratios.**

Self Check 2

Write the ratio 12 to 9 as a fraction in simplest form.

Now Try **Problems 17 and 23**

> ***Caution!*** Since ratios are comparisons of two numbers, it would be *incorrect* in Example 2 to write the ratio $\frac{7}{2}$ as the mixed number $3\frac{1}{2}$. Ratios written as improper fractions are perfectly acceptable—just make sure the numerator and denominator have no common factors other than 1.

To write a ratio in simplest form, we remove any common factors of the numerator and denominator as well as any common units.

Self Check 3

CARRY-ON LUGGAGE

a. Write the ratio of the height to the length of the carry-on space shown in the illustration in Example 3 as a fraction in simplest form.

b. Write the ratio of the length of the carry-on space to its height in simplest form.

Now Try **Problem 27**

EXAMPLE 3 ***Carry-on Luggage*** An airline allows its passengers to carry a piece of luggage onto an airplane only if it will fit in the space shown below.

a. Write the ratio of the width of the space to its length as a fraction in simplest form.

b. Write the ratio of the length of the space to its width as a fraction in simplest form.

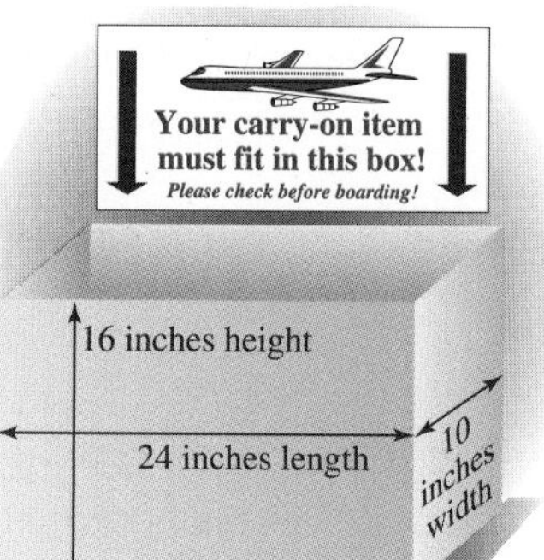

Strategy To write each ratio as a fraction, we will identify the quantity before the word *to* and the quantity after it.

WHY The first quantity mentioned is the numerator of the fraction and the second quantity mentioned is the denominator.

Solution

a. The ratio of the width of the space **to** its length is $\frac{10 \text{ inches}}{24 \text{ inches}}$.

To write a ratio in simplest form, we remove the common factors *and* the common units of the numerator and denominator.

$$\frac{10 \text{ inches}}{24 \text{ inches}} = \frac{\overset{1}{\cancel{2}} \cdot 5 \, \cancel{\text{inches}}}{\underset{1}{\cancel{2}} \cdot 12 \, \cancel{\text{inches}}}$$

Factor 10 as $2 \cdot 5$ and 24 as $2 \cdot 12$. Then remove the common factor of 2 and the common units of inches from the numerator and denominator.

$$= \frac{5}{12}$$

The width-to-length ratio of the carry-on space is $\frac{5}{12}$ (read as "5 to 12").

b. The ratio of the length of the space **to** its width is $\frac{24 \text{ inches}}{10 \text{ inches}}$.

$$\frac{24 \text{ inches}}{10 \text{ inches}} = \frac{\overset{1}{\cancel{2}} \cdot 12 \, \cancel{\text{inches}}}{\underset{1}{\cancel{2}} \cdot 5 \, \cancel{\text{inches}}}$$

Factor 24 and 10. Then remove the common factor of 2 and the common units of inches from the numerator and denominator.

$$= \frac{12}{5}$$

The length-to-width ratio of the carry-on space is $\frac{12}{5}$ (read as "12 to 5").

Caution! Example 3 shows that order is important when writing a ratio. The width-to-length ratio is $\frac{5}{12}$ while the length-to-width ratio is $\frac{12}{5}$.

2 Simplify ratios involving decimals and mixed numbers.

EXAMPLE 4 Write the ratio 0.3 to 1.2 as a fraction in simplest form.

Strategy After writing the ratio as a fraction, we will multiply it by a form of 1 to obtain an equivalent ratio of whole numbers.

WHY A ratio of whole numbers is easier to understand than a ratio of decimals.

Solution

The ratio 0.3 **to** 1.2 can be written as $\frac{0.3}{1.2}$.

To write this as a ratio of *whole numbers,* we need to move the decimal points in the numerator and denominator one place to the right. Recall that to find the product of a decimal and 10, we simply move the decimal point one place to the right. Therefore, it follows that $\frac{10}{10}$ is the form of 1 that we should use to build $\frac{0.3}{1.2}$ into an equivalent ratio.

$\frac{0.3}{1.2} = \frac{0.3}{1.2} \cdot \frac{\mathbf{10}}{\mathbf{10}}$ Multiply the ratio by a form of 1.

$\frac{0.3}{1.2} = \frac{0.3 \cdot \mathbf{10}}{1.2 \cdot \mathbf{10}}$ Multiply the numerators. Multiply the denominators.

$= \frac{3}{12}$ Do the multiplications by moving each decimal point one place to the right. $0.3 \cdot 10 = 3$ and $1.2 \cdot 10 = 12$.

$= \frac{1}{4}$ Simplify the fraction: $\frac{3}{12} = \frac{\overset{1}{\cancel{3}}}{\underset{1}{\cancel{3}} \cdot 4} = \frac{1}{4}$.

Self Check 4

Write the ratio 0.8 to 2.4 as a fraction in simplest form.

Now Try **Problems 29 and 33**

THINK IT THROUGH ***Student Loan Calculations***

"A consistent majority of students who borrow to pay for their higher education believe they could not have gone to college without student loans. Over 70% agree that student loans were very or extremely important in allowing them access to education after high school."

National Student Loan Survey, 2002

Many student loan programs calculate a *debt-to-income ratio* to assist them in determining whether the borrower has sufficient income to repay the loan. A debt-to-income ratio compares an applicant's monthly debt payments (mortgages, credit cards, auto loans, etc.) to their gross monthly income. Most education lenders require borrower debt-to-income ratios of $\frac{2}{5}$ or less, according to the Nellie Mae Debt Management Edvisor. Calculate the debt-to-income ratio for each loan applicant shown below. Then determine whether it makes them eligible for a student loan.

	Applicant #1	Applicant #2	Applicant #3
Monthly debt payments	$250	$1,000	$1,200
Gross monthly income	$1,000	$2,000	$3,000
Debt-to-income ratio			
Is the ratio $\leq \frac{2}{5}$?			

Self Check 5

Write the ratio $3\frac{1}{3}$ to $1\frac{1}{9}$ as a fraction in simplest form.

Now Try **Problem 37**

EXAMPLE 5 Write the ratio $4\frac{2}{3}$ to $1\frac{1}{6}$ as a fraction in simplest form.

Strategy After writing the ratio as a fraction, we will use the method for simplifying a complex fraction to obtain an equivalent ratio of whole numbers.

WHY A ratio of whole numbers is easier to understand than a ratio of mixed numbers.

Solution

The ratio of $4\frac{2}{3}$ **to** $1\frac{1}{6}$ can be written as $\dfrac{4\frac{2}{3}}{1\frac{1}{6}}$.

The resulting ratio is a complex fraction. To write the ratio in simplest form, we perform the division indicated by the main fraction bar (shown in red).

$$\dfrac{4\frac{2}{3}}{1\frac{1}{6}} = \dfrac{\frac{14}{3}}{\frac{7}{6}}$$ Write $4\frac{2}{3}$ and $1\frac{1}{6}$ as improper fractions.

$$= \frac{14}{3} \div \frac{7}{6}$$ Write the division indicated by the main fraction bar using a ÷ symbol.

$$= \frac{14}{3} \cdot \frac{6}{7}$$ Use the rule for dividing fractions: Multiply the first fraction by the reciprocal of $\frac{7}{6}$, which is $\frac{6}{7}$.

$$= \frac{14 \cdot 6}{3 \cdot 7}$$ Multiply the numerators. Multiply the denominators.

$$= \frac{2 \cdot \overset{1}{\cancel{7}} \cdot 2 \cdot \overset{1}{\cancel{3}}}{\underset{1}{\cancel{3}} \cdot \underset{1}{\cancel{7}}}$$ To simplify the fraction, factor 14 as $2 \cdot 7$ and 6 as $2 \cdot 3$. Then remove the common factors 3 and 7.

$$= \frac{4}{1}$$ Multiply the remaining factors in the numerator. Multiply the remaining factors in the denominator.

We would normally simplify the result $\frac{4}{1}$ and write it as 4. But since a ratio compares two numbers, we leave the result in fractional form.

3 Convert units to write ratios.

When a ratio compares 2 quantities, both quantities must be measured in the same units. For example, inches must be compared to inches, pounds to pounds, and seconds to seconds.

Self Check 6

Write the ratio *6 feet to 3 yards* as a fraction in simplest form. (*Hint:* 3 feet = 1 yard.)

Now Try **Problem 41**

EXAMPLE 6 Write the ratio *12 ounces to 2 pounds* as a fraction in simplest form.

Strategy We will convert 2 pounds to ounces and write a ratio that compares ounces to ounces. Then we will simplify the ratio.

WHY A ratio compares two quantities that have the *same* units. When the units are different, it's usually easier to write the ratio using the smaller unit of measurement. Since ounces are smaller than pounds, we will compare in ounces.

Solution

To express 2 pounds in ounces, we use the fact that there are 16 ounces in one pound.

$2 \cdot 16$ ounces = 32 ounces

We can now express the ratio *12 ounces to 2 pounds* using the same units:

12 **ounces** to 32 **ounces**

Next, we write the ratio in fraction form and simplify.

$$\frac{12 \text{ ounces}}{32 \text{ ounces}} = \frac{3 \cdot \overset{1}{\cancel{4}} \cancel{\text{ounces}}}{\underset{1}{\cancel{4}} \cdot 8 \cancel{\text{ounces}}}$$

To simplify, factor 12 as $3 \cdot 4$ and 32 as $4 \cdot 8$. Then remove the common factor of 4 and the common units of ounces from the numerator and denominator.

$$= \frac{3}{8}$$

The ratio in simplest form is $\frac{3}{8}$.

4 Write rates as fractions.

When we compare two quantities that have different units (and neither unit can be converted to the other), we call the comparison a **rate,** and we can write it as a fraction. For example, on the label of the can of paint shown on the right, we see that 1 quart of paint is needed for every 200 square feet to be painted. Writing this as a rate in fractional form, we have

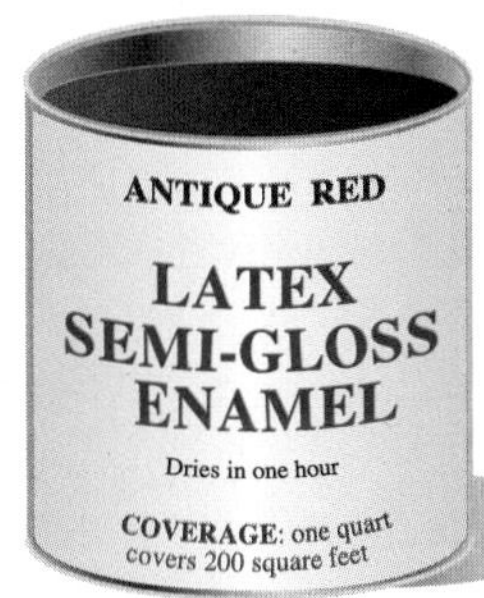

$$\frac{1 \text{ quart}}{200 \text{ square feet}}$$

Read as "1 quart per 200 square feet."

The Language of Mathematics The word *per* is associated with the operation of division, and it means "for each" or "for every." For example, when we say 1 quart of paint *per* 200 square feet, we mean 1 quart of paint *for every* 200 square feet.

Rates

A **rate** is a quotient of two quantities that have different units.

When writing a rate, always include the units. Some other examples of rates are:

- 16 computers **for** 75 students
- 1,550 feet **in** 4.5 seconds
- 88 tomatoes **from** 3 plants
- 250 miles **on** 2 gallons of gasoline

The Language of Mathematics As seen above, words such as *per, for, in, from,* and *on* are used to separate the two quantities that are compared in a rate.

Writing a Rate as a Fraction

To **write a rate as a fraction,** write the first quantity mentioned as the numerator and the second quantity mentioned as the denominator, and then simplify, if possible. Write the units as part of the fraction.

Self Check 7

GROWTH RATES The fastest-growing flowering plant on record grew 12 feet in 14 days. Write the rate of growth as a fraction in simplest form.

Now Try **Problems 49 and 53**

EXAMPLE 7 ***Snowfall*** According to the *Guinness Book of World Records,* a total of 78 inches of snow fell at Mile 47 Camp, Cooper River Division, Arkansas, in a 24-hour period in 1963. Write the rate of snowfall as a fraction in simplest form.

Strategy We will use a fraction to compare the amount of snow that fell (in inches) to the amount of time in which it fell (in hours). Then we will simplify it.

WHY A rate is a quotient of two quantities with different units.

Solution

78 inches **in** 24 hours can be written as $\frac{78 \text{ inches}}{24 \text{ hours}}$.

Now, we simplify the fraction.

$$\frac{78 \text{ inches}}{24 \text{ hours}} = \frac{\overset{1}{\cancel{6}} \cdot 13 \text{ inches}}{4 \cdot \underset{1}{\cancel{6}} \text{ hours}}$$ To simplify, factor 78 as 6 · 13 and 24 as 4 · 6. Then remove the common factor of 6 from the numerator and denominator.

$$= \frac{13 \text{ inches}}{4 \text{ hours}}$$ Since the units are different, they cannot be removed.

The snow fell at a rate of 13 inches per 4 hours.

5 Find unit rates.

Unit Rate

A **unit rate** is a rate in which the denominator is 1.

To illustrate the concept of a unit rate, suppose a driver makes the 354-mile trip from Pittsburgh to Indianapolis in 6 hours. Then the motorist's rate (or more specifically, rate of speed) is given by

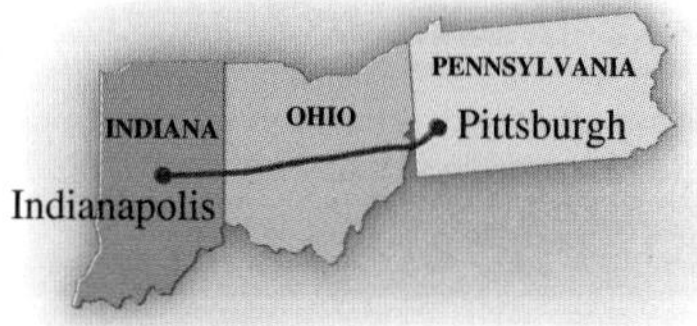

$$\frac{354 \text{ miles}}{6 \text{ hours}} = \frac{\overset{1}{\cancel{6}} \cdot 59 \text{ miles}}{\underset{1}{\cancel{6}} \cdot \text{hours}}$$ Factor 354 as 6 · 59 and remove the common factor of 6 from the numerator and denominator.

$$= \frac{59 \text{ miles}}{1 \text{ hour}}$$ Since the units are different, they cannot be removed. Note that the denominator is 1.

We can also find the unit rate by dividing 354 by 6.

Rate: $\frac{354 \text{ miles}}{6 \text{ hours}}$

$$\begin{array}{r} 59 \\ 6\overline{)354} \\ -30 \\ \hline 54 \\ -54 \\ \hline 0 \end{array}$$

This quotient is the numerical part of the unit rate, written as a fraction. → **Unit rate:** $\frac{59 \text{ miles}}{1 \text{ hour}}$

The numerical part of the denominator is always 1.

The unit rate $\frac{59 \text{ miles}}{1 \text{ hour}}$ can be expressed in any of the following forms:

$59 \frac{\text{miles}}{\text{hour}}$, 59 miles per hour, 59 miles/hour, or 59 mph

> ***The Language of Mathematics*** A slash mark / is often used to write a unit rate. In such cases, we read the slash mark as "per." For example, 33 pounds/gallon is read as 33 pounds *per* gallon.

Writing a Rate as a Unit Rate

To **write a rate as a unit rate,** divide the numerator of the rate by the denominator.

EXAMPLE 8 ***Coffee*** There are 384 calories in a 16-ounce cup of caramel Frappuccino blended coffee with whip cream. Write this rate as a unit rate. (*Hint:* Find the number of calories in 1 ounce.)

Strategy We will translate the rate from its given form in words to fractional form. Then we will perform the indicated division.

WHY To write a rate as a unit rate, we divide the numerator of the rate by the denominator.

Solution

384 calories **in** 16 ounces can be written as $\frac{384 \text{ calories}}{16 \text{ ounces}}$.

To find the number of calories in 1 ounce of the coffee (the unit rate), we perform the division as indicated by the fraction bar:

$$\begin{array}{r} 24 \\ 16\overline{)384} \\ -32 \\ \hline 64 \\ -64 \\ \hline 0 \end{array}$$

Divide the numerator of the rate by the denominator.

For the caramel Frappuccino blended coffee with whip cream, the unit rate is $\frac{24 \text{ calories}}{1 \text{ ounce}}$, which can be written as 24 calories per ounce or 24 calories/ounce.

Self Check 8

NUTRITION There are 204 calories in a 12-ounce can of cranberry juice. Write this rate as a unit rate. (*Hint:* Find the number of calories in 1 ounce.)

Now Try **Problem 57**

Self Check 9

FULL-TIME JOBS Joan earns $436 per 40-hour week managing a dress shop. Write this rate as a unit rate. (*Hint:* Find her hourly rate of pay.)

Now Try **Problem 61**

EXAMPLE 9 ***Part-time Jobs*** A student earns $74 for working 8 hours in a bookstore. Write this rate as a unit rate. (*Hint:* Find his hourly rate of pay.)

Strategy We will translate the rate from its given form in words to fractional form. Then we will perform the indicated division.

WHY To write a rate as a unit rate, we divide the numerator of the rate by the denominator.

Solution

$74 **for** working 8 hours can be written as $\frac{\$74}{8 \text{ hours}}$.

To find the rate of pay for 1 hour of work (the unit rate), we divide 74 by 8.

$$\begin{array}{r} 9.25 \\ 8\overline{)74.00} \\ -72 \\ \hline 2\,0 \\ -1\,6 \\ \hline 40 \\ -40 \\ \hline 0 \end{array}$$

Write a decimal point and two additional zeros to the right of 4.

The unit rate of pay is $\frac{\$9.25}{1 \text{ hour}}$, which can be written as $9.25 per hour or $9.25/hr.

6 Find the best buy based on unit price.

If a grocery store sells a 5-pound package of hamburger for $18.75, a consumer might want to know what the hamburger costs per pound. When we find the cost of 1 pound of the hamburger, we are finding a **unit price.** To find the unit price of an item, we begin by comparing its price to the number of units.

$$\frac{\$18.75}{5 \text{ pounds}} \begin{array}{l} \leftarrow \text{Price} \\ \leftarrow \text{Number of units} \end{array}$$

Then we divide the price by the number of units.

$$\begin{array}{r} 3.75 \\ 5\overline{)18.75} \end{array}$$

The unit price of the hamburger is $3.75 per pound.

Other examples of unit prices are:

- $8.15 per ounce
- $200 per day
- $0.75 per foot

Unit Price

A **unit price** is a rate that tells how much is paid for *one* unit (or *one* item). It is the quotient of price to the number of units.

$$\text{Unit price} = \frac{\text{price}}{\text{number of units}}$$

When shopping, it is often difficult to determine the best buys because the items that we purchase come in so many different sizes and brands. Comparison shopping can be made easier by finding unit prices. *The best buy is the item that has the lowest unit price.*

EXAMPLE 10 Comparison Shopping

Olives come packaged in a 10-ounce jar, which sells for \$2.49, or in a 6-ounce jar, which sells for \$1.53. Which is the better buy?

Strategy We will find the unit price for each jar of olives. Then we will identify which jar has the lower unit price.

WHY The better buy is the jar of olives that has the lower unit price.

Solution

To find the unit price of each jar of olives, we write the quotient of its price and its weight, and then perform the indicated division. Before dividing, we convert each price from dollars to cents so that the unit price can be expressed in cents per ounce.

The 10-ounce jar:

$$\frac{\$2.49}{10\text{ oz}} = \frac{249¢}{10\text{ oz}}$$ Write the rate: $\frac{\text{price}}{\text{number of units}}$. Then change \$2.49 to 249 cents.

$$= 24.9¢ \text{ per oz}$$ Divide 249 by 10 by moving the decimal point 1 place to the left.

The 6-ounce jar:

$$\frac{\$1.53}{6\text{ oz}} = \frac{153¢}{6\text{ oz}}$$ Write the rate: $\frac{\text{price}}{\text{number of units}}$. Then change \$1.53 to 153 cents.

$$= 25.5¢ \text{ per oz}$$ Do the division.

$$\begin{array}{r} 25.5 \\ 6\overline{)153.0} \\ -12 \\ \hline 33 \\ -30 \\ \hline 3\,0 \\ -3\,0 \\ \hline 0 \end{array}$$

One ounce for 24.9¢ is a better buy than one ounce for 25.5¢. The unit price is less when olives are packaged in 10-ounce jars, so that is the better buy.

Self Check 10

COMPARISON SHOPPING A fast-food restaurant sells a 12-ounce cola for 72¢ and a 16-ounce cola for 99¢. Which is the better buy?

Now Try **Problems 65 and 107**

ANSWERS TO SELF CHECKS

1. a. $\frac{4}{9}$ **b.** $\frac{8}{15}$ **2.** $\frac{4}{3}$ **3. a.** $\frac{2}{3}$ **b.** $\frac{3}{2}$ **4.** $\frac{1}{3}$ **5.** $\frac{3}{1}$ **6.** $\frac{2}{3}$ **7.** $\frac{6\text{ feet}}{7\text{ days}}$ **8.** 17 calories/oz **9.** \$10.90 per hour **10.** the 12-oz cola

SECTION 3.1 STUDY SET

VOCABULARY

Fill in the blanks.

1. A ______ is the quotient of two numbers or the quotient of two quantities that have the same units.
2. A ______ is the quotient of two quantities that have different units.
3. A ______ rate is a rate in which the denominator is 1.
4. A unit ______ is a rate that tells how much is paid for one unit or one item.

CONCEPTS

5. To write the ratio $\frac{15}{24}$ in lowest terms, we remove any common factors of the numerator and denominator. What common factor do they have?
6. Complete the solution. Write the ratio $\frac{14}{21}$ in lowest terms.

$$\frac{14}{21} = \frac{2 \cdot 7}{\square \cdot \square} = \frac{2 \cdot \overset{1}{\cancel{7}}}{\square \cdot \underset{1}{\cancel{7}}} = \frac{\square}{\square}$$

7. Consider the ratio $\frac{0.5}{0.6}$. By what number should we multiply numerator and denominator to make this a ratio of whole numbers?

8. What should be done to write the ratio $\frac{15 \text{ inches}}{22 \text{ inches}}$ in simplest form?

9. Write $\frac{11 \text{ minutes}}{1 \text{ hour}}$ so that it compares the same units and then simplify.

10. **a.** Consider the rate $\frac{\$248}{16 \text{ hours}}$. What division should be performed to find the unit rate in dollars per hour?

b. Suppose 3 pairs of socks sell for \$7.95: $\frac{\$7.95}{3 \text{ pairs}}$. What division should be performed to find the unit price of one pair of socks?

NOTATION

11. FLAGS

a. Write the ratio of the flag's length to its width using a fraction, using the word *to*, and using a colon.

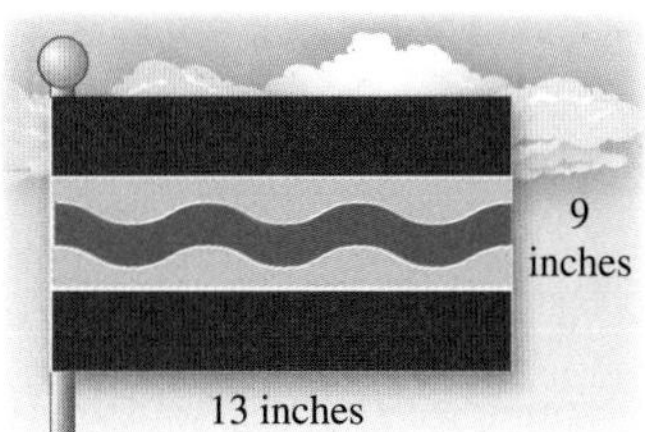

b. WEST AFRICA Write the ratio (in fractional form) of the number of red stripes to the number of white stripes on the flag of Liberia.

12. The rate $\frac{55 \text{ miles}}{1 \text{ hour}}$ can be expressed as

- 55 ______ ____ ______ (in three words)
- 55 ______/______ (in two words with a slash)
- 55 ____ ___ ___ (in three letters)

GUIDED PRACTICE

Write each ratio as a fraction. See Example 1.

13. 5 to 8 **14.** 3 to 23

15. 11:16 **16.** 9:25

Write each ratio as a fraction in simplest form. See Example 2.

17. 25 to 15 **18.** 45 to 35

19. 63:36 **20.** 54:24

21. 22:33 **22.** 14:21

23. 17 to 34 **24.** 19 to 38

Write each ratio as a fraction in simplest form. See Example 3.

25. 4 ounces to 12 ounces **26.** 3 inches to 15 inches

27. 24 miles to 32 miles **28.** 56 yards to 64 yards

Write each ratio as a fraction in simplest form. See Example 4.

29. 0.3 to 0.9 **30.** 0.2 to 0.6

31. 0.65 to 0.15 **32.** 2.4 to 1.5

33. 3.8:7.8 **34.** 4.2:8.2

35. 7:24.5 **36.** 5:22.5

Write each ratio as a fraction in simplest form. See Example 5.

37. $2\frac{1}{3}$ to $4\frac{2}{3}$ **38.** $1\frac{1}{4}$ to $1\frac{1}{2}$

39. $10\frac{1}{2}$ to $1\frac{3}{4}$ **40.** $12\frac{3}{4}$ to $2\frac{1}{8}$

Write each ratio as a fraction in simplest form. See Example 6.

41. 12 minutes to 1 hour **42.** 8 ounces to 1 pound

43. 3 days to 1 week **44.** 4 inches to 1 yard

45. 18 months to 2 years **46.** 8 feet to 4 yards

47. 21 inches to 3 feet **48.** 32 seconds to 2 minutes

Write each rate as a fraction in simplest form. See Example 7.

49. 64 feet in 6 seconds
50. 45 applications for 18 openings
51. 75 days on 20 gallons of water
52. 3,000 students over a 16-year career
53. 84 made out of 100 attempts
54. 16 right compared to 34 wrong
55. 18 beats every 12 measures
56. 10 inches as a result of 30 turns

Write each rate as a unit rate. See Example 8.

57. 60 revolutions in 5 minutes
58. 14 trips every 2 months
59. \$50,000 paid over 10 years
60. 245 presents for 35 children

Write each rate as a unit rate. See Example 9.

61. 12 errors in 8 hours

62. 114 times in a 12-month period

63. 4,007,500 people living in 12,500 square miles

64. 117.6 pounds of pressure on 8 square inches

Find the unit price of each item. See Example 10.

65. They charged $48 for 12 minutes.

66. 150 barrels cost $4,950.

67. Four sold for $272.

68. 7,020 pesos will buy six tickets.

69. 65 ounces sell for 78 cents.

70. For 7 dozen, you will pay $10.15.

71. $3.50 for 50 feet

72. $4 billion over a 5-month span

CONCEPT EXTENSIONS

73. Write the ratio of the longest side of the triangle shown below to the shortest side.

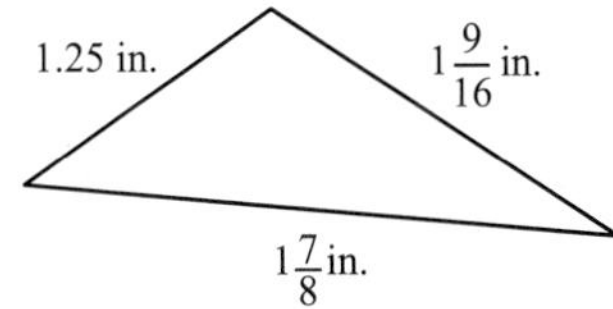

74. SOCIAL SECURITY

a. In 1960, there were about 5 workers paying into the Social Security System for every person receiving benefits from it. Write this as a ratio using a colon.

b. By 2030, the government predicts that there will be about 2 workers paying into the Social Security System for every person receiving benefits from it. Write this as a ratio using a colon.

c. Why is the changing ratio a concern?

(Source: Social Security Administration)

75. a. Ratios comparing three quantities that have the same units can be written in the form ▢ : ▢ : ▢ . Refer to the illustration in the next column. Write such a ratio that compares the number of red, green, and blue stars, in that order.

b. Write a ratio that compares the number of blue, red, and green stars, in that order.

76. PACKAGING The ice cream sold in grocery stores used to come in 2 quart (one-half gallon) containers. The new container standard throughout the industry is now 1.5 quarts. Even though the container size became smaller, many grocery stores sell the ice cream at the same price. In that case, did the unit cost of ice cream increase or decrease? Use an example to explain your reasoning.

APPLICATIONS

77. GEAR RATIOS Refer to the illustration below.

a. Write the ratio of the number of teeth of the smaller gear to the number of teeth of the larger gear as a fraction in simplest form.

b. Write the ratio of the number of teeth of the larger gear to the number of teeth of the smaller gear as a fraction in simplest form.

78. CARDS The suit of hearts from a deck of playing cards is shown below. What is the ratio of the number of face cards to the total number of cards in the suit? (*Hint:* A face card is a Jack, Queen, or King.)

79. SKIN Refer to the cross-section of human skin shown on the next page. Write the ratio of the thickness of the stratum corneum to the thickness of the dermis in simplest form. (*Source:* Philips Research Laboratories)

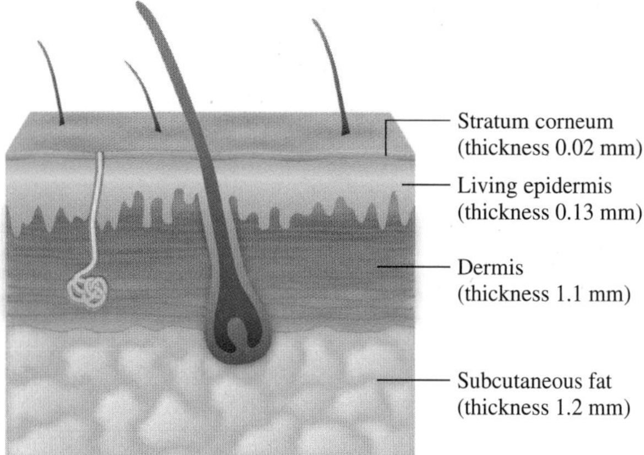

80. PAINTING A 9.5-mil thick coat of fireproof paint is applied with a roller to a wall. (A *mil* is a unit of measure equal to 1/1,000 of an inch.) The coating dries to a thickness of 5.7 mils. Write the ratio of the thickness of the coating when wet to the thickness when dry as a fraction in simplest form.

81. BAKING A recipe for sourdough bread calls for $5\frac{1}{4}$ cups of all-purpose flour and $1\frac{3}{4}$ cups of water. Write the ratio of flour to water in simplest form.

82. DESSERTS Refer to the recipe card shown below. Write the ratio of milk to sugar in simplest form.

Frozen Chocolate Slush
(Serves 8)
Once frozen, this chocolate can be cut into cubes and stored in sealed plastic bags for a spur-of-the-moment dessert.

$\frac{1}{2}$ cup Dutch cocoa powder, sifted
$1\frac{1}{2}$ cups sugar
$3\frac{1}{2}$ cups skim milk

83. RECREATION DIRECTOR A total of 966 boys and girls are members of a community recreation center.

a. If 504 are boys, how many members are girls?

b. Express the ratio of girls to boys who are members of the recreation center using a fraction, using the word to, and using a colon.

©BananaStock/SuperStock

84. Two lengths are in the ratio 7:4.

a. Write the ratio in two other ways.

b. Use the illustration to show what a ratio 7:4 means.

85. BUDGETS Refer to the circle graph below that shows a monthly budget for a family. Write each ratio in simplest form.

a. Find the total amount for the monthly budget.

b. Write the ratio of the amount budgeted for rent to the total budget.

c. Write the ratio of the amount budgeted for food to the total budget.

d. Write the ratio of the amount budgeted for the phone to the total budget.

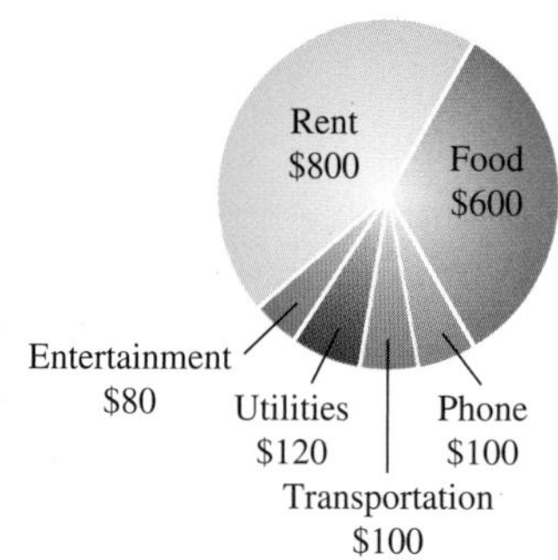

86. TAXES Refer to the list of tax deductions shown below. Write each ratio in simplest form.

a. Write the ratio of the real estate tax deduction to the total deductions.

b. Write the ratio of the charitable contributions to the total deductions.

c. Write the ratio of the mortgage interest deduction to the union dues deduction.

Item	Amount
Medical expenses	$875
Real estate taxes	$1,250
Charitable contributions	$1,750
Mortgage interest	$4,375
Union dues	$500
Total deductions	$8,750

87. ART HISTORY Leonardo da Vinci drew the human figure shown within a square. Write the ratio of the length of the man's outstretched arms to his height. Express the answer in three ways. (*Hint:* All four sides of a square are the same length.)

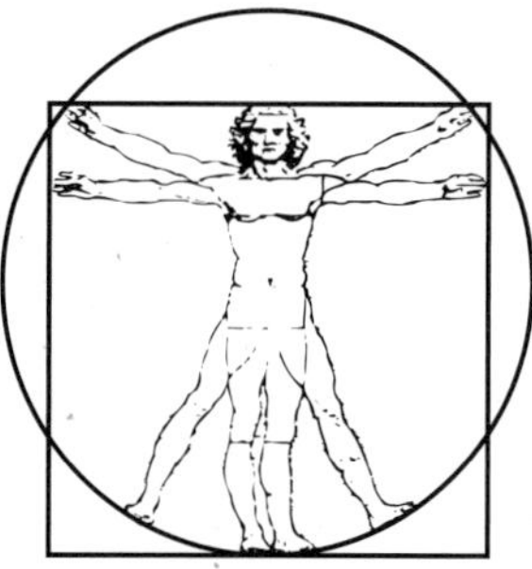

88. FLAGS The checkered flag is composed of 24 equal-sized squares. What is the ratio of the width of the flag to its length? Express the answer in three ways. (*Hint:* All four sides of a square are the same length.)

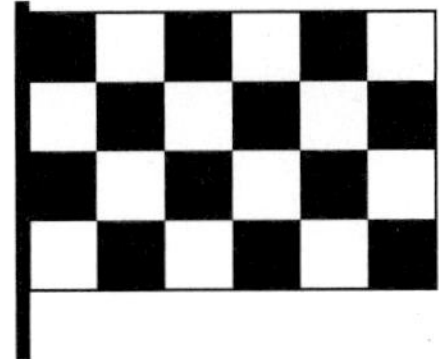

89. BANKRUPTCY After declaring bankruptcy, a company could pay its creditors only 5¢ on the dollar. Write this as a ratio in simplest form.

90. EGGS An average-sized ostrich egg weighs 3 pounds and an average-sized chicken egg weighs 2 ounces. Write the ratio of the weight of an ostrich egg to the weight of a chicken egg in simplest form.

91. CPR A paramedic performed 210 compressions to 7 breaths on an adult with no pulse. What compressions-to-breaths rate did the paramedic use?

92. FACULTY–STUDENT RATIOS At a college, there are 125 faculty members and 2,000 students. Find the rate of faculty to students. (This is often referred to as the faculty–student *ratio*, even though the units are different.)

93. AIRLINE COMPLAINTS An airline had 3.29 complaints for every 1,000 passengers. Write this as a rate of whole numbers.

94. FINGERNAILS On average, fingernails grow 0.02 inch per week. Write this rate using whole numbers.

95. INTERNET SALES A website determined that it had 112,500 hits in one month. Of those visiting the site, 4,500 made purchases.

a. Those that visited the site, but did not make a purchase, are called *browsers*. How many browsers visited the website that month?

b. What was the browsers-to-buyers unit rate for the website that month?

96. TYPING A secretary typed a document containing 330 words in 5 minutes. Write this rate as a unit rate.

97. UNIT PRICES A 12-ounce can of cola sells for 84¢. Find the unit price in cents per ounce.

98. DAYCARE A daycare center charges $32 for 8 hours of supervised care. Find the unit price in dollars per hour for the daycare.

99. PARKING A parking meter requires 25¢ for 20 minutes of parking. Find the unit price to park.

100. GASOLINE COST A driver pumped 17 gallons of gasoline into the tank of his pickup truck at a cost of $66.13. Find the unit price of the gasoline.

101. LANDSCAPING A 50-pound bag of grass seed sells for $222.50. Find the unit price of grass seed.

102. UNIT COSTS A 24-ounce package of green beans sells for $1.29. Find the unit price in cents per ounce.

103. DRAINING TANKS An 11,880-gallon tank of water can be emptied in 27 minutes. Find the unit rate of flow of water out of the tank.

104. PAY RATE Ricardo worked for 27 hours to help insulate a hockey arena. For his work, he received $337.50. Find his hourly rate of pay.

105. AUTO TRAVEL A car's odometer reads 34,746 at the beginning of a trip. Five hours later, it reads 35,071.

a. How far did the car travel?

b. What was its rate of speed?

106. RATES OF SPEED An airplane travels from Chicago to San Francisco, a distance of 1,883 miles, in 3.5 hours. Find the rate of speed of the plane.

107. COMPARISON SHOPPING A 6-ounce can of orange juice sells for 89¢, and an 8-ounce can sells for $1.19. Which is the better buy?

108. COMPARISON SHOPPING A 30-pound bag of planting mix costs $12.25, and an 80-pound bag costs $30.25. Which is the better buy?

109. COMPARISON SHOPPING A certain brand of cold and sinus medication is sold in 20-tablet boxes for $4.29 and in 50-tablet boxes for $9.59. Which is the better buy?

110. COMPARISON SHOPPING Which tire shown is the better buy?

111. COMPARING SPEEDS A car travels 345 miles in 6 hours, and a truck travels 376 miles in 6.2 hours. Which vehicle is going faster?

112. READING One seventh-grader read a 54-page book in 40 minutes. Another read an 80-page book in 62 minutes. If the books were equally difficult, which student read faster?

113. GAS MILEAGE One car went 1,235 miles on 51.3 gallons of gasoline, and another went 1,456 miles on 55.78 gallons. Which car got the better gas mileage?

114. ELECTRICITY RATES In one community, a bill for 575 kilowatt-hours(kwh) of electricity is \$38.81. In a second community, a bill for 831 kwh is \$58.10. In which community is electricity cheaper?

115. YOGURT Which package of yogurt is the better buy?

FAT-FREE PEACH YOGURT
44791 09265 3
4.79
Six 4-OZ CARTONS

FAT-FREE PEACH YOGURT
44791 09265 3
2.99
Four 4-OZ CARTONS

116. BOTTLED WATER Which package of bottled water is the better buy?

WRITING

117. Are the ratios 3 to 1 and 1 to 3 the same? Explain why or why not.

118. Give three examples of ratios (or rates) that you have encountered in the past week.

119. How will the topics studied in this section make you a better shopper?

120. What is a unit rate? Give some examples.

Objectives

1 Write proportions.

2 Determine whether proportions are true or false.

3 Solve a proportion to find an unknown term.

4 Write proportions to solve application problems.

SECTION 3.2 Proportions

ARE YOU READY?

The following problems review some basic skills that are needed when working with proportions.

1. Simplify: $\frac{48}{120}$

2. Multiply: $5\frac{3}{5} \cdot 1\frac{11}{14}$

3. Multiply: 3.06×1.82

4. Divide: $4.1\overline{)14.637}$

One of the most useful concepts in mathematics is the *equation.* An **equation** is a statement indicating that two expressions are equal. All equations contain an = symbol. Some examples of equations are:

$$4 + 4 = 8, \quad 15.6 - 4.3 = 11.3, \quad \frac{1}{2} \cdot 10 = 5, \quad \text{and} \quad -16 \div 8 = -2$$

Each of the equations shown above is true. Equations can also be false. For example,

$$3 + 2 = 6 \quad \text{and} \quad -40 \div (-5) = -8$$

are false equations.

In this section, we will work with equations that state that two ratios (or rates) are equal.

1 Write proportions.

Like any tool, a ladder can be dangerous if used improperly. When setting up an extension ladder, users should follow the *4-to-1 rule:* For every 4 feet of ladder height, position the legs of the ladder 1 foot away from the base of the wall. The 4-to-1 rule for ladders can be expressed using a ratio.

$$\frac{4 \text{ feet}}{1 \text{ foot}} = \frac{4 \not{\text{feet}}}{1 \not{\text{foot}}} = \frac{4}{1}$$ Remove the common units of feet.

The figure on the right shows how the 4-to-1 rule was used to properly position the legs of a ladder 3 feet from the base of a 12-foot-high wall. We can write a ratio comparing the ladder's height to its distance from the wall.

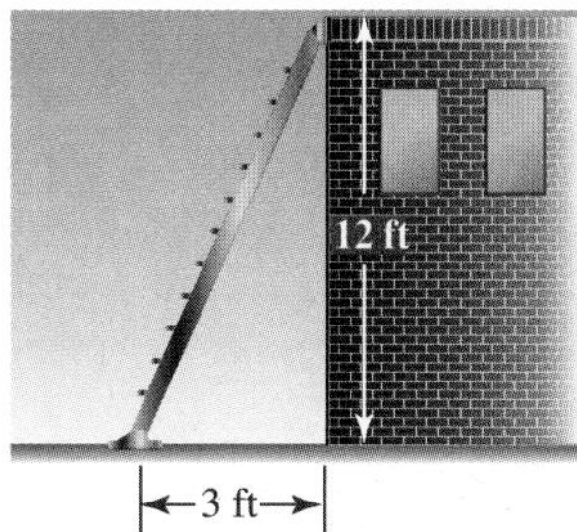

$$\frac{12 \text{ feet}}{3 \text{ feet}} = \frac{12 \cancel{\text{feet}}}{3 \cancel{\text{feet}}} = \frac{12}{3}$$ Remove the common units of feet.

Since this ratio satisfies the 4-to-1 rule, the two ratios $\frac{4}{1}$ and $\frac{12}{3}$ must be equal. Therefore, we have

$$\frac{4}{1} = \frac{12}{3}$$

Equations like this, which show that two ratios are equal, are called *proportions.*

Proportion

A **proportion** is a statement that two ratios (or rates) are equal.

Some examples of proportions are

- $\frac{1}{2} = \frac{3}{6}$ Read as "1 is to 2 as 3 is to 6."
- $\frac{3 \text{ waiters}}{7 \text{ tables}} = \frac{9 \text{ waiters}}{21 \text{ tables}}$ Read as "3 waiters are to 7 tables as 9 waiters are to 21 tables."

EXAMPLE 1 Write each statement as a proportion.

a. 22 is to 6 as 11 is to 3.

b. 1,000 administrators is to 8,000 teachers as 1 administrator is to 8 teachers.

Strategy We will locate the word *as* in each statement and identify the ratios (or rates) before and after it.

WHY The word *as* translates to the = symbol that is needed to write the statement as a proportion (equation).

Solution

a. This proportion states that two ratios are equal.

22 is **to** 6 as 11 is **to** 3.

$$\frac{22}{6} = \frac{11}{3}$$

Recall that the word "to" is used to separate the numbers being compared.

b. This proportion states that two rates are equal.

1,000 administrators is **to** 8,000 teachers as 1 administrator is **to** 8 teachers

$$\frac{1{,}000 \text{ administrators}}{8{,}000 \text{ teachers}} = \frac{1 \text{ administrator}}{8 \text{ teachers}}$$

When proportions involve rates, the units are often written outside of the proportion, as shown below:

$$\text{Administrators} \rightarrow \frac{1{,}000}{8{,}000} = \frac{1}{8} \leftarrow \text{Administrators}$$
$$\text{Teachers} \rightarrow \quad \leftarrow \text{Teachers}$$

Self Check 1

Write each statement as a proportion.

a. 16 is to 28 as 4 is to 7.

b. 300 children is to 500 adults as 3 children is to 5 adults.

Now Try **Problems 17 and 19**

2 Determine whether proportions are true or false.

Since a proportion is an equation, a proportion can be true or false. A proportion is true if its ratios (or rates) are equal and false if it its ratios (or rates) are not equal. One way to determine whether a proportion is true is to use the fraction simplifying skills of module 2.

Self Check 2

Determine whether each proportion is true or false by simplifying.

a. $\frac{4}{5} = \frac{16}{20}$ **b.** $\frac{30}{24} = \frac{28}{16}$

Now Try **Problem 23**

EXAMPLE 2 Determine whether each proportion is true or false by simplifying.

a. $\frac{3}{8} = \frac{21}{56}$ **b.** $\frac{30}{4} = \frac{45}{12}$

Strategy We will simplify any ratios in the proportion that are not in simplest form. Then we will compare them to determine whether they are equal.

WHY If the ratios are equal, the proportion is true. If they are not equal, the proportion is false.

Solution

a. On the left side of the proportion $\frac{3}{8} = \frac{21}{56}$, the ratio $\frac{3}{8}$ is in simplest form. On the right side, the ratio $\frac{21}{56}$ can be simplified.

$$\frac{21}{56} = \frac{3 \cdot \overset{1}{\cancel{7}}}{\underset{1}{\cancel{7}} \cdot 8} = \frac{3}{8}$$ Factor 21 and 56 and then remove the common factor of 7 in the numerator and denominator.

Since the ratios on the left and right sides of the proportion are equal, the proportion is true.

b. Neither ratio in the proportion $\frac{30}{4} = \frac{45}{12}$ is in simplest form. To simplify each ratio, we proceed as follows:

$$\frac{30}{4} = \frac{\overset{1}{\cancel{2}} \cdot 15}{\underset{1}{\cancel{2}} \cdot 2} = \frac{15}{2} \qquad \frac{45}{12} = \frac{\overset{1}{\cancel{3}} \cdot 15}{\underset{1}{\cancel{3}} \cdot 4} = \frac{15}{4}$$

Since the ratios on the left and right sides of the proportion are not equal $\left(\frac{15}{2} \neq \frac{15}{4}\right)$, the proportion is false.

There is another way to determine whether a proportion is true or false. Before we can discuss it, we need to introduce some more vocabulary of proportions.

Each of the four numbers in a proportion is called a **term.** The first and fourth terms are called the **extremes,** and the second and third terms are called the **means.**

First term (extreme) → 1, Third term (mean) → 3, Second term (mean) → 2, Fourth term (extreme) → 6:

$$\frac{1}{2} = \frac{3}{6}$$

In the proportion shown above, the *product of the extremes is equal to the product of the means.*

$$1 \cdot 6 = 6 \quad \text{and} \quad 2 \cdot 3 = 6$$

These products can be found by multiplying diagonally in the proportion. We call $1 \cdot 6$ and $2 \cdot 3$ **cross products.**

Cross products

$$1 \cdot 6 = 6 \qquad 2 \cdot 3 = 6$$

$$\frac{1}{2} = \frac{3}{6}$$

Note that the cross products are equal. This example illustrates the following property of proportions.

Cross-Products Property (Means-Extremes Property)

To determine whether a proportion is true or false, first multiply along one diagonal, and then multiply along the other diagonal.

- If the cross products are *equal,* the proportion is true.
- If the cross products are *not equal,* the proportion is false.

(If the product of the extremes is *equal* to the product of the means, the proportion is true. If the product of the extremes is *not equal* to the product of the means, the proportion is false.)

EXAMPLE 3 Determine whether each proportion is true or false.

a. $\frac{3}{7} = \frac{9}{21}$ **b.** $\frac{8}{3} = \frac{13}{5}$

Strategy We will check to see whether the cross products are equal (the product of the extremes is equal to the product of the means).

WHY If the cross products are equal, the proportion is true. If the cross products are not equal, the proportion is false.

Solution

a. $3 \cdot 21 = 63$ $7 \cdot 9 = 63$

$$\frac{3}{7} = \frac{9}{21}$$ Each cross product is 63.

Since the cross products are equal, the proportion is true.

b. $8 \cdot 5 = 40$ $3 \cdot 13 = 39$

$$\frac{8}{3} = \frac{13}{5}$$ One cross product is 40 and the other is 39.

Since the cross products are not equal, the proportion is false.

Self Check 3

Determine whether the proportion

$$\frac{6}{13} = \frac{18}{39}$$

is true or false.

Now Try **Problem 25**

Caution! We cannot remove common factors "across" an = symbol. When this is done, the true proportion from Example 3 part a, $\frac{3}{7} = \frac{9}{21}$, is changed into the false proportion $\frac{1}{7} = \frac{9}{7}$.

$$\frac{\overset{1}{\cancel{3}}}{7} = \frac{9}{\underset{7}{\cancel{21}}}$$

EXAMPLE 4 Determine whether each proportion is true or false.

a. $\frac{0.9}{0.6} = \frac{2.4}{1.5}$ **b.** $\frac{2\frac{1}{3}}{3\frac{1}{2}} = \frac{4\frac{2}{3}}{7}$

Strategy We will check to see whether the cross products are equal (the product of the extremes is equal to the product of the means).

WHY If the cross products are equal, the proportion is true. If the cross products are not equal, the proportion is false.

Self Check 4

Determine whether each proportion is true or false.

a. $\frac{9.9}{13.2} = \frac{1.125}{1.5}$

b. $\frac{3\frac{3}{16}}{2\frac{1}{2}} = \frac{4\frac{1}{4}}{3\frac{1}{3}}$

Now Try **Problems 31 and 35**

Solution

a. $1.5 \times 0.9 = 1.35$ $\quad$ $2.4 \times 0.6 = 1.44$

$$\frac{0.9}{0.6} = \frac{2.4}{1.5}$$ One cross product is 1.35 and the other is 1.44.

Since the cross products are not equal, the proportion is not true.

b.

$$2\frac{1}{3} \cdot 7 = \frac{7}{3} \cdot \frac{7}{1} = \frac{49}{3} \qquad 3\frac{1}{2} \cdot 4\frac{2}{3} = \frac{7}{2} \cdot \frac{14}{3} = \frac{7 \cdot \overset{1}{\cancel{2}} \cdot 7}{\underset{1}{\cancel{2}} \cdot 3} = \frac{49}{3}$$

$$\frac{2\frac{1}{3}}{3\frac{1}{2}} = \frac{4\frac{2}{3}}{7}$$ Each cross product is $\frac{49}{3}$.

Since the cross products are equal, the proportion is true.

When two pairs of numbers such as 2, 3 and 8, 12 form a true proportion, we say that they are **proportional.** To show that 2, 3 and 8, 12 are proportional, we check to see whether the equation

$$\frac{2}{3} = \frac{8}{12}$$

is a true proportion. To do so, we find the cross products.

$$2 \cdot 12 = 24 \qquad 3 \cdot 8 = 24$$

Since the cross products are equal, the proportion is true, and the numbers are proportional.

Self Check 5

Determine whether 6, 11 and 54, 99 are proportional.

Now Try **Problem 37**

EXAMPLE 5 Determine whether 3, 7 and 36, 91 are proportional.

Strategy We will use the given pairs of numbers to write two ratios and form a proportion. Then we will find the cross products.

WHY If the cross products are equal, the proportion is true, and the numbers are proportional. If the cross products are not equal, the proportion is false, and the numbers are not proportional.

Solution

The pair of numbers 3 and 7 form one ratio and the pair of numbers 36 and 91 form a second ratio. To write a proportion, we set the ratios equal. Then we find the cross products.

$$3 \cdot 91 = 273 \qquad 7 \cdot 36 = 252$$

$$\frac{3}{7} = \frac{36}{91}$$ One cross product is 273 and the other is 252.

Since the cross products are not equal, the numbers are not proportional.

3 Solve a proportion to find an unknown term.

Suppose that we know three of the four terms in the following proportion.

$$\frac{?}{5} = \frac{24}{20}$$

In mathematics, we often let a letter represent an unknown number. We call such a letter a **variable.** To find the unknown term, we let the variable x represent it in the proportion and we can write:

$$\frac{x}{5} = \frac{24}{20}$$

If the proportion is to be true, the cross products must be equal.

$x \cdot 20 = 5 \cdot 24$ Find the cross products for $\frac{x}{5} = \frac{24}{20}$ and set them equal.

$x \cdot 20 = 120$ To simplify the right side of the equation, do the multiplication: $5 \cdot 24 = 120$.

On the left side of the equation, the unknown number x is multiplied by 20. To undo the multiplication by 20 and isolate x, we divide both sides of the equation by 20.

$$\frac{x \cdot 20}{\mathbf{20}} = \frac{120}{\mathbf{20}}$$

We can simplify the fraction on the left side of the equation by removing the common factor of 20 from the numerator and denominator. On the right side, we perform the division indicated by the fraction bar.

$$\frac{x \cdot \overset{1}{\cancel{20}}}{\underset{1}{\cancel{20}}} = 6$$

To simplify the left side of the equation, remove the common factor of 20 in the numerator and denominator.
To simplify the right side of the equation, do the division: $120 \div 20 = 6$.

Since the product of any number and 1 is that number, it follows that the numerator $x \cdot 1$ on the left side can be replaced by x.

$$\frac{x}{1} = 6$$

Since the quotient of any number and 1 is that number, it follows that $\frac{x}{1}$ on the left side of the equation can be replaced with x. Therefore,

$$x = 6$$

We have found that the unknown term in the proportion is 6 and we can write:

$$\frac{\mathbf{6}}{5} = \frac{24}{20}$$

To check this result, we find the cross products.

Check:

$$\frac{6}{5} \stackrel{?}{=} \frac{24}{20} \qquad 20 \cdot 6 = \mathbf{120} \qquad 5 \cdot 24 = \mathbf{120}$$

Since the cross products are equal, the result, 6, checks.

In the previous example, when we find the value of the variable x that makes the given proportion true, we say that we have *solved the proportion* to find the unknown term.

The Language of Mathematics We solve proportions by writing a series of steps that result in an equation of the form $x =$ **a number** or **a number** $= x$. We say that the variable x is *isolated* on one side of the equation. *Isolated* means alone or by itself.

Solving a Proportion to Find an Unknown Term

1. Set the cross products equal to each other to form an equation.
2. Isolate the variable on one side of the equation by dividing both sides by the number that is multiplied by that variable.
3. Check by substituting the result into the original proportion and finding the cross products.

Self Check 6

Solve the proportion: $\frac{15}{x} = \frac{20}{32}$

Now Try **Problem 41**

EXAMPLE 6 Solve the proportion: $\frac{12}{20} = \frac{3}{x}$

Strategy We will set the cross products equal to each other to form an equation.

WHY Then we can isolate the variable x on one side of the equation to find the unknown term that it represents.

Solution

$\frac{12}{20} = \frac{3}{x}$ This is the proportion to solve.

$12 \cdot x = 20 \cdot 3$ Set the cross products equal to each other to form an equation.

$12 \cdot x = 60$ To simplify the right side of the equation, multiply: $20 \cdot 3 = 60$.

$\frac{12 \cdot x}{\mathbf{12}} = \frac{60}{\mathbf{12}}$ To undo the multiplication by 12 and isolate x, divide both sides by 12.

$x = 5$ To simplify the left side, remove the common factor of 12. To simplify the right side of the equation, do the division: $60 \div 12 = 5$.

$$\begin{array}{r} 5 \\ 12\overline{)60} \\ -60 \\ \hline 0 \end{array}$$

Thus, x is 5. To check this result, we substitute 5 for x in the original proportion.

Check:

$\frac{12}{20} \stackrel{?}{=} \frac{3}{5}$ $5 \cdot 12 = \mathbf{60}$

$20 \cdot 3 = \mathbf{60}$

Since the cross products are equal, the result, 5, checks.

Self Check 7

Solve the proportion:
$\frac{6.7}{x} = \frac{33.5}{38}$

Now Try **Problem 45**

EXAMPLE 7 Solve the proportion: $\frac{3.5}{7.2} = \frac{x}{15.84}$

Strategy We will set the cross products equal to each other to form an equation.

WHY Then we can isolate the variable x on one side of the equation to find the unknown term that it represents.

Solution

$\frac{3.5}{7.2} = \frac{x}{15.84}$ This is the proportion to solve.

$3.5 \cdot 15.84 = 7.2 \cdot x$ Set the cross products equal to each other to form an equation.

$55.44 = 7.2 \cdot x$ To simplify the left side of the equation, multiply: $3.5 \cdot 15.84 = 55.44$.

$\frac{55.44}{\mathbf{7.2}} = \frac{7.2 \cdot x}{\mathbf{7.2}}$ To undo the multiplication by 7.2 and isolate x, divide both sides by 7.2.

$7.7 = x$ To simplify the left side of the equation, do the division: $55.44 \div 7.2 = 7.7$. To simplify the right side, remove the common factor of 7.2.

$$\begin{array}{r} 15.84 \\ \times\ 3.5 \\ \hline 7920 \\ 47520 \\ \hline 55.440 \end{array}$$

$$\begin{array}{r} 7.7 \\ 7.2\overline{)55.44} \\ -50\ 4 \\ \hline 5\ 04 \\ -5\ 04 \\ \hline 0 \end{array}$$

Thus, x is 7.7. Check the result in the original proportion.

Using Your CALCULATOR **Solving Proportions with a Calculator**

To solve the proportion in Example 7, we set the cross products equal and divided both sides by 7.2 to isolate the variable x.

$$\frac{3.5 \cdot 15.84}{7.2} = x$$

We can find x by entering these numbers and pressing these keys on a calculator.

3.5 [×] 15.84 [÷] 7.2 [=] [7.7]

On some calculators, the [ENTER] key is pressed to find the result. Thus, x is 7.7.

EXAMPLE 8

Solve the proportion $\frac{x}{4\frac{1}{5}} = \frac{5\frac{1}{2}}{16\frac{1}{2}}$. Write the result as a mixed number.

Strategy We will set the cross products equal to each other to form an equation.

WHY Then we can isolate the variable x on one side of the equation to find the unknown term that it represents.

Solution

$$\frac{x}{4\frac{1}{5}} = \frac{5\frac{1}{2}}{16\frac{1}{2}}$$ This is the proportion to solve.

$$x \cdot 16\frac{1}{2} = 4\frac{1}{5} \cdot 5\frac{1}{2}$$ Set the cross products equal to each other to form an equation.

$$x \cdot \frac{33}{2} = \frac{21}{5} \cdot \frac{11}{2}$$ Write each mixed number as an improper fraction.

$$\frac{x \cdot \frac{33}{2}}{\frac{33}{2}} = \frac{\frac{21}{5} \cdot \frac{11}{2}}{\frac{33}{2}}$$ To undo the multiplication by $\frac{33}{2}$ and isolate x, divide both sides by $\frac{33}{2}$.

$$x = \frac{21}{5} \cdot \frac{11}{2} \cdot \frac{2}{33}$$ To simplify the left side, remove the common factor of $\frac{33}{2}$ in the numerator and denominator. Perform the division on the right side indicated by the complex fraction bar. Multiply the numerator of the complex fraction by the reciprocal of $\frac{33}{2}$, which is $\frac{2}{33}$.

$$x = \frac{21 \cdot 11 \cdot 2}{5 \cdot 2 \cdot 33}$$ Multiply the numerators. Multiply the denominators.

$$x = \frac{\overset{1}{\cancel{3}} \cdot 7 \cdot \overset{1}{\cancel{11}} \cdot \overset{1}{\cancel{2}}}{5 \cdot \underset{1}{\cancel{2}} \cdot \underset{1}{\cancel{3}} \cdot \underset{1}{\cancel{11}}}$$ To simplify the fraction, factor 21 and 33, and then remove the common factors 2, 3, and 11 in the numerator and denominator.

$$x = \frac{7}{5}$$ Multiply the remaining factors in the numerator. Multiply the remaining factors in the denominator.

$$x = 1\frac{2}{5}$$ Write the improper fraction as a mixed number.

Thus, x is $1\frac{2}{5}$. Check this result in the original proportion.

Self Check 8

Solve the proportion:

$$\frac{x}{2\frac{1}{3}} = \frac{2\frac{1}{4}}{1\frac{1}{2}}$$

Write the result as a mixed number.

Now Try **Problem 49**

4 Write proportions to solve application problems.

Proportions can be used to solve application problems from a wide variety of fields such as medicine, accounting, construction, and business. It is easy to spot problems that can be solved using a proportion. You will be given a ratio (or rate) and asked to find the missing part of another ratio (or rate). It is helpful to follow the five-step problem-solving strategy seen earlier in the text to solve proportion problems.

Self Check 9

CONCERT TICKETS If 9 tickets to a concert cost $112.50, find the cost of 15 tickets.

Now Try **Problem 79**

EXAMPLE 9 ***Shopping*** If 5 apples cost $1.15, find the cost of 16 apples.

Analyze

- We can express the fact that 5 apples cost $1.15 using the rate: $\frac{5 \text{ apples}}{\$1.15}$.
- What is the cost of 16 apples?

Form We will let the variable c represent the unknown cost of 16 apples. If we compare the number of apples to their cost, we know that the two rates must be equal and we can write a proportion.

5 apples **is** to $1.15 16 apples **is** to $$c$.

$$\frac{5}{1.15} = \frac{16}{c}$$

5 apples → 5; Cost of 5 apples → 1.15; 16 ← 16 apples; c ← Cost of 16 apples

The units can be written outside of the proportion.

Solve To find the cost of 16 apples, we solve the proportion for c.

$5 \cdot c = 1.15 \cdot 16$ Set the cross products equal to each other to form an equation.

$5 \cdot c = 18.4$ To simplify the right side of the equation, multiply: 1.15(16) = 18.4.

$\frac{5 \cdot c}{5} = \frac{18.4}{5}$ To undo the multiplication by 5 and isolate c, divide both sides by 5.

$c = 3.68$ To simplify the left side, remove the common factor of 5. On the right side, do the division: $18.4 \div 5 = 3.68$.

$$\begin{array}{r} 3.68 \\ 5\overline{)18.40} \\ -15 \\ \hline 3\,4 \\ -3\,0 \\ \hline 40 \\ -40 \\ \hline 0 \end{array}$$

State Sixteen apples will cost $3.68.

Check If 5 apples cost $1.15, then 15 apples would cost 3 times as much: $3 \cdot \$1.15 = \$3.45$. It seems reasonable that 16 apples would cost $3.68.

In Example 9, we could have compared the cost of the apples to the number of apples:

$1.15 **is** to 5 apples **as** $$c$ is **to** 16 apples. This would have led to the proportion

$$\frac{1.15}{5} = \frac{c}{16}$$

Cost of 5 apples → 1.15; 5 apples → 5; c ← Cost of 16 apples; 16 ← 16 apples

If we solve this proportion for c, we obtain the same result: 3.68.

Caution! When solving problems using proportions, make sure that the units of the numerators are the same and the units of the denominators are the same. For Example 9, it would be incorrect to write

$$\frac{1.15}{5} = \frac{16}{c}$$

Cost of 5 apples → 1.15; 5 apples → 5; 16 ← 16 apples; c ← Cost of 16 apples

EXAMPLE 10 *Scale Drawings* A **scale** is a ratio (or rate) that compares the size of a model, drawing, or map to the size of an actual object. The airplane shown below is drawn using a scale of 1 inch: 6 feet. This means that 1 inch on the drawing is actually 6 feet on the plane. The distance from wing tip to wing tip (the wingspan) on the drawing is 4.5 inches. What is the actual wingspan of the plane?

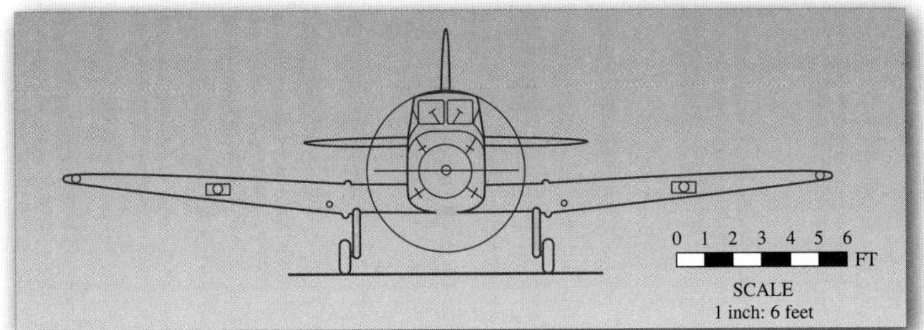

Analyze

- The airplane is drawn using a scale of 1 inch: 6 feet, which can be written as a rate in fraction form as: $\frac{1 \text{ inch}}{6 \text{ feet}}$.
- The wingspan of the airplane on the drawing is 4.5 inches.
- What is the actual wingspan of the plane?

Form We will let w represent the unknown actual wingspan of the plane. If we compare the measurements on the drawing to their actual measurement of the plane, we know that those two rates must be equal and we can write a proportion.

1 inch corresponds **to** 6 feet **as** 4.5 inches corresponds **to** w feet.

Measure on the drawing → 1, Measure on the plane → 6; 4.5 ← Measure on the drawing, w ← Measure on the plane

$$\frac{1}{6} = \frac{4.5}{w}$$

Solve To find the actual wingspan of the airplane, we solve the proportion for w.

$1 \cdot w = 6 \cdot 4.5$ Set the cross products equal to form an equation.

$w = 27$ To simplify each side of the equation, do the multiplication.

$$\begin{array}{r} \overset{3}{4.5} \\ \times\ 6 \\ \hline 27.0 \end{array}$$

State The actual wingspan of the plane is 27 feet.

Check Every 1 inch on the scale drawing corresponds to an actual length of 6 feet on the plane. Therefore, a 5-inch measurement corresponds to an actual wingspan of $5 \cdot 6$ feet, or 30 feet. It seems reasonable that a 4.5-inch measurement corresponds to an actual wingspan of 27 feet.

Self Check 10

SCALE MODELS In a scale model of a city, a 300-foot-tall building is 4 inches high. An observation tower in the model is 9 inches high. How tall is the actual tower?

Now Try **Problem 96**

EXAMPLE 11 *Baking* A recipe for chocolate cake calls for $1\frac{1}{2}$ cups of sugar for every $2\frac{1}{4}$ cups of flour. If a baker has only $\frac{1}{2}$ cup of sugar on hand, how much flour should he add to it to make chocolate cake batter?

Analyze

- The rate of $1\frac{1}{2}$ cups of sugar for every $2\frac{1}{4}$ cups of flour can be expressed as:

$$\frac{1\frac{1}{2} \text{ cups sugar}}{2\frac{1}{4} \text{ cups flour}}$$

- How much flour should be added to $\frac{1}{2}$ cups of sugar?

Self Check 11

BAKING See Example 11. How many cups of flour will be needed to make several chocolate cakes that will require a total of $12\frac{1}{2}$ cups of sugar?

Now Try **Problem 103**

Form We will let the variable f represent the unknown cups of flour. If we compare the cups of sugar to the cups of flour, we know that the two rates must be equal and we can write a proportion.

$1\frac{1}{2}$ cups of sugar is **to** $2\frac{1}{4}$ cups of flour **as** $\frac{1}{2}$ cup of sugar is **to** f cups of flour

$$\frac{1\frac{1}{2}}{2\frac{1}{4}} = \frac{\frac{1}{2}}{f}$$

Cups of sugar → $1\frac{1}{2}$; Cups of flour → $2\frac{1}{4}$; $\frac{1}{2}$ ← Cup of sugar; f ← Cups of flour

Solve To find the amount of flour that is needed, we solve the proportion for f.

$$\frac{1\frac{1}{2}}{2\frac{1}{4}} = \frac{\frac{1}{2}}{f}$$ This is the proportion to solve.

$$1\frac{1}{2} \cdot f = 2\frac{1}{4} \cdot \frac{1}{2}$$ Set the cross products equal to each other to form an equation.

$$\frac{3}{2} \cdot f = \frac{9}{4} \cdot \frac{1}{2}$$ Write each mixed number as an improper fraction.

$$\frac{\frac{3}{2} \cdot f}{\frac{3}{2}} = \frac{\frac{9}{4} \cdot \frac{1}{2}}{\frac{3}{2}}$$ To undo the multiplication by $\frac{3}{2}$ and isolate f, divide both sides by $\frac{3}{2}$.

$$f = \frac{9}{4} \cdot \frac{1}{2} \cdot \frac{2}{3}$$ To simplify the left side, remove the common factor of $\frac{3}{2}$ in the numerator and denominator. Perform the division on the right side indicated by the complex fraction bar. Multiply the numerator of the complex fraction by the reciprocal of $\frac{3}{2}$, which is $\frac{2}{3}$.

$$f = \frac{9 \cdot 1 \cdot 2}{4 \cdot 2 \cdot 3}$$ Multiply the numerators. Multiply the denominators.

$$f = \frac{\overset{1}{\cancel{3}} \cdot 3 \cdot 1 \cdot \overset{1}{\cancel{2}}}{4 \cdot \underset{1}{\cancel{2}} \cdot \underset{1}{\cancel{3}}}$$ To simplify the fraction, factor 9 and then remove the common factors 2 and 3 in the numerator and denominator.

$$f = \frac{3}{4}$$ Multiply the remaining factors in the numerator. Multiply the remaining factors in the denominator.

State The baker should use $\frac{3}{4}$ cups of flour.

Check The rate of $1\frac{1}{2}$ cups of sugar for every $2\frac{1}{4}$ cups of flour is about 1 to 2. The rate of $\frac{1}{2}$ cup of sugar to $\frac{3}{4}$ cup flour is also about 1 to 2. The result, $\frac{3}{4}$, seems reasonable.

Success Tip In Example 11, an alternate approach would be to write each term of the proportion in its equivalent decimal form and then solve for f.

Fractions and mixed numbers		**Decimals**
$\frac{1\frac{1}{2}}{2\frac{1}{4}} = \frac{\frac{1}{2}}{f}$	→	$\frac{1.5}{2.25} = \frac{0.5}{f}$

ANSWERS TO SELF CHECKS

1. a. $\frac{16}{28} = \frac{4}{7}$ **b.** $\frac{300 \text{ children}}{500 \text{ adults}} = \frac{3 \text{ children}}{5 \text{ adults}}$ **2. a.** true **b.** false **3.** true **4. a.** true **b.** true **5.** yes **6.** 24 **7.** 7.6 **8.** $3\frac{1}{2}$ **9.** \$187.50 **10.** 675 ft **11.** $18\frac{3}{4}$

SECTION 3.2 STUDY SET

VOCABULARY

Fill in the blanks.

1. A ________ is a statement that two ratios (or rates) are equal.

2. In $\frac{1}{2} = \frac{5}{10}$, the terms 1 and 10 are called the ________ of the proportion and the terms 2 and 5 are called the ________ of the proportion.

3. The ______ products for the proportion $\frac{4}{7} = \frac{36}{x}$ are $4 \cdot x$ and $7 \cdot 36$.

4. When two pairs of numbers form a proportion, we say that the numbers are ____________.

5. A letter that is used to represent an unknown number is called a ________.

6. When we find the value of x that makes the proportion $\frac{3}{8} = \frac{x}{16}$ true, we say that we have ________ the proportion.

7. We solve proportions by writing a series of steps that result in an equation of the form x = a number or a number = x. We say that the variable x is ________ on one side of the equation.

8. A ______ is a ratio (or rate) that compares the size of a model, drawing, or map to the size of an actual object.

CONCEPTS

Fill in the blanks.

9. If the cross products of a proportion are equal, the proportion is ______. If the cross products are *not equal,* the proportion is ______.

10. The proportion $\frac{2}{5} = \frac{4}{10}$ will be true if the product $\square \cdot 10$ is equal to the product $\square \cdot 4$.

11. Complete the cross products.

$\square \cdot 10 = \square \qquad 2 \cdot \square = \square$

$$\frac{9}{2} = \frac{45}{10}$$

12. In the equation $6 \cdot x = 2 \cdot 12$, to undo the multiplication by 6 and isolate x, ________ both sides of the equation by 6.

13. Label the missing units in the proportion.

Teacher's aides → 12 / □ → 100 = 3 ← □ / 25 ← Children

$$\frac{12}{100} = \frac{3}{25}$$

14. Consider the following problem: *For every 15 feet of chain link fencing, 4 support posts are used. How many support posts will be needed for 300 feet of chain link fencing?* Which of the proportions below could be used to solve this problem?

i. $\frac{15}{4} = \frac{300}{x}$ **ii.** $\frac{15}{4} = \frac{x}{300}$

iii. $\frac{4}{15} = \frac{300}{x}$ **iv.** $\frac{4}{15} = \frac{x}{300}$

NOTATION

Complete each step.

15. Solve the proportion: $\frac{2}{3} = \frac{x}{9}$

$2 \cdot 9 = \square$

$\square = 3 \cdot x$

$\frac{18}{\square} = \frac{3 \cdot x}{\square}$

$\square = x$

The solution is $\square$.

16. Solve the proportion: $\frac{14}{x} = \frac{49}{17.5}$

$14 \cdot \square = x \cdot 49$

$\square = x \cdot 49$

$\frac{245}{\square} = \frac{x \cdot 49}{\square}$

$\square = x$

The solution is $\square$.

GUIDED PRACTICE

Write each statement as a proportion. **See Example 1.**

17. 20 is to 30 as 2 is to 3.

18. 9 is to 36 as 1 is to 4.

19. 400 sheets is to 100 beds as 4 sheets is to 1 bed.

20. 50 shovels is to 125 laborers as 2 shovels is to 5 laborers.

Determine whether each proportion is true or false by simplifying. See Example 2.

21. $\frac{7}{9} = \frac{70}{81}$

22. $\frac{2}{5} = \frac{8}{20}$

23. $\frac{21}{14} = \frac{18}{12}$

24. $\frac{42}{38} = \frac{95}{60}$

Determine whether each proportion is true or false by finding cross products. See Example 3.

25. $\frac{4}{32} = \frac{2}{16}$

26. $\frac{6}{27} = \frac{4}{18}$

27. $\frac{9}{19} = \frac{38}{80}$

28. $\frac{40}{29} = \frac{29}{22}$

Determine whether each proportion is true or false by finding cross products. See Example 4.

29. $\frac{0.5}{0.8} = \frac{1.1}{1.3}$

30. $\frac{0.6}{1.4} = \frac{0.9}{2.1}$

31. $\frac{1.2}{3.6} = \frac{1.8}{5.4}$

32. $\frac{3.2}{4.5} = \frac{1.6}{2.7}$

33. $\frac{1\frac{4}{5}}{3\frac{3}{7}} = \frac{2\frac{3}{16}}{4\frac{1}{6}}$

34. $\frac{2\frac{1}{2}}{1\frac{1}{5}} = \frac{3\frac{3}{4}}{2\frac{9}{10}}$

35. $\frac{\frac{1}{5}}{1\frac{1}{6}} = \frac{1\frac{1}{7}}{11\frac{2}{3}}$

36. $\frac{11\frac{1}{4}}{2\frac{1}{2}} = \frac{\frac{3}{4}}{\frac{1}{6}}$

Determine whether the numbers are proportional. See Example 5.

37. 18, 54 and 3, 9

38. 4, 3 and 12, 9

39. 8, 6 and 21, 16

40. 15, 7 and 13, 6

Solve each proportion. Check each result. See Example 6.

41. $\frac{5}{10} = \frac{3}{c}$

42. $\frac{7}{14} = \frac{2}{x}$

43. $\frac{2}{3} = \frac{x}{6}$

44. $\frac{3}{6} = \frac{x}{8}$

Solve each proportion. Check each result. See Example 7.

45. $\frac{0.6}{9.6} = \frac{x}{4.8}$

46. $\frac{0.4}{3.4} = \frac{x}{13.6}$

47. $\frac{2.75}{x} = \frac{1.5}{1.2}$

48. $\frac{9.8}{x} = \frac{2.8}{5.4}$

Solve each proportion. Check each result. Write each result as a fraction or mixed number. See Example 8.

49. $\frac{x}{1\frac{1}{2}} = \frac{10\frac{1}{2}}{4\frac{1}{2}}$

50. $\frac{x}{3\frac{1}{3}} = \frac{1\frac{1}{2}}{1\frac{9}{11}}$

51. $\frac{x}{1\frac{1}{6}} = \frac{2\frac{5}{8}}{3\frac{1}{2}}$

52. $\frac{x}{2\frac{2}{3}} = \frac{1\frac{1}{20}}{3\frac{1}{2}}$

TRY IT YOURSELF

Solve each proportion.

53. $\frac{4{,}000}{x} = \frac{3.2}{2.8}$

54. $\frac{0.4}{1.6} = \frac{96.7}{x}$

55. $\frac{12}{6} = \frac{x}{\frac{1}{4}}$

56. $\frac{15}{10} = \frac{x}{\frac{1}{3}}$

57. $\frac{x}{800} = \frac{900}{200}$

58. $\frac{x}{200} = \frac{1{,}800}{600}$

59. $\frac{x}{2.5} = \frac{3.7}{9.25}$

60. $\frac{8.5}{x} = \frac{4.25}{1.7}$

61. $\frac{0.8}{2} = \frac{x}{5}$

62. $\frac{0.9}{0.3} = \frac{6}{x}$

63. $\frac{x}{4\frac{1}{10}} = \frac{3\frac{3}{4}}{1\frac{7}{8}}$

64. $\frac{x}{2\frac{1}{4}} = \frac{\frac{1}{2}}{\frac{1}{5}}$

65. $\frac{340}{51} = \frac{x}{27}$

66. $\frac{480}{36} = \frac{x}{15}$

67. $\frac{0.4}{1.2} = \frac{6}{x}$

68. $\frac{5}{x} = \frac{2}{4.4}$

69. $\frac{4.65}{7.8} = \frac{x}{5.2}$

70. $\frac{8.6}{2.4} = \frac{x}{6}$

71. $\frac{\frac{3}{4}}{\frac{1}{2}} = \frac{0.25}{x}$

72. $\frac{\frac{7}{8}}{\frac{1}{2}} = \frac{0.25}{x}$

CONCEPT EXTENSIONS

73. The proportion $\frac{3}{8} = \frac{15}{40}$ is true. Use the numbers 3, 8, 15, and 40 to write two other true proportions.

74. LOOK ALIKES . . .

a. Solve: $\frac{3}{4} = \frac{9}{x}$ **b.** Add: $\frac{3}{4} + \frac{9}{14}$

c. Subtract: $\frac{3}{4} - \frac{9}{14}$ **d.** Multiply: $\frac{3}{4} \cdot \frac{9}{14}$

e. Divide: $\frac{3}{4} \div \frac{9}{14}$

75. Are the numbers 0.75 and 1.2 proportional to the numbers $4\frac{1}{6}$ and $\frac{19}{8}$?

76. Write a true proportion that involves only the numbers 2, 6, and 18.

77. BASKETBALL Two players were shooting free throws after practice. John made 40 out of 60 shots and Richard made 60 out of 90 shots. Does it appear that the players have the same ability to shoot free throws? Explain your reasoning.

78. DRAWING The smaller picture on the left has dimensions 3 inches by 5 inches. The larger picture on the right has dimensions 7.5 inches by 12.5 inches. Are the pictures proportional? Explain your reasoning.

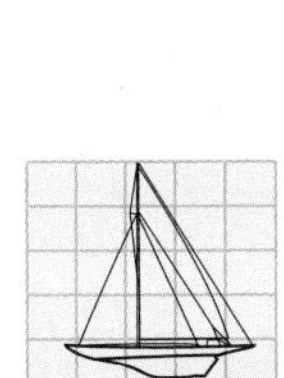

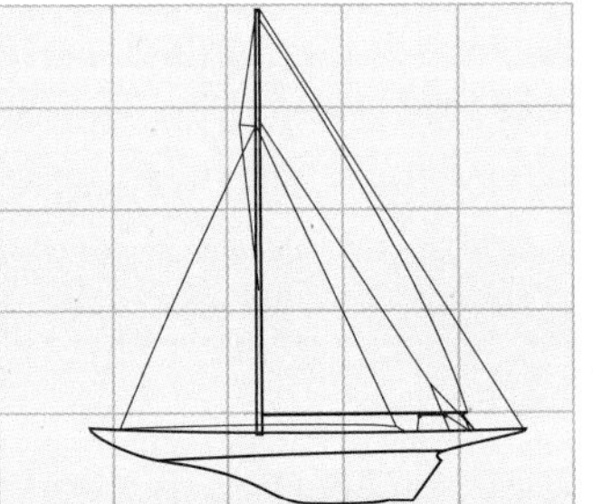

APPLICATIONS

To solve each problem, write and then solve a proportion.

79. SCHOOL LUNCHES A manager of a school cafeteria orders 750 pudding cups. What will the order cost if she purchases them wholesale, 6 cups for $1.75?

80. CLOTHES SHOPPING As part of a spring clearance, a men's store put dress shirts on sale, 2 for $25.98. How much will a businessman pay if he buys five shirts?

81. ANNIVERSARY GIFTS A florist sells a dozen long-stemmed red roses for $57.99. In honor of their 16th wedding anniversary, a man wants to buy 16 roses for his wife. What will the roses cost? (*Hint:* How many roses are in one dozen?)

82. COOKING A recipe for spaghetti sauce requires four 16-ounce bottles of ketchup to make 2 gallons of sauce. How many bottles of ketchup are needed to make 10 gallons of sauce? (*Hint:* Read the problem very carefully.)

83. BUSINESS PERFORMANCE The following bar graph shows the yearly costs and the revenue received by a business. Are the ratios of costs to revenue for 2011 and 2012 equal?

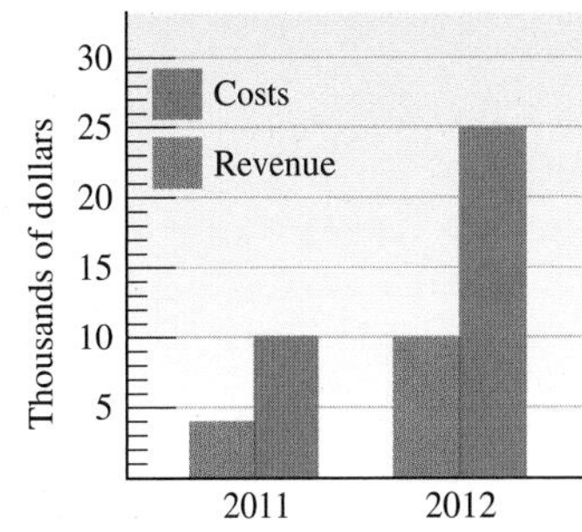

84. RAMPS Write a ratio of the rise to the run for each ramp shown. Set the ratios equal.

a. Is the resulting proportion true?

b. Is one ramp steeper than the other?

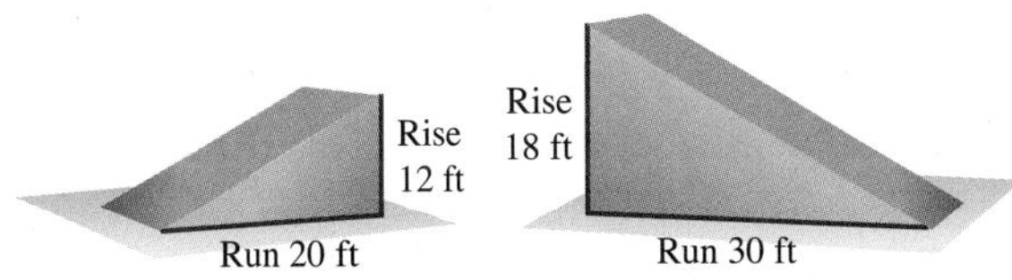

85. MIXING PERFUMES A perfume is to be mixed in the ratio of 3 drops of pure essence to 7 drops of alcohol. How many drops of pure essence should be mixed with 56 drops of alcohol?

86. MAKING COLOGNE A cologne can be made by mixing 2 drops of pure essence with 5 drops of distilled water. How much water should be used with 15 drops of pure essence?

87. LAB WORK In a red blood cell count, a drop of the patient's diluted blood is placed on a grid like that shown below. Instead of counting each and every red blood cell in the 25-square grid, a technician counts only the number of cells in the five highlighted squares. Then he or she uses a proportion to estimate the total red blood cell count. If there are 195 red blood cells in the blue squares, about how many red blood cells are in the entire grid?

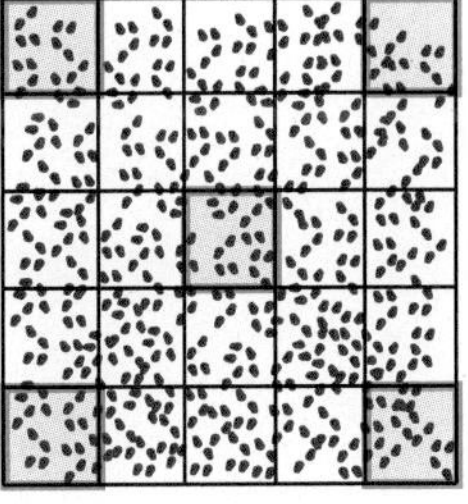

88. DOSAGES The proper dosage of a certain medication for a 30-pound child is shown. At this rate, what would be the dosage for a 45-pound child?

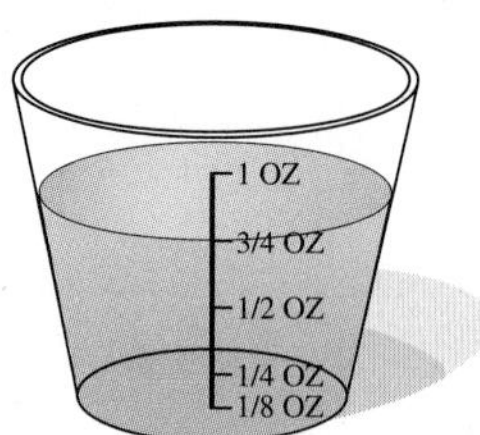

89. WAVES If the peak height to wavelength ratio is greater than 1:7, a wave becomes unstable and it breaks forward. (See the figure below.) What is the maximum height a wave with wavelength 637 feet can have before it breaks forward?

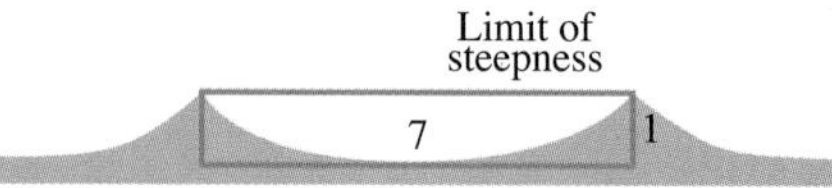

90. TWITTER According to a June, 2010 article in the Blog Herald, approximately 7,500 tweets are sent every 10 seconds. At this rate, about how many tweets are sent in one minute?

91. ERGONOMICS The science of ergonomics coordinates the design of working conditions with the requirements of the worker. The illustration gives guidelines for the dimensions (in inches) of a computer workstation to be used by a person whose height is 69 inches. Find a set of workstation dimensions for a person 5 feet 11 inches tall. Round to the nearest tenth.

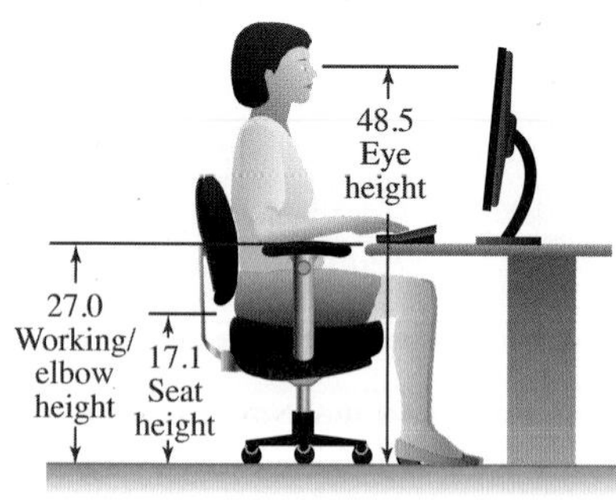

92. PHOTO ENLARGEMENTS The 3-by-5 photo is to be blown up to the larger size. Find x.

93. CAPTURE–RELEASE METHOD To estimate the ground squirrel population on his acreage, a farmer trapped, tagged, and then released a dozen squirrels. Two weeks later, the farmer trapped 35 squirrels and noted that 3 were tagged. Use this information to estimate the number of ground squirrels on his acreage.

94. CONCRETE A 2:3 concrete mix means that for every two parts of sand, three parts of gravel are used. How much sand should be used in a mix composed of 25 cubic feet of gravel?

95. WALLPAPERING Read the instructions on the label of wallpaper adhesive. Estimate the amount of adhesive needed to paper 500 square feet of kitchen walls if a heavy wallpaper will be used.

> COVERAGE: One-half gallon will hang approximately 4 single rolls (140 sq ft), depending on the weight of the wall covering and the condition of the wall.

96. DRAFTING In a scale drawing, a 280-foot antenna tower is drawn 7 inches high. The building next to it is drawn 2 inches high. How tall is the actual building?

97. BLUEPRINTS The scale for the drawing in the blueprint tells the reader that a $\frac{1}{4}$-inch length $\left(\frac{1}{4}''\right)$ on the drawing corresponds to an actual size of 1 foot (1′0″). Suppose the length of the kitchen is $2\frac{1}{2}$ inches on the blueprint. How long is the actual kitchen?

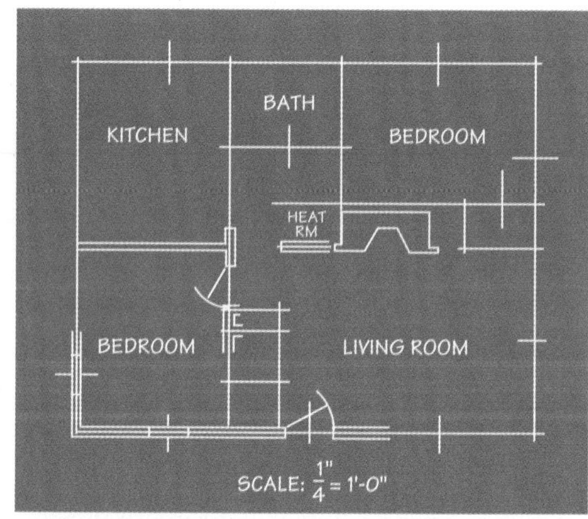

98. MODEL RAILROADS An HO scale model railroad engine is 6 inches long. If the HO scale is 1 to 87, how long is a real engine, in inches? In feet?

99. MODEL RAILROADS An N scale model railroad caboose is 4.5 inches long. If the N scale is 1 to 160, how long is a real caboose, in inches? In feet?

100. THE TITANIC A 1:144 scale model of the *Titanic* is to be built. If the ship was 882 feet long, find the length of the model.

101. CAROUSELS The ratio in the illustration below indicates that 1 inch on the model carousel is equivalent to 160 inches on the actual carousel. How wide should the model be if the actual carousel is 35 feet wide? (*Hint:* Convert 35 feet to inches.)

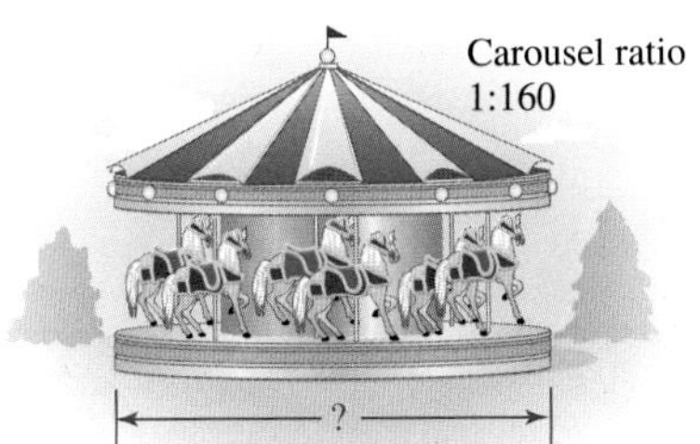

102. MIXING FUELS The instructions on a can of oil intended to be added to lawn mower gasoline read as shown. Are these instructions correct? (*Hint*: There are 128 ounces in 1 gallon.)

Recommended	Gasoline	Oil
50 to 1	6 gal	16 oz

103. MAKING COOKIES A recipe for chocolate chip cookies calls for $1\frac{1}{4}$ cups of flour and 1 cup of sugar. The recipe will make $3\frac{1}{2}$ dozen cookies. How many cups of flour will be needed to make 12 dozen cookies?

104. MAKING BROWNIES A recipe for brownies calls for 4 eggs and $1\frac{1}{2}$ cups of flour. If the recipe makes 15 brownies, how many cups of flour will be needed to make 130 brownies?

from Campus to Careers
Chef

Nick White/Getty Images

105. COMPUTER SPEED Using the *Mathematica 3.0* program, a Dell Dimension XPS R350 (Pentium II) computer can perform a set of 15 calculations in 2.85 seconds. How long will it take the computer to perform 100 such calculations?

106. QUALITY CONTROL Out of a sample of 500 men's shirts, 17 were rejected because of crooked collars. How many crooked collars would you expect to find in a run of 15,000 shirts?

107. DOGS Refer to the illustration below. A Saint Bernard website lists the "ideal proportions for the *height at the withers* to *body length* as 5: 6." What is the ideal height at the withers for a Saint Bernard whose body length is $37\frac{1}{2}$ inches?

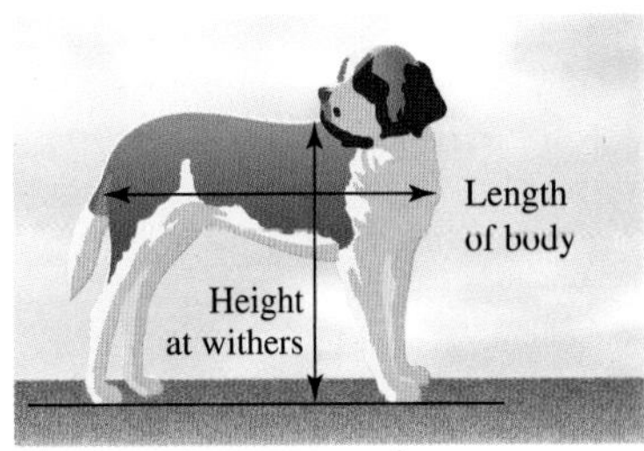

108. MILEAGE Under normal conditions, a Hummer can travel 325 miles on a full tank (25 gallons) of diesel. How far can it travel on its auxiliary tank, which holds 17 gallons of diesel?

109. PAYCHECKS Billie earns $412 for a 40-hour week. If she missed 10 hours of work last week, how much did she get paid?

110. STAFFING A school board has determined that there should be 3 teachers for every 50 students. Complete the table by filling in the number of teachers needed at each school.

	Glenwood High	Goddard Junior High	Sellers Elementary
Enrollment	2,700	1,900	850
Teachers			

WRITING

111. Explain the difference between a ratio and a proportion.

112. The following paragraph is from a book about dollhouses. What concept from this section is mentioned?

> *Today, the internationally recognized scale for dollhouses and miniatures is 1 in. = 1 ft. This is small enough to be defined as a miniature, yet not too small for all details of decoration and furniture to be seen clearly.*

113. Write a problem that could be solved using the following proportion.

$$\frac{4}{639} = \frac{10}{x}$$

Ounces of cashews → 4; Calories → 639; 10 ← Ounces of cashews; x ← Calories

114. Write a problem about a situation you encounter in your daily life that could be solved by using a proportion.

115. MINIATURES A high-wheeler bicycle is shown below. A model of it is to be made using a scale of 2 inches to 15 inches. The following proportion was set up to determine the height of the front wheel of the model. Explain the error.

$$\frac{2}{15} = \frac{48}{h}$$

48 in.

116. Explain how to tell whether $\frac{3.2}{3.7} = \frac{5.44}{6.29}$ is a true proportion.

Objectives

1. Identify the parts of a triangle.
2. Identify corresponding parts of congruent triangles.
3. Determine whether two triangles are similar.
4. Use similar triangles to find unknown lengths in application problems.

SECTION 3.3 Similar Triangles

ARE YOU READY?

The following problems review some basic skills that are needed when working with similar triangles.

1. Are $\frac{3}{2}$ and $\frac{48}{32}$ proportional?

2. Solve the proportion: $\frac{12}{8} = \frac{36}{x}$

3. Solve the proportion: $\frac{0.05}{x} = \frac{0.0025}{6}$

4. a. How many sides does a triangle have?

b. How many angles does a triangle have?

In our everyday lives, we see many types of triangles. Triangular-shaped kites, sails, roofs, tortilla chips, and ramps are just a few examples. In this section, we will discuss how to compare the size and shape of two given triangles. From this comparison, we can make observations about their side lengths and angle measures.

1 Identify the parts of a triangle.

A **triangle** is a closed geometric figure with three **line segments** for its sides, as shown below. The **point** where two sides of a triangle meet is called a **vertex** of the triangle (plural **vertices**). Since points are often labeled with capital letters, we can use capital letters to name triangles. For example, when referring to the triangle below, with vertices A, B, and C, we can use the notation ΔABC (read as "triangle ABC").

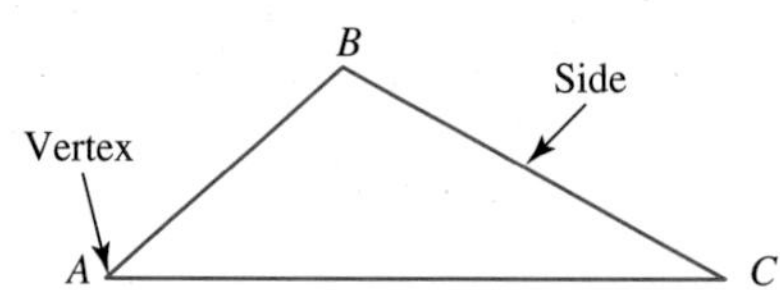

> ***The Language of Mathematics*** When naming a triangle, we may begin with any vertex. Then we move around the figure in a clockwise (or counterclockwise) direction as we list the remaining vertices. Other ways of naming the triangle shown above are ΔACB, ΔBCA, ΔBAC, ΔCAB, and ΔCBA.

ΔABC shown on the previous page is formed by three line segments and it has three angles. These six parts of the triangle can be written as:

$\overline{AB}$	Read as "line segment AB."	$\angle A$	Read as "angle A."
$\overline{BC}$	Read as "line segment BC."	$\angle B$	Read as "angle B."
$\overline{CA}$	Read as "line segment CA."	$\angle C$	Read as "angle C."

We can measure the length of each side of ΔABC using a ruler. For example, if $\overline{AC}$ is 2 inches long, we can write:

$\text{m}(\overline{AC}) = 2$ Read as "the measure of line segment AC is 2."

We can use a protractor to find the measure of each angle of ΔABC. For example, if $\angle A$ measures 30°, we can write:

$\text{m}(\angle A) = 30°$ Read as "the measure of angle A is 30 degrees."

2 Identify corresponding parts of congruent triangles.

Simply put, two geometric figures are **congruent** if they have the same shape and size. For example, if $\triangle ABC$ and $\triangle DEF$ shown below are congruent, we can write

$\triangle ABC \cong \triangle DEF$ Read as "Triangle ABC is congruent to triangle DEF."

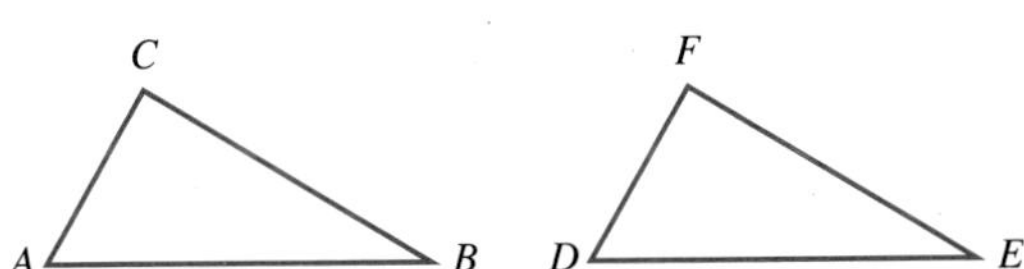

One way to determine whether two triangles are congruent is to see if one triangle can be moved onto the other triangle in such a way that it fits exactly. When we write $\triangle ABC \cong \triangle DEF$, we are showing how the vertices of one triangle are matched to the vertices of the other triangle to obtain a "perfect fit." We call this matching of points a **correspondence.**

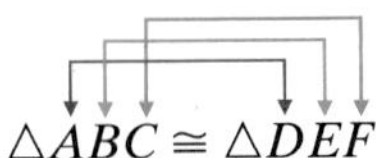

$A \leftrightarrow D$ Read as "Point A corresponds to point D."

$B \leftrightarrow E$ Read as "Point B corresponds to point E."

$C \leftrightarrow F$ Read as "Point C corresponds to point F."

When we establish a correspondence between the vertices of two congruent triangles, we also establish a correspondence between the angles and the sides of the triangles. Corresponding angles and corresponding sides of congruent triangles are called **corresponding parts.** *Corresponding parts of congruent triangles are always congruent.* That is, corresponding parts of congruent triangles always have the same measure. For the congruent triangles shown above, we have six pairs of congruent parts:

Angles: $\text{m}(\angle A) = \text{m}(\angle D)$ $\text{m}(\angle B) = \text{m}(\angle E)$ $\text{m}(\angle C) = \text{m}(\angle F)$

Sides: $\text{m}(\overline{BC}) = \text{m}(\overline{EF})$ $\text{m}(\overline{AC}) = \text{m}(\overline{DF})$ $\text{m}(\overline{AB}) = \text{m}(\overline{DE})$

Congruent Triangles

Two triangles are congruent if and only if their vertices can be matched so that the corresponding sides and the corresponding angles are congruent.

Self Check 1

Refer to the figure below, where $\triangle ABC \cong \triangle EDF$.

a. Name the six congruent corresponding parts of the triangles.

b. Find $m(\angle C)$.

c. Find $m(\overline{FE})$.

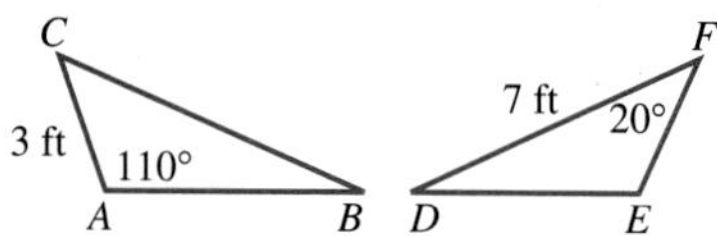

Now Try **Problem 29**

EXAMPLE 1 Refer to the figure below, where $\triangle XYZ \cong \triangle PQR$.

a. Name the six congruent corresponding parts of the triangles.

b. Find $m(\angle P)$.

c. Find $m(\overline{XZ})$.

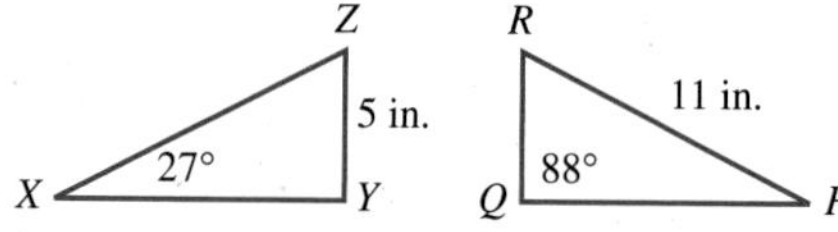

Strategy We will establish the correspondence between the vertices of $\triangle XYZ$ and the vertices of $\triangle PQR$.

WHY This will, in turn, establish a correspondence between the congruent corresponding angles and sides of the triangles.

Solution

a. The correspondence between the vertices is

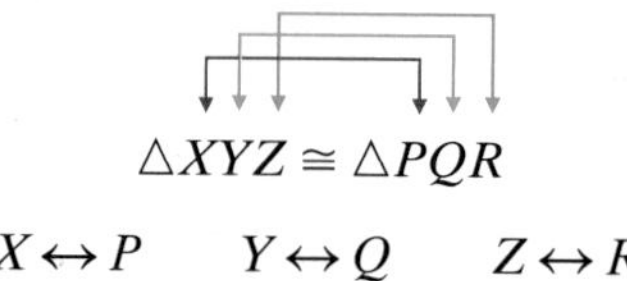

$$\triangle XYZ \cong \triangle PQR$$

$$X \leftrightarrow P \qquad Y \leftrightarrow Q \qquad Z \leftrightarrow R$$

Corresponding parts of congruent triangles are congruent. Therefore, the congruent corresponding angles are

$$\angle X \cong \angle P \qquad \angle Y \cong \angle Q \qquad \angle Z \cong \angle R$$

The congruent corresponding sides are

$$\overline{YZ} \cong \overline{QR} \qquad \overline{XZ} \cong \overline{PR} \qquad \overline{XY} \cong \overline{PQ}$$

b. From the figure, we see that $m(\angle X) = 27°$. Since $\angle X \cong \angle P$, it follows that $m(\angle P) = 27°$.

c. From the figure, we see that $m(\overline{PR}) = 11$ inches. Since $\overline{XZ} \cong \overline{PR}$, it follows that $m(\overline{XZ}) = 11$ inches.

3 Determine whether two triangles are similar.

We have seen that congruent triangles have the same shape and size. **Similar triangles** have the same shape, but not necessarily the same size. That is, one triangle is an exact scale model of the other triangle. If the triangles in the figure below are similar, we can write $\triangle ABC \sim \triangle DEF$ (read the symbol $\sim$ as "is similar to").

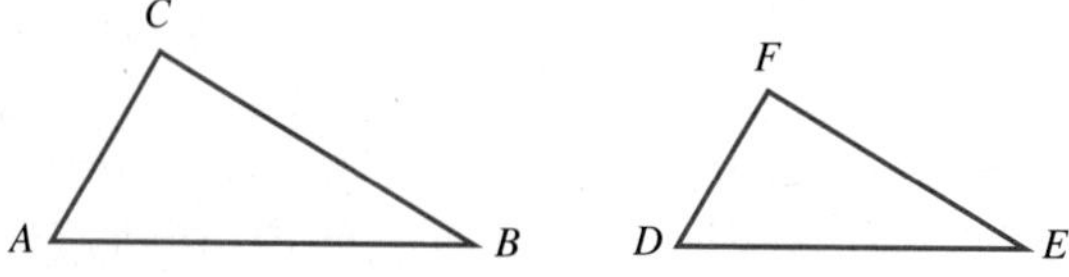

Success Tip Note that congruent triangles are always similar, but similar triangles are not always congruent.

The formal definition of similar triangles requires that we establish a correspondence between the vertices of the triangles. The definition also involves the word *proportional.*

Recall that a **proportion** is a mathematical statement that two ratios (fractions) are equal. An example of a proportion is

$$\frac{1}{2} = \frac{4}{8} \quad \text{Because } 1 \cdot 8 = 2 \cdot 4.$$

In this case, we say that $\frac{1}{2}$ and $\frac{4}{8}$ are *proportional.*

Similar Triangles

If two triangles are **similar**, their vertices can be matched so that:

- Corresponding angles are congruent
- The lengths of corresponding sides are proportional.

EXAMPLE 2 Refer to the figure below. If $\triangle PQR \sim \triangle CDE$, name the congruent angles and the sides that are proportional.

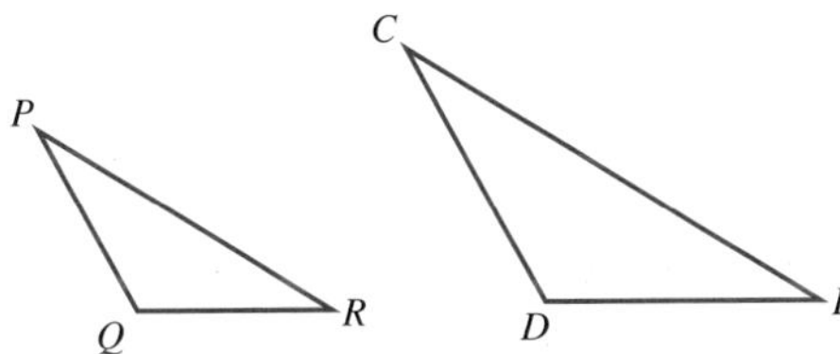

Strategy We will establish the correspondence between the vertices of $\triangle PQR$ and the vertices of $\triangle CDE$.

WHY This will, in turn, establish a correspondence between the congruent corresponding angles and proportional sides of the triangles.

Solution When we write $\triangle PQR \sim \triangle CDE$, a correspondence between the vertices of the triangles is established.

$$\triangle PQR \sim \triangle CDE$$

Since the triangles are similar, corresponding angles are congruent:

$$\angle P \cong \angle C \qquad \angle Q \cong \angle D \qquad \angle R \cong \angle E$$

The lengths of the corresponding sides are proportional. To simplify the notation, we will now let $PQ = m(\overline{PQ})$, $CD = m(\overline{CD})$, $QR = m(\overline{QR})$, and so on.

$$\frac{PQ}{CD} = \frac{QR}{DE} \qquad \frac{QR}{DE} = \frac{PR}{CE} \qquad \frac{PQ}{CD} = \frac{PR}{CE}$$

Written in a more compact way, we have

$$\frac{PQ}{CD} = \frac{QR}{DE} = \frac{PR}{CE}$$

Self Check 2

If $\triangle GEF \sim \triangle IJH$, name the congruent angles and the sides that are proportional.

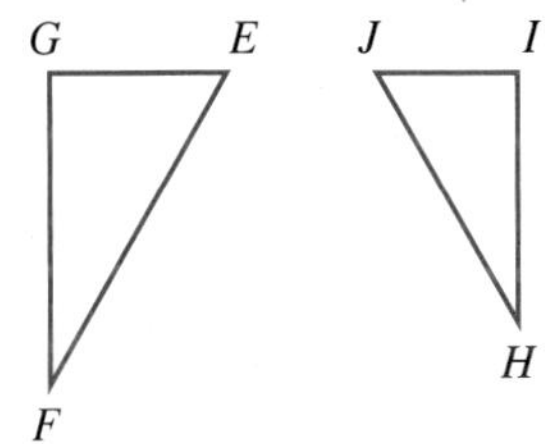

Now Try **Problem 31**

It is possible to conclude that two triangles are similar without having to show that all three pairs of corresponding angles are congruent and that the lengths of all three pairs of corresponding sides are proportional.

The following *theorem* simplifies things. It states that we need only find two pairs of corresponding angles that are congruent to show two triangles are similar. (A **theorem** is a mathematical statement that can be proven. The proof of this theorem is beyond the scope of this module. It is discussed in more formal geometry classes.)

AA Similarity Theorem

Given a correspondence between two triangles, if two pairs of corresponding angles have the same measure, the triangles are similar.

For the triangles shown below, we can conclude that $\Delta ABC \sim \Delta DEF$ because two pairs of corresponding angles have the same measure: $m(\angle A) = m(\angle D)$ and $m(\angle B) = m(\angle E)$.

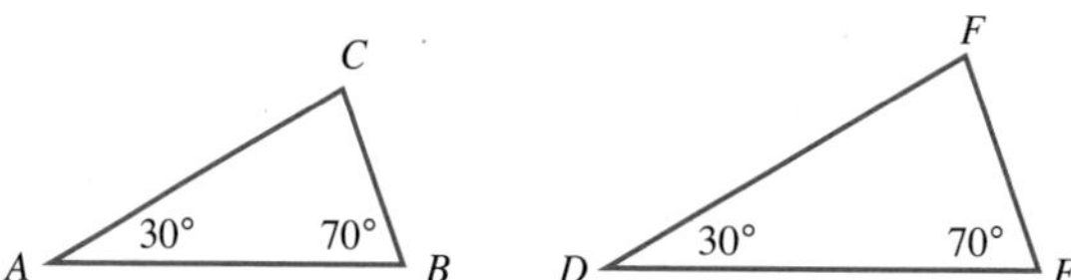

Once we have determined that $\Delta ABC \sim \Delta DEF$, we know three pairs of corresponding sides are proportional and we can write three true proportions:

$$\frac{AB}{DE} = \frac{BC}{EF}, \quad \frac{BC}{EF} = \frac{CA}{FD}, \quad \text{and} \quad \frac{CA}{FD} = \frac{AB}{DE}$$

Read AB as "the length of segment AB."

Self Check 3

In the figure below, find:

a. x **b.** y

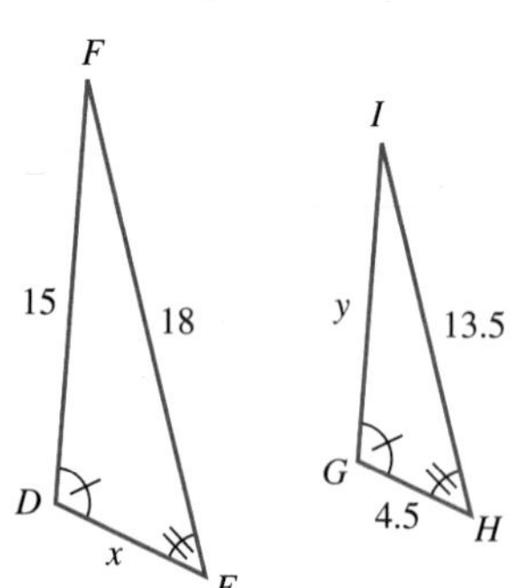

Now Try **Problem 41**

EXAMPLE 3 In the figure below find: **a.** x **b.** y

Strategy To find x, we will write a proportion of corresponding sides so that x is the only unknown. Then we will solve the proportion for x. We will use a similar method to find y.

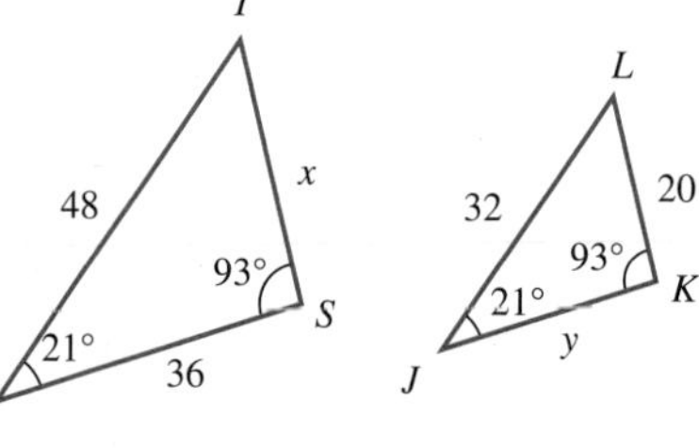

WHY Since $m(\angle R) = m(\angle J)$ and $m(\angle S) = m(\angle K)$, it follows from the AA similarity theorem that $\Delta RST \sim \Delta JKL$. And if the triangles are similar, we can write true proportions involving pairs of corresponding sides.

Solution

a. When we write $\Delta RST \sim \Delta JKL$, a correspondence between the vertices of the two triangles is established.

$$\Delta RST \sim \Delta JKL$$

To find x (which represents the length of $\overline{ST}$), we write a proportion of corresponding side lengths in such a way that x is the only unknown. Then we solve the proportion.

$\frac{RT}{JL} = \frac{ST}{KL}$ Each fraction is a ratio of a side length of $\triangle RST$ to its corresponding side length of $\triangle JKL$.

$\frac{48}{32} = \frac{x}{20}$ Substitute: $RT = 48$, $JL = 32$, $ST = x$, and $KL = 20$.

$$48(20) = 32x$$ Find each cross product and set them equal.

$$960 = 32x$$ Do the multiplication.

$$\frac{960}{32} = \frac{32x}{32}$$ To isolate x, undo the multiplication by 32 by dividing both sides by 32.

$$30 = x$$ Do the division: 960 ÷ 32 = 30.

Thus, x is 30.

$$\begin{array}{r} 48 \\ \times 20 \\ \hline 960 \end{array} \qquad \begin{array}{r} 30 \\ 32\overline{)960} \\ -96 \\ \hline 00 \\ -00 \\ \hline 0 \end{array}$$

b. To find y (which represents the length of JK), we write a proportion of corresponding side lengths in such a way that y is the only unknown. Then we solve the proportion.

$$\frac{RT}{JL} = \frac{RS}{JK}$$

$$\frac{48}{32} = \frac{36}{y}$$ Substitute: $RT = 48$, $JL = 32$, $RS = 36$, and $JK = y$.

$$48y = 32(36)$$ Find each cross product and set them equal.

$$48y = 1{,}152$$ Do the multiplication.

$$\frac{48y}{48} = \frac{1{,}152}{48}$$ To isolate y, undo the multiplication by 48 by dividing both sides by 48.

$$y = 24$$ Do the division: 1,152 ÷ 48 = 24.

Thus, y is 24.

$$\begin{array}{r} 36 \\ \times 32 \\ \hline 72 \\ 1080 \\ \hline 1152 \end{array} \qquad \begin{array}{r} 24 \\ 48\overline{)1{,}152} \\ -96 \\ \hline 192 \\ -192 \\ \hline 0 \end{array}$$

4 Use similar triangles to find unknown lengths in application problems.

Similar triangles and proportions can be used to find lengths that would normally be difficult to measure. For example, we can use the properties of similar triangles to calculate the height of a tree while standing safely on the ground.

EXAMPLE 4 ***Finding the Height of a Tree*** A tree casts a shadow 18 feet long at the same time as a woman 5 feet tall casts a shadow 1.5 feet long. Find the height of the tree.

Solution Refer to the illustration below. One triangle is drawn in such a way that the woman, her shadow, and the sun's rays form its sides. A second triangle is drawn so that the tree, its shadow, and the sun's rays form its sides.

Each triangle has a right angle. Since the sun's rays strike the ground at the same angle, the angles highlighted with a tick mark have the same measure. Therefore, two angles of the smaller triangle have the same measures as two angles of the larger triangle; the triangles are similar.

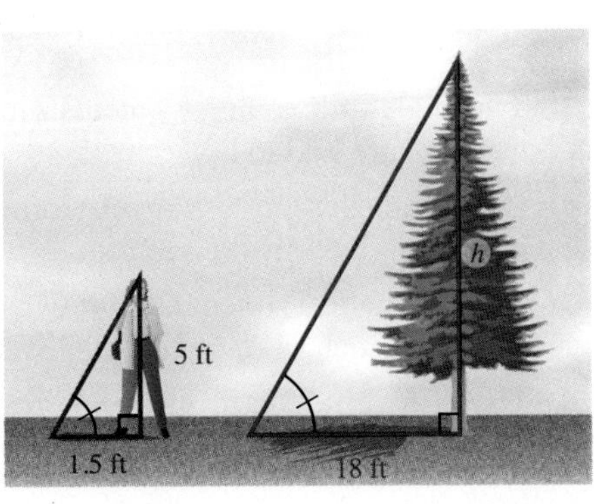

Self Check 4

Find the height of the tree in Example 4 if the woman is 5 feet 6 inches tall and her shadow is 1.5 feet long.

Now Try **Problem 49**

If we let $h =$ the height of the tree, we can find h by solving the following proportion.

$$\frac{h}{5} = \frac{18}{1.5} \quad \frac{\text{Height of the tree}}{\text{Height of the woman}} = \frac{\text{Length of shadow of the tree}}{\text{Length of shadow of the woman}}$$

$1.5h = 5(18)$ In a proportion, the product of the extremes equals the product of the means.

$1.5h = 90$ Perform the multiplication.

$\frac{1.5h}{\mathbf{1.5}} = \frac{90}{\mathbf{1.5}}$ To undo the multiplication by 1.5, divide both sides by 1.5.

$h = 60$ Divide: $90 \div 1.5 = 60$.

The tree is 60 feet tall.

Check $\frac{18}{1.5} = 12$ and $\frac{60}{5} = 12$. The ratios are the same. The result checks.

At times, theorems beyond the scope of this module are needed to show that two triangles are similar. For example, suppose $\overline{PR}$ is parallel to $\overline{MN}$ in the figure below. A theorem from geometry called the **vertical angle theorem** tells us that $\angle PQR \cong \angle NQM$. This is shown in the figure with the single tick marks. Another theorem, called the **alternate interior angles theorem,** tells us that $\angle N \cong \angle P$. This is shown in the figure with the double tick marks. Since two pairs of corresponding angles have the same measure, it follows from the AA similarity theorem that $\Delta PQR \sim \Delta NQM$.

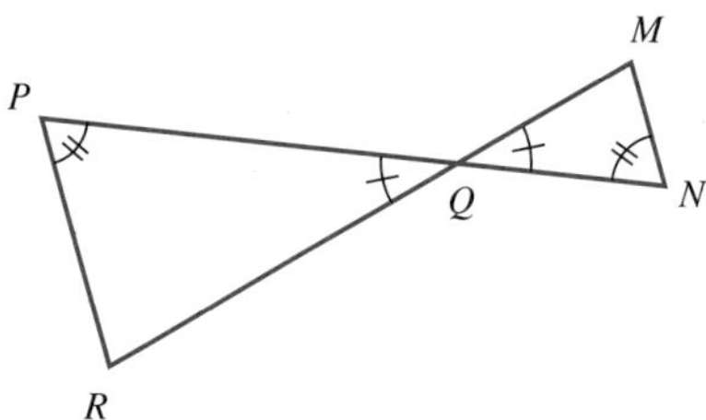

Once we know that $\Delta PQR \sim \Delta NQM$, we can write three true proportions:

$$\frac{PQ}{NQ} = \frac{QR}{QM} \qquad \frac{QR}{QM} = \frac{RP}{MN} \qquad \frac{RP}{MN} = \frac{PQ}{NQ}$$

ANSWERS TO SELF CHECKS

1. a. $\angle A \cong \angle E, \angle B \cong \angle D, \angle C \cong \angle F, \overline{AB} \cong \overline{ED}, \overline{BC} \cong \overline{DF}, \overline{CA} \cong \overline{FE}$ **b.** 20° **c.** 3 ft
2. $\angle G \cong \angle I, \angle E \cong \angle J, \angle F \cong \angle H; \frac{EG}{JI} = \frac{GF}{IH}, \frac{GF}{IH} = \frac{FE}{HJ}, \frac{EG}{JI} = \frac{FE}{HJ}$ **3. a.** 6 **b.** 11.25
4. 66 ft

SECTION 3.3 STUDY SET

VOCABULARY

Fill in the blanks.

1. ________ triangles are the same size and the same shape.

2. When we match the vertices of $\triangle ABC$ with the vertices of $\triangle DEF$, as shown below, we call this matching of points a ____________.

$A \leftrightarrow D \quad B \leftrightarrow E \quad C \leftrightarrow F$

3. Two angles or two line segments with the same measure are said to be ________.

4. If two triangles are ______, they have the same shape but not necessarily the same size.

5. A mathematical statement that two ratios (fractions) are equal, such as $\frac{x}{18} = \frac{4}{9}$, is called a ________.

6. The _____ products for the proportion $\frac{10}{3} = \frac{5}{x}$ are $10x$ and 15.

7. A point where two sides of a polygon intersect is called a ______ of the polygon.

8. Atriangle has three ______ and three vertices.

CONCEPTS

9. Refer to the triangles below.

a. Do these triangles appear to be congruent? Explain why or why not.

b. Do these triangles appear to be similar? Explain why or why not.

10. a. Draw a triangle that is congruent to $\triangle CDE$ shown below. Label it $\triangle ABC$.

b. Draw a triangle that is similar to, but not congruent to, $\triangle CDE$. Label it $\triangle MNO$.

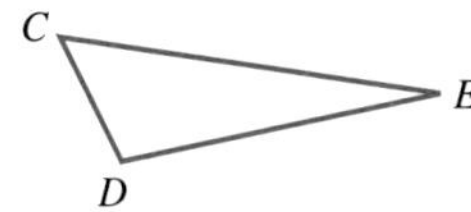

11. Name the six corresponding parts of the congruent triangles shown below.

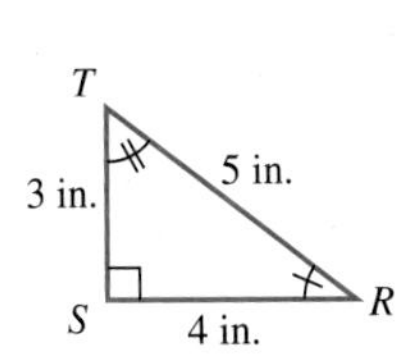

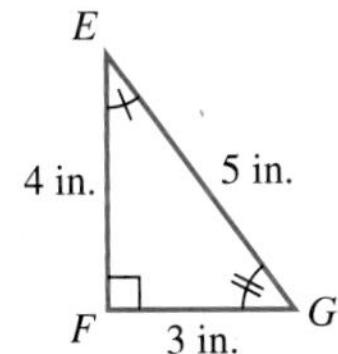

12. The two triangles shown in the following illustration are similar. Complete the proportion.

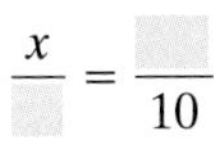

$$\frac{x}{\square} = \frac{\square}{10}$$

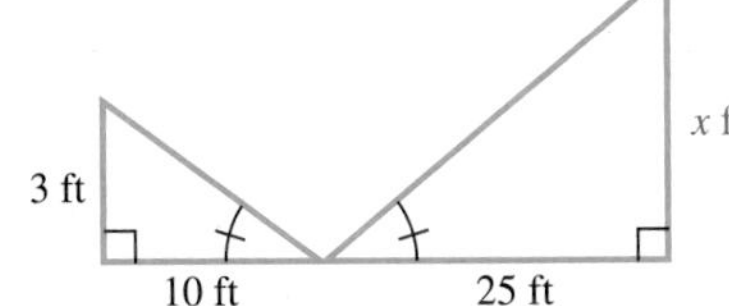

13. Two similar triangles are shown below. Fill in the blanks to make the proportions true.

$$\frac{AB}{DE} = \frac{\square}{EF} \qquad \frac{BC}{\square} = \frac{CA}{FD} \qquad \frac{CA}{FD} = \frac{AB}{\square}$$

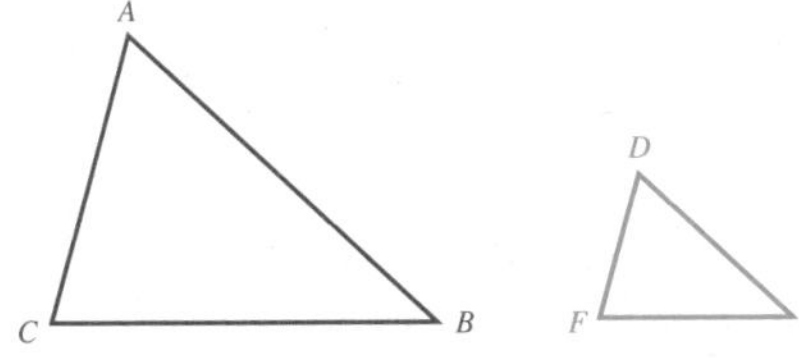

Fill in the blanks.

14. If two triangles are similar, their vertices can be matched so that:

- Corresponding angles are ________ .
- The lengths of corresponding sides are ___________.

15. If two angles of one triangle have the same measure as two angles of a second triangle, the triangles are ______.

16. If two triangles are ______, their corresponding sides are in proportion.

17. Congruent triangles are always similar, but similar triangles are not always ________.

18. For certain application problems, similar triangles and __________ can be used to find lengths that would normally be difficult to measure.

NOTATION

Fill in the blanks.

19. The symbol $\cong$ is read as "___ ___________ ___."

20. The symbol $\sim$ is read as "___ ________ ___."

21. The symbol $\overline{AB}$ is read as "_________ AB."

22. We read $m(\overline{AB})$ as "the ________ of segment AB."

23. We read $\angle ABC$ as "______ ABC."

24. The symbol $m(\angle A)$ means the ________ of angle A.

25. We read "$\triangle ABC$" as "________ ABC."

26. The symbol ⌉ indicates a ______ angle.

Complete each step.

27. Solve for x: $\frac{12}{18} = \frac{x}{24}$

$$12 \cdot 24 = 18 \cdot \square$$
$$\square = 18x$$
$$\frac{288}{\square} = \frac{18x}{\square}$$
$$16 = x$$

28. Solve for x: $\frac{14}{x} = \frac{49}{17.5}$

$$14 \cdot \square = 49x$$
$$\square = 49x$$
$$\frac{245}{\square} = \frac{49x}{\square}$$
$$5 = x$$

GUIDED PRACTICE

29. Refer to the figure on the next page, where $\triangle BCD \cong \triangle MNO$. **See Example 1.**

a. Name the six congruent corresponding parts of the triangles. **See Example 1.**

b. Find $m(\angle N)$.

c. Find $m(\overline{MO})$.

d. Find $m(\overline{CD})$.

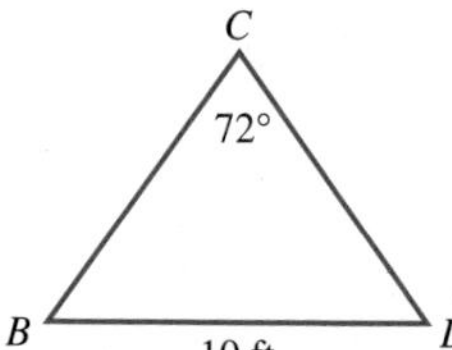

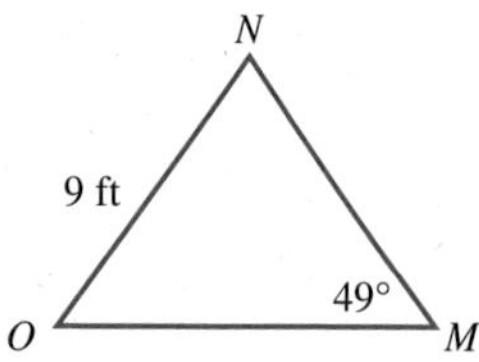

30. Refer to the figure below, where $\triangle DCG \cong \triangle RST$. **See Example 1.**

a. Name the six congruent corresponding parts of the triangles. **See Example 1.**

b. Find $m(\angle R)$.

c. Find $m(\overline{DG})$.

d. Find $m(\overline{ST})$.

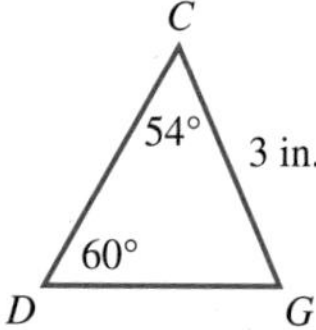

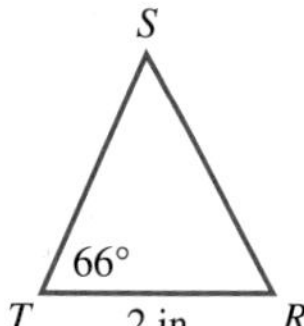

31. Refer to the similar triangles shown below. **See Example 2.**

a. Name 3 pairs of congruent angles.

b. Complete each proportion.

$$\frac{LM}{HJ} = \frac{\square}{JE} \qquad \frac{MR}{JE} = \frac{\square}{HE} \qquad \frac{\square}{HJ} = \frac{LR}{HE}$$

c. We can write the answer to part b in a more compact form:

$$\frac{LM}{\square} = \frac{MR}{\square} = \frac{\square}{HE}$$

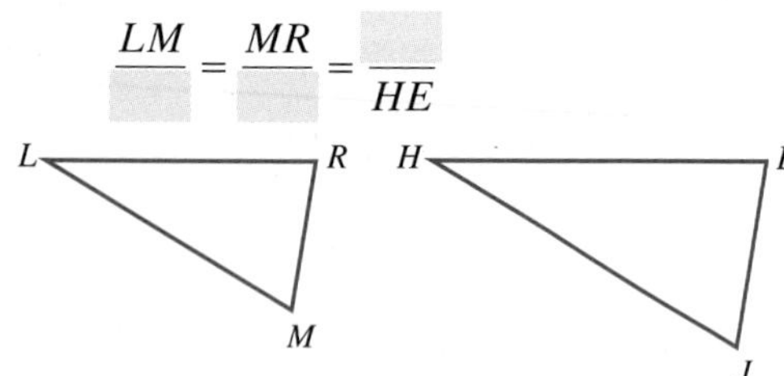

32. Refer to the similar triangles shown in the next column. **See Example 2.**

a. Name 3 pairs of congruent angles.

b. Complete each proportion.

$$\frac{WY}{DF} = \frac{\square}{FE} \qquad \frac{WX}{\square} = \frac{YX}{FE} \qquad \frac{\square}{EF} = \frac{WY}{DF}$$

c. We can write the answer to part b in a more compact form:

$$\frac{\square}{DF} = \frac{YX}{\square} = \frac{WX}{\square}$$

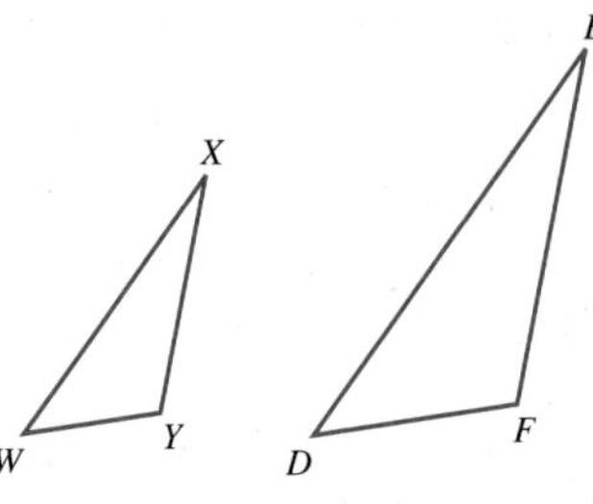

Tell whether the triangles are similar. **See Objective 2.**

33.

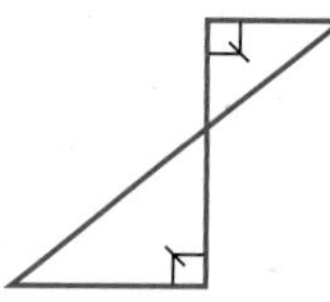

34.

35.

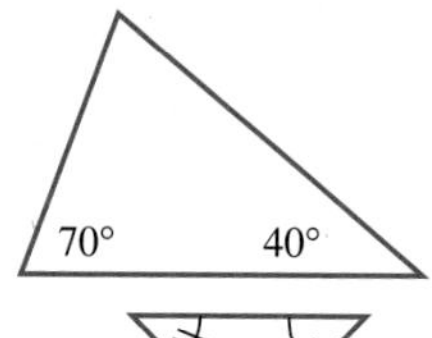

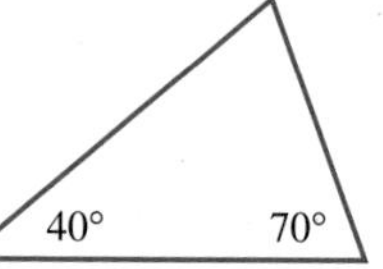

36.

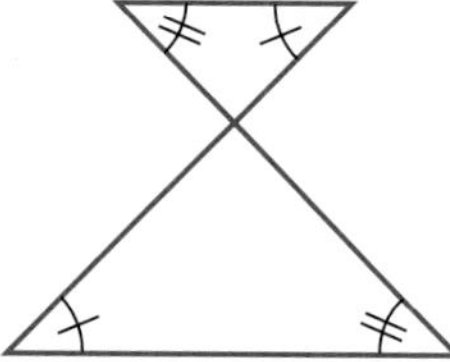

Each pair of triangles is similar. Find the missing side length. **See Example 3.**

37.

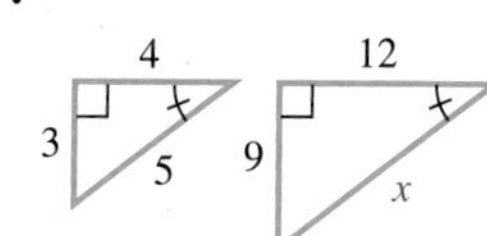

38.

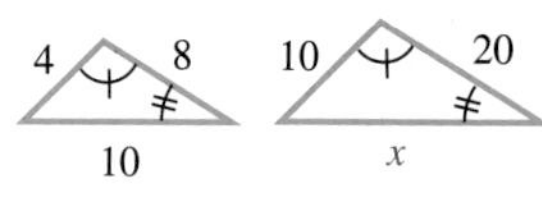

39.

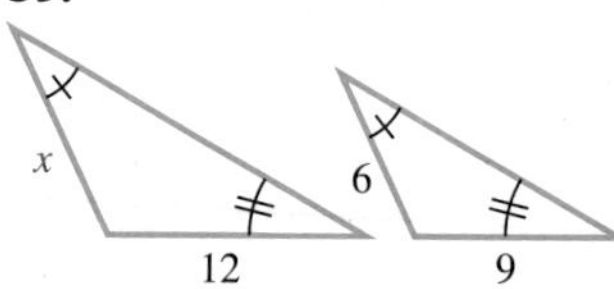

40.

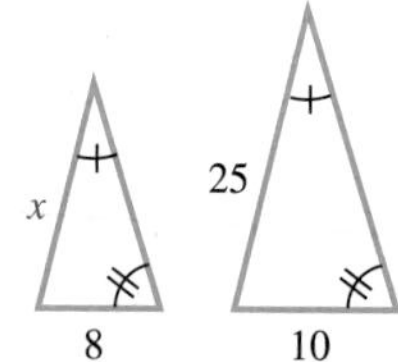

In Problems 41 and 42, $\triangle MSN \sim \triangle TPR$. Find x and y. **See Example 3.**

41.

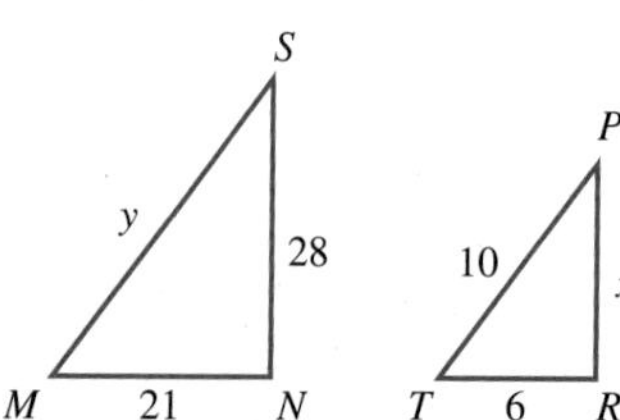

42.

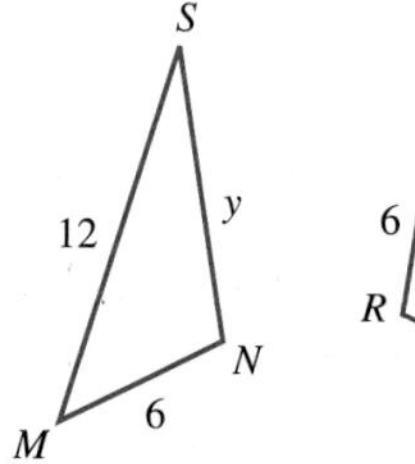

In Problems 43 and 44, $\triangle MSN \sim \triangle TPN$. Find x and y.
See Example 3.

43.

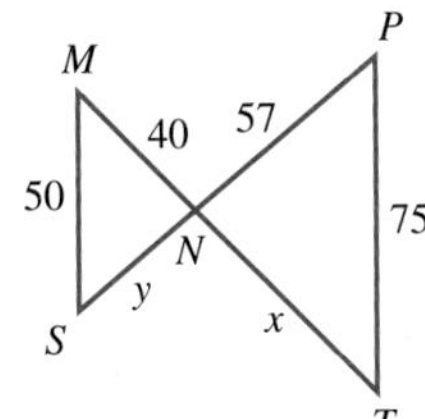

44.

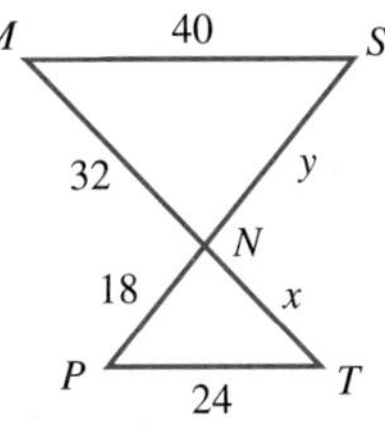

CONCEPT EXTENSIONS

45. The triangles below are similar. Find the perimeter of the triangle on the right.

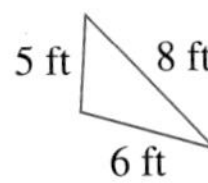

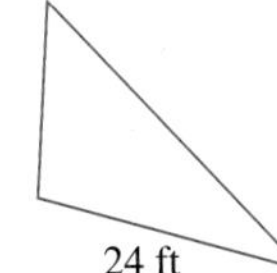

46. The triangles below are similar. Find the area of the triangle on the right.

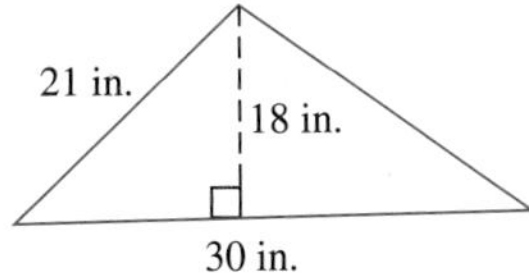

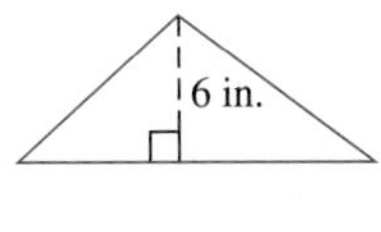

47. Find each ratio (larger triangle to smaller triangle) of the corresponding sides of the similar triangles shown below.

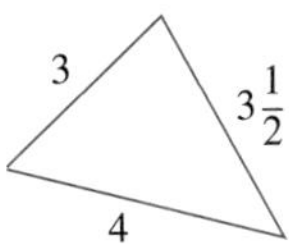

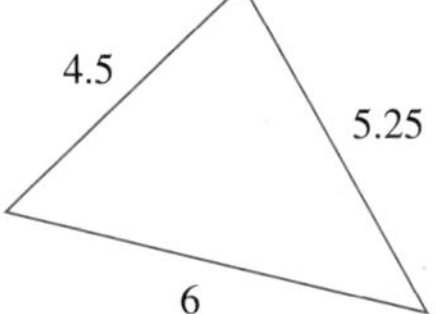

48. The two figures below are similar. Find x, y, and z. Round to the nearest tenth.

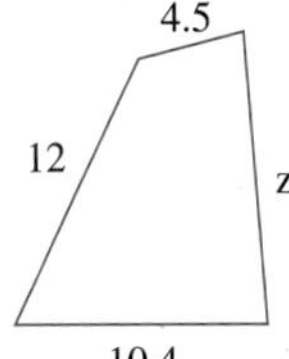

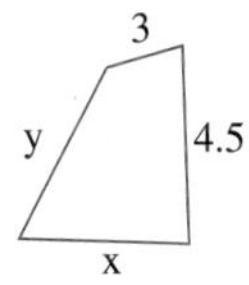

APPLICATIONS

49. HEIGHT OF A TREE The tree shown in the next column casts a shadow 24 feet long when a man 6 feet tall casts a shadow 4 feet long. Find the height of the tree.

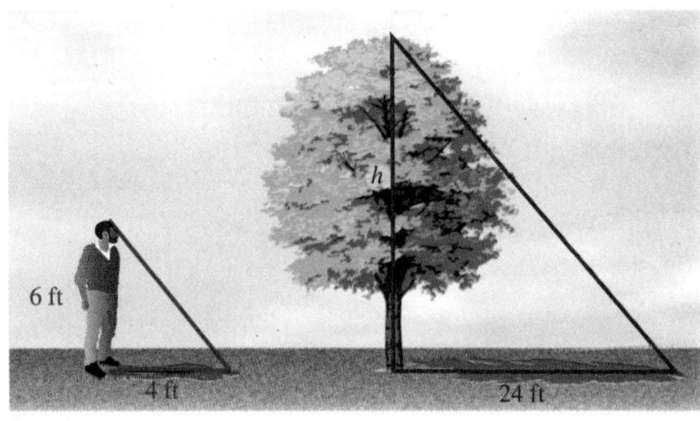

50. HEIGHT OF A BUILDING A man places a mirror on the ground and sees the reflection of the top of a building, as shown below. Find the height of the building. (**Hint:** When a beam of light strikes a mirror, it is reflected at the same angle as it hits the mirror.)

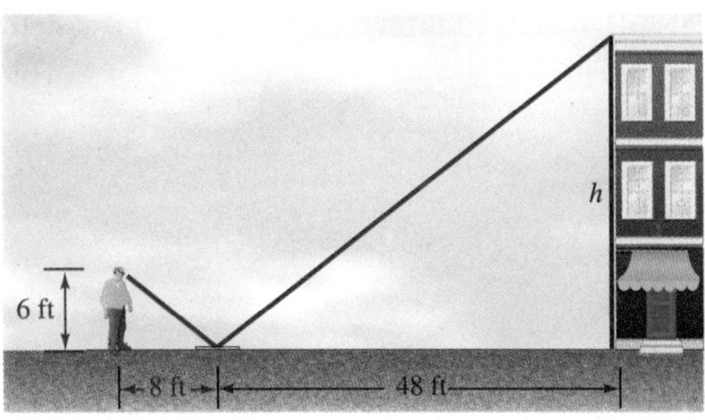

51. WASHINGTON, D.C. The Washington Monument casts a shadow of $166\frac{1}{2}$ feet at the same time as a 5-foot-tall tourist casts a shadow of $1\frac{1}{2}$ feet. Find the height of the monument.

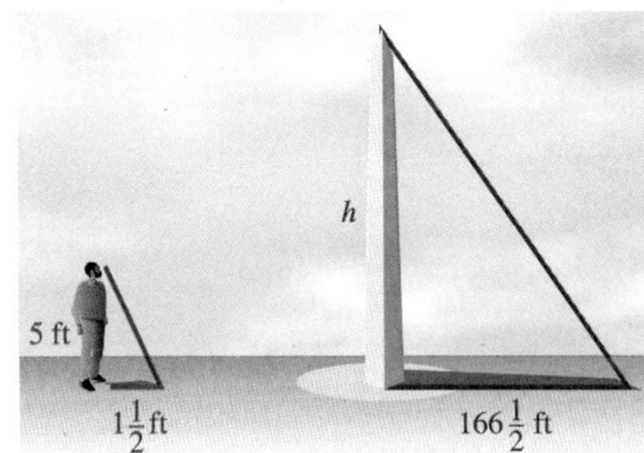

52. HEIGHT OF A TREE A tree casts a shadow of 29 feet at the same time as a vertical yardstick casts a shadow of 2.5 feet. Find the height of the tree.

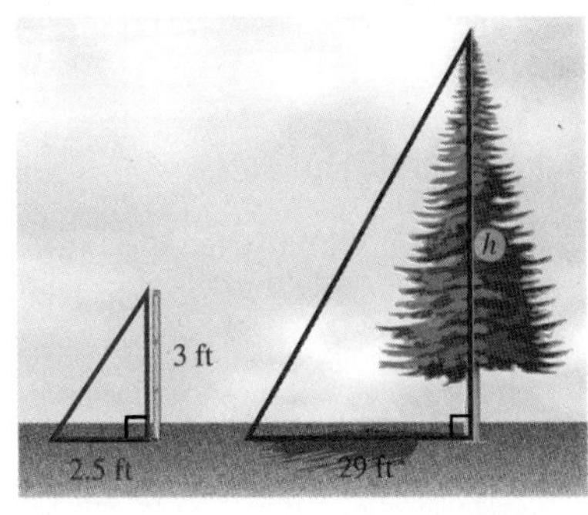

53. FLIGHT PATH An airplane ascends 200 feet as it flies a horizontal distance of 1,000 feet, as shown in the following figure. How much altitude is gained as it flies a horizontal distance of 1 mile? (*Hint:* 1 mile = 5,280 feet.)

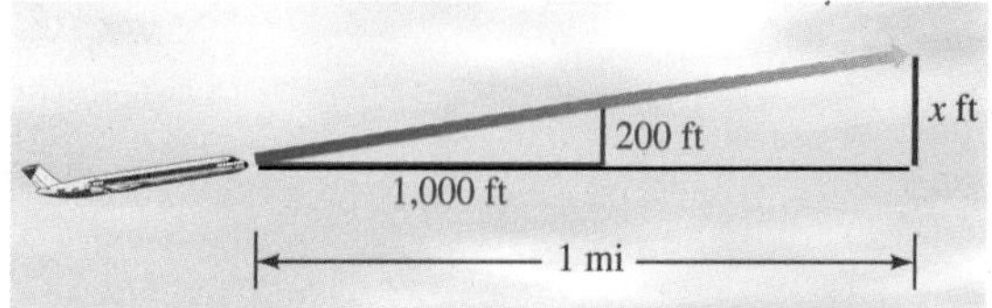

54. SURVEYOR A surveying crew needs to find the width of the river shown in the illustration below. Because of a dangerous current, they decide to stay on the west side of the river and use geometry to find its width. Their approach is to create two similar right triangles on dry land. Then they write and solve a proportion to find w. What is the width of the river?

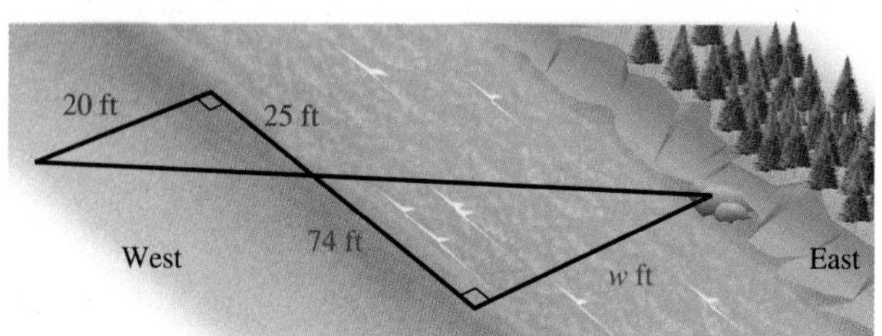

55. GRAPHIC ARTS The compass in the illustration is used to draw circles with different radii (plural for radius). For the setting shown, what radius will the resulting circle have?

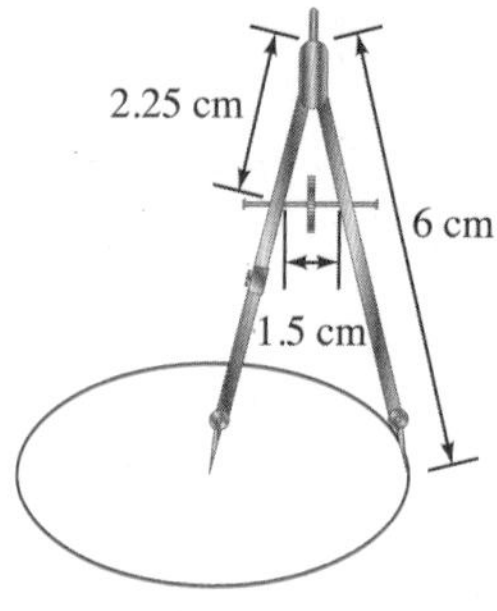

56. SKI RUNS A ski course with $\frac{1}{2}$ mile of horizontal run falls 100 feet in every 300 feet of run. Find the height of the hill.

WRITING

57. Tell whether the statement is true or false. Explain your answer.

a. Congruent triangles are always similar.

b. Similar triangles are always congruent.

58. Explain how the concepts studied in this section can be used to find the height of an object such as a tree or flagpole while standing safely on the ground.

Objectives

1. Use a ruler to measure lengths in inches.
2. Define American units of length.
3. Convert from one American unit of length to another.
4. Define American units of weight.
5. Convert from one American unit of weight to another.
6. Define American units of capacity.
7. Convert from one American unit of capacity to another.
8. Define units of time.
9. Convert from one unit of time to another.

SECTION 3.4
American Units of Measurement

ARE YOU READY?

The following problems review some basic skills that are needed when working with American units of measurement.

1. Simplify: $\dfrac{2 \cdot 2 \cdot 2 \cdot 3 \cdot 5 \cdot 3}{2 \cdot 2 \cdot 2 \cdot 2 \cdot 2 \cdot 3 \cdot 5 \cdot 11}$

2. a. Write $2\frac{1}{2}$ as an improper fraction.

b. Write $\frac{7}{4}$ as a mixed number.

3. Multiply: $\frac{9}{4} \cdot 12$

4. Multiply: $60 \cdot 3 \cdot \frac{1}{40}$

5. a. Multiply: $\begin{array}{r} 26 \\ \times\ 16 \\ \hline \end{array}$

b. Divide: $8\overline{)20}$

6. What fraction of the figure is shaded?

Two common systems of measurement are the **American** (or **English**) **system** and the **metric system.** We will discuss American units of measurement in this section and metric units in the next. Some common American units are *inches, feet, miles, ounces, pounds, tons, cups, pints, quarts,* and *gallons.* These units are used when measuring length, weight, and capacity.

A newborn baby is 20 inches long.

First-class postage for a letter that weighs less than 1 ounce is 44¢.

Milk is sold in gallon containers.

1 Use a ruler to measure lengths in inches.

A ruler is one of the most common tools used for measuring distances or lengths. The figure below shows part of a ruler. Most rulers are 12 inches (1 foot) long. Since 12 inches = 1 foot, a ruler is divided into 12 equal lengths of 1 inch. Each inch is divided into halves of an inch, quarters of an inch, eighths of an inch, and sixteenths of an inch.

The left end of a ruler can be (but sometimes isn't) labeled with a 0. Each point on a ruler, like each point on a number line, has a number associated with it. That number is the distance between the point and 0. Several lengths on the ruler are shown below.

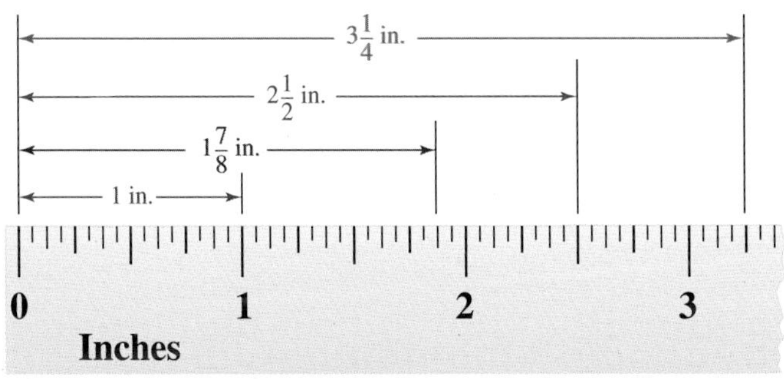

Actual size

EXAMPLE 1 Find the length of the paper clip shown here.

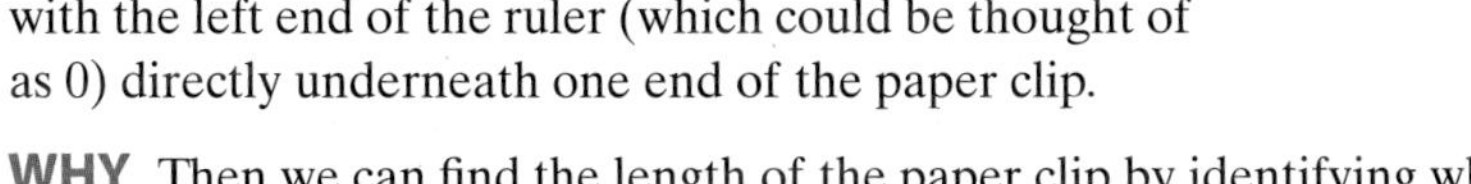

Strategy We will place a ruler below the paper clip, with the left end of the ruler (which could be thought of as 0) directly underneath one end of the paper clip.

WHY Then we can find the length of the paper clip by identifying where its other end lines up on the tick marks printed in black on the ruler.

Solution

Since the tick marks between 0 and 1 on the ruler create eight equal spaces, the ruler is scaled in eighths of an inch. The paper clip is $1\frac{3}{8}$ inches long.

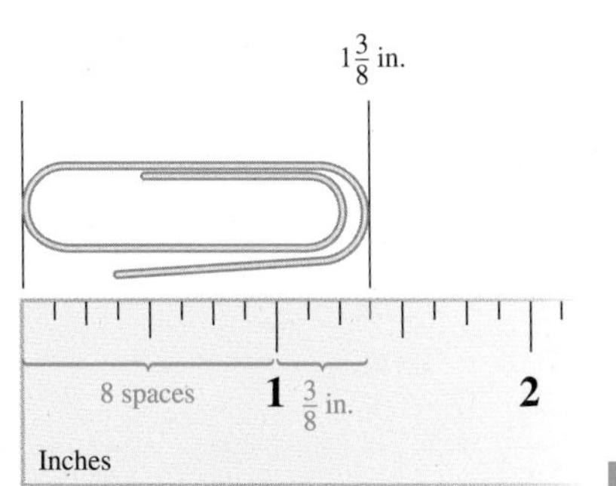

Self Check 1

Find the length of the jumbo paper clip.

Now Try **Problem 27**

Self Check 2

Find the width of the circle.

Now Try **Problem 29**

EXAMPLE 2 Find the length of the nail shown below.

Strategy We will place a ruler below the nail, with the left end of the ruler (which could be thought of as 0) directly underneath the head of the nail.

WHY Then we can find the length of the nail by identifying where its pointed end lines up on the tick marks printed in black on the ruler.

Solution

Since the tick marks between 0 and 1 on the ruler create sixteen equal spaces, the ruler is scaled in sixteenths of an inch.

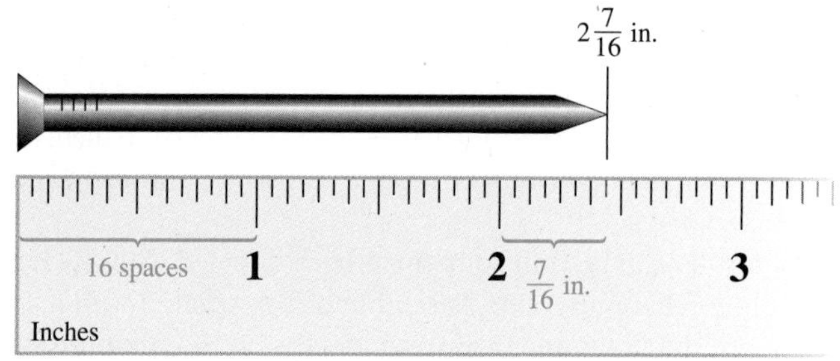

The nail is $2\frac{7}{16}$ inches long.

2 Define American units of length.

The American system of measurement uses the units of **inch, foot, yard,** and **mile** to measure length. These units are related in the following ways.

American Units of Length

1 foot (ft) = 12 inches (in.)	1 yard (yd) = 36 inches
1 yard = 3 feet	1 mile (mi) = 5,280 feet

The abbreviation for each unit is written within parentheses.

The Language of Mathematics According to some sources, the inch was originally defined as the length from the tip of the thumb to the first knuckle. In some languages the word for *inch* is similar to or the same as *thumb*. For example, in Spanish, *pulgada* is inch and *pulgar* is thumb. In Swedish, *tum* is inch and *tumme* is thumb. In Italian, *pollice* is both inch and thumb.

3 Convert from one American unit of length to another.

To convert from one unit of length to another, we use *unit conversion factors.* To find the unit conversion factor between yards and feet, we begin with this fact:

$$3 \text{ ft} = 1 \text{ yd}$$

If we divide both sides of this equation by 1 yard, we get

$$\frac{3 \text{ ft}}{\mathbf{1 \text{ yd}}} = \frac{1 \text{ yd}}{\mathbf{1 \text{ yd}}}$$

$$\frac{3 \text{ ft}}{1 \text{ yd}} = 1$$ Simplify the right side of the equation. A number divided by itself is 1: $\frac{1 \text{ yd}}{1 \text{ yd}} = 1$.

The fraction $\frac{3\text{ ft}}{1\text{ yd}}$ is called a **unit conversion factor,** because its value is 1. It can be read as "3 feet per yard." Since this fraction is equal to 1, multiplying a length by this fraction does not change its measure; it changes only the *units* of measure.

To convert units of length in the American system of measurement, we use the following unit conversion factors. Each conversion factor shown below is a form of 1.

To convert from	Use the unit conversion factor	To convert from	Use the unit conversion factor
feet to inches	$\frac{12\text{ in.}}{1\text{ ft}}$	inches to feet	$\frac{1\text{ ft}}{12\text{ in.}}$
yards to feet	$\frac{3\text{ ft}}{1\text{ yd}}$	feet to yards	$\frac{1\text{ yd}}{3\text{ ft}}$
yards to inches	$\frac{36\text{ in.}}{1\text{ yd}}$	inches to yards	$\frac{1\text{ yd}}{36\text{ in.}}$
miles to feet	$\frac{5{,}280\text{ ft}}{1\text{ mi}}$	feet to miles	$\frac{1\text{ mi}}{5{,}280\text{ ft}}$

EXAMPLE 3 Convert 8 yards to feet.

Strategy We will multiply 8 yards by a carefully chosen unit conversion factor.

WHY If we multiply by the proper unit conversion factor, we can eliminate the unwanted units of yards and convert to feet.

Solution

To convert from yards to feet, we must use a unit conversion factor that relates feet to yards. Since there are 3 feet per yard, we multiply 8 yards by the unit conversion factor $\frac{3\text{ ft}}{1\text{ yd}}$.

$$8\text{ yd} = \frac{8\text{ yd}}{1} \cdot \frac{\mathbf{3\ ft}}{\mathbf{1\ yd}}$$ Write 8 yd as a fraction: 8 yd $= \frac{8\text{ yd}}{1}$. Then multiply by a form of 1: $\frac{3\text{ ft}}{1\text{ yd}}$.

$$= \frac{8\text{ }\not{\text{yd}}}{1} \cdot \frac{3\text{ ft}}{1\text{ }\not{\text{yd}}}$$ Remove the common units of yards from the numerator and denominator. Notice that the units of feet remain.

$$= 8 \cdot 3\text{ ft}$$ Simplify.

$$= 24\text{ ft}$$ Multiply: $8 \cdot 3 = 24$.

8 yards is equal to 24 feet.

Self Check 3

Convert 9 yards to feet.

Now Try **Problem 35**

Success Tip Notice that in Example 3, we eliminated the units of yards and introduced the units of feet by multiplying by the appropriate unit conversion factor. In general, a unit conversion factor is a fraction with the following form:

$$\frac{\text{Unit we want to introduce}}{\text{Unit we want to eliminate}}$$ ← Numerator / ← Denominator

EXAMPLE 4 Convert $1\frac{3}{4}$ feet to inches.

Strategy We will multiply $1\frac{3}{4}$ feet by a carefully chosen unit conversion factor.

Self Check 4

Convert $1\frac{1}{2}$ feet to inches.

Now Try **Problem 39**

WHY If we multiply by the proper unit conversion factor, we can eliminate the unwanted units of feet and convert to inches.

Solution

To convert from feet to inches, we must choose a unit conversion factor whose numerator contains the units we want to introduce (inches), and whose denominator contains the units we want to eliminate (feet). Since there are 12 inches per foot, we will use

$$\frac{12 \text{ in.}}{1 \text{ ft}}$$
← This is the unit we want to introduce. (12 in.)
← This is the unit we want to eliminate (the original unit). (1 ft)

To perform the conversion, we multiply.

$1\frac{3}{4} \text{ ft} = \frac{7}{4} \text{ ft} \cdot \frac{\mathbf{12 \text{ in.}}}{\mathbf{1 \text{ ft}}}$ Write $1\frac{3}{4}$ as an improper fraction: $1\frac{3}{4} = \frac{7}{4}$. Then multiply by a form of 1: $\frac{12 \text{ in.}}{1 \text{ ft}}$.

$= \frac{7}{4} \cancel{\text{ft}} \cdot \frac{12 \text{ in.}}{1 \cancel{\text{ft}}}$ Remove the common units of feet from the numerator and denominator. Notice that the units of inches remain.

$= \frac{7 \cdot 12}{4 \cdot 1} \text{ in.}$ Multiply the fractions.

$= \frac{7 \cdot 3 \cdot \overset{1}{\cancel{4}}}{\underset{1}{\cancel{4}} \cdot 1} \text{ in.}$ To simplify the fraction, factor 12. Then remove the common factor of 4 from the numerator and denominator.

$= 21 \text{ in.}$ Simplify.

$1\frac{3}{4}$ feet is equal to 21 inches.

> ***Caution!*** When converting lengths, if no common units appear in the numerator and denominator to remove, you have chosen the wrong conversion factor.

Sometimes we must use two (or more) unit conversion factors to eliminate the given units while introducing the desired units. The following example illustrates this concept.

Self Check 5

MARATHONS The *marathon* is a long-distance race with an official distance of 26 miles 385 yards. Convert 385 yards to miles. Give the exact answer and a decimal approximation, rounded to the nearest hundredth of a mile.

Now Try **Problem 43**

EXAMPLE 5 ***Football*** A football field (including both end zones) is 120 yards long. Convert this length to miles. Give the exact answer and a decimal approximation, rounded to the nearest hundredth of a mile.

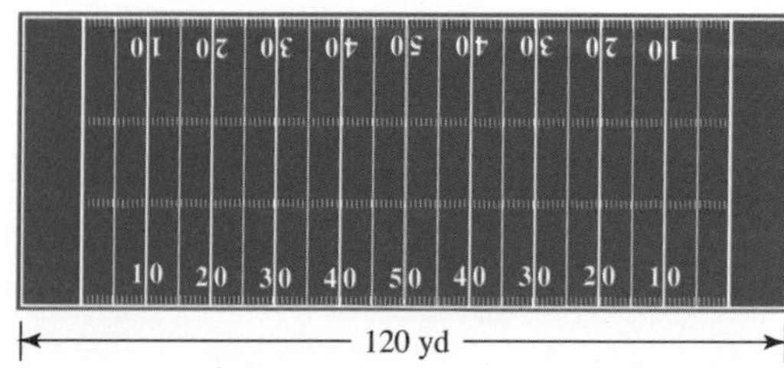

Strategy We will use a two-part multiplication process that converts 120 yards to feet and then convert that result to miles.

WHY We must use a two-part process because the table on page 50 does not contain a single unit conversion factor that converts from yards to miles.

Solution

Since there are 3 feet per yard, we can convert 120 yards to feet by multiplying by the unit conversion factor $\frac{3\text{ft}}{1\text{yd}}$. Since there is 1 mile for every 5,280 feet, we can convert that result to miles by multiplying by the unit conversion factor $\frac{1\text{ mi}}{5{,}280\text{ ft}}$.

$$120\text{ yd} = \frac{120\text{ yd}}{1} \cdot \frac{3\text{ ft}}{1\text{ yd}} \cdot \frac{1\text{ mi}}{5{,}280\text{ ft}}$$

Write 120 yd as a fraction: $120\text{ yd} = \frac{120\text{ yd}}{1}$. Then multiply by two unit conversion factors: $\frac{3\text{ ft}}{1\text{ yd}} = 1$ and $\frac{1\text{ mi}}{5{,}280\text{ ft}} = 1$.

$$= \frac{120\text{ }\cancel{\text{yd}}}{1} \cdot \frac{3\text{ }\cancel{\text{ft}}}{1\text{ }\cancel{\text{yd}}} \cdot \frac{1\text{ mi}}{5{,}280\text{ }\cancel{\text{ft}}}$$

Remove the common units of yards and feet in the numerator and denominator. Notice that all the units are removed except for miles.

$$= \frac{120 \cdot 3}{5{,}280}\text{ mi}$$

Multiply the fractions.

$$= \frac{\overset{1}{\cancel{2}} \cdot \overset{1}{\cancel{2}} \cdot \overset{1}{\cancel{2}} \cdot \overset{1}{\cancel{3}} \cdot \overset{1}{\cancel{5}} \cdot 3}{\underset{1}{\cancel{2}} \cdot \underset{1}{\cancel{2}} \cdot \underset{1}{\cancel{2}} \cdot 2 \cdot 2 \cdot \underset{1}{\cancel{3}} \cdot \underset{1}{\cancel{5}} \cdot 11}\text{ mi}$$

To simplify the fraction, prime factor 120 and 5,280, and remove the common factors 2, 3, and 5.

$$= \frac{3}{44}\text{ mi}$$

Multiply the remaining factors in the numerator. Multiply the remaining factors in the the

A football field (including the end zones) is *exactly* $\frac{3}{44}$ miles long.

We can also present this conversion as a decimal. If we divide 3 by 44 (as shown on the right), and round the result to the nearest hundredth, we see that a football field (including the end zones) is *approximately* 0.07 mile long.

$$\begin{array}{r} 0.068 \\ 44\overline{)3.000} \\ -\ 0 \\ \hline 3\ 00 \\ -\ 2\ 64 \\ \hline 360 \\ -\ 352 \\ \hline 8 \end{array}$$

4 Define American units of weight.

The American system of measurement uses the units of **ounce, pound,** and **ton** to measure weight. These units are related in the following ways.

American Units of Weight

1 pound (lb) = 16 ounces (oz)   1 ton (T) = 2,000 pounds

The abbreviation for each unit is written within parentheses.

5 Convert from one American unit of weight to another.

To convert units of weight in the American system of measurement, we use the following unit conversion factors. Each conversion factor shown below is a form of 1.

To convert from	Use the unit conversion factor	To convert from	Use the unit conversion factor
pounds to ounces	$\frac{16\text{ oz}}{1\text{ lb}}$	ounces to pounds	$\frac{1\text{ lb}}{16\text{ oz}}$
tons to pounds	$\frac{2{,}000\text{ lb}}{1\text{ ton}}$	pounds to tons	$\frac{1\text{ ton}}{2{,}000\text{ lb}}$

Self Check 6

Convert 60 ounces to pounds.

Now Try **Problem 47**

EXAMPLE 6 Convert 40 ounces to pounds.

Strategy We will multiply 40 ounces by a carefully chosen unit conversion factor.

WHY If we multiply by the proper unit conversion factor, we can eliminate the unwanted units of ounces and convert to pounds.

Solution

To convert from ounces to pounds, we must chose a unit conversion factor whose numerator contains the units we want to introduce (pounds), and whose denominator contains the units we want to eliminate (ounces). Since there is 1 pound for every 16 ounces, we will use

$$\frac{1 \text{ lb}}{16 \text{ oz}}$$ ← 1 lb: This is the unit we want to introduce. ← 16 oz: This is the unit we want to eliminate (the original unit).

To perform the conversion, we multiply.

$$40 \text{ oz} = \frac{40 \text{ oz}}{1} \cdot \frac{\mathbf{1\ lb}}{\mathbf{16\ oz}}$$ Write 40 oz as a fraction: $40 \text{ oz} = \frac{40 \text{ oz}}{1}$. Then multiply by a form of 1: $\frac{1 \text{ lb}}{16 \text{ oz}}$.

$$= \frac{40 \not{\text{oz}}}{1} \cdot \frac{1 \text{ lb}}{16 \not{\text{oz}}}$$ Remove the common units of ounces from the numerator and denominator. Notice that the units of pounds remain.

$$= \frac{40}{16} \text{ lb}$$ Multiply the fractions.

There are two ways to complete the solution. First, we can remove any common factors of the numerator and denominator to simplify the fraction. Then we can write the result as a mixed number.

$$\frac{40}{16} \text{ lb} = \frac{5 \cdot \overset{1}{\not{8}}}{2 \cdot \underset{1}{\not{8}}} \text{ lb} = \frac{5}{2} \text{ lb} = 2\frac{1}{2} \text{ lb}$$

A second approach is to divide the numerator by the denominator and express the result as a decimal.

$$\frac{40}{16} \text{ lb} = 2.5 \text{ lb}$$ Perform the division: $40 \div 16$.

$$\begin{array}{r} 2.5 \\ 16\overline{)40.0} \\ -32 \\ \hline 8\,0 \\ -8\,0 \\ \hline 0 \end{array}$$

40 ounces is equal to $2\frac{1}{2}$ lb (or 2.5 lb).

Self Check 7

Convert 60 pounds to ounces.

Now Try **Problem 51**

EXAMPLE 7 Convert 25 pounds to ounces.

Strategy We will multiply 25 pounds by a carefully chosen unit conversion factor.

WHY If we multiply by the proper unit conversion factor, we can eliminate the unwanted units of pounds and convert to ounces.

Solution

To convert from pounds to ounces, we must chose a unit conversion factor whose numerator contains the units we want to introduce (ounces), and whose denominator contains the units we want to eliminate (pounds). Since there are 16 ounces per pound, we will use

$$\frac{16 \text{ oz}}{1 \text{ lb}}$$ ← 16 oz: This is the unit we want to introduce. ← 1 lb: This is the unit we want to eliminate (the original unit).

To perform the conversion, we multiply.

$25\text{ lb} = \dfrac{25\text{ lb}}{1} \cdot \dfrac{\mathbf{16\text{ oz}}}{\mathbf{1\text{ lb}}}$	Write 25 lb as a fraction: $25\text{ lb} = \frac{25\text{ lb}}{1}$. Then multiply by a form of 1: $\frac{16\text{ oz}}{1\text{ lb}}$.
$= \dfrac{25\cancel{\text{ lb}}}{1} \cdot \dfrac{16\text{ oz}}{1\cancel{\text{ lb}}}$	Remove the common units of pounds from the numerator and denominator. Notice that the units of ounces remain.
$= 25 \cdot 16\text{ oz}$	Simplify.
$= 400\text{ oz}$	Multiply: $25 \cdot 16 = 400$.

$$\begin{array}{r} 25 \\ \times\ 16 \\ \hline 150 \\ 250 \\ \hline 400 \end{array}$$

25 pounds is equal to 400 ounces.

6 Define American units of capacity.

The American system of measurement uses the units of **ounce, cup, pint, quart,** and **gallon** to measure capacity. These units are related as follows.

The Language of Mathematics The word *capacity* means the amount that can be contained. For example, a gas tank might have a *capacity* of 12 gallons.

American Units of Capacity

1 cup (c) = 8 fluid ounces (fl oz)	1 pint (pt) = 2 cups
1 quart (qt) = 2 pints	1 gallon (gal) = 4 quarts

The abbreviation for each unit is written within parentheses.

7 Convert from one American unit of capacity to another.

To convert units of capacity in the American system of measurement, we use the following unit conversion factors. Each conversion factor shown below is a form of 1.

To convert from	Use the unit conversion factor	To convert from	Use the unit conversion factor
cups to ounces	$\frac{8\text{ fl oz}}{1\text{ c}}$	ounces to cups	$\frac{1\text{ c}}{8\text{ fl oz}}$
pints to cups	$\frac{2\text{ c}}{1\text{ pt}}$	cups to pints	$\frac{1\text{ pt}}{2\text{ c}}$
quarts to pints	$\frac{2\text{ pt}}{1\text{ qt}}$	pints to quarts	$\frac{1\text{ qt}}{2\text{ pt}}$
gallons to quarts	$\frac{4\text{ qt}}{1\text{ gal}}$	quarts to gallons	$\frac{1\text{ gal}}{4\text{ qt}}$

Self Check 8

Convert 2.5 pints to fluid ounces.

Now Try **Problem 55**

© Felix Wirth/Corbis

EXAMPLE 8 ***Cooking*** If a recipe calls for 3 pints of milk, how many fluid ounces of milk should be used?

Strategy We will use a two-part multiplication process that converts 3 pints to cups and then converts that result to fluid ounces.

WHY We must use a two-part process because the table on page 449 does not contain a single unit conversion factor that converts from pints to fluid ounces.

Solution

Since there are 2 cups per pint, we can convert 3 pints to cups by multiplying by the unit conversion factor $\frac{2\text{ c}}{1\text{ pt}}$. Since there are 8 fluid ounces per cup, we can convert that result to fluid ounces by multiplying by the unit conversion factor $\frac{8\text{ fl oz}}{1\text{ c}}$.

$$3\text{ pt} = \frac{3\text{ pt}}{1} \cdot \frac{2\text{ c}}{1\text{ pt}} \cdot \frac{8\text{ fl oz}}{1\text{ c}}$$

Write 3 pt as a fraction: $3\text{ pt} = \frac{3\text{ pt}}{1}$. Multiply by two unit conversion factors: $\frac{2\text{ c}}{1\text{ pt}} = 1$ and $\frac{8\text{ fl oz}}{1\text{ c}} = 1$.

$$= \frac{3\not{\text{pt}}}{1} \cdot \frac{2\not{\text{c}}}{1\not{\text{pt}}} \cdot \frac{8\text{ fl oz}}{1\not{\text{c}}}$$

Remove the common units of pints and cups in the numerator and denominator. Notice that all the units are removed except for fluid ounces.

$$= 3 \cdot 2 \cdot 8\text{ fl oz}$$

Simplify.

$$= 48\text{ fl oz}$$

Multiply.

Since 3 pints is equal to 48 fluid ounces, 48 fluid ounces of milk should be used.

8 Define units of time.

The American system of measurement (and the metric system) use the units of **second, minute, hour,** and **day** to measure time. These units are related as follows.

Units of Time

1 minute (min) = 60 seconds (sec) 1 hour (hr) = 60 minutes

1 day = 24 hours

The abbreviation for each unit is written within parentheses.

To convert units of time, we use the following unit conversion factors. Each conversion factor shown below is a form of 1.

To convert from	Use the unit conversion factor	To convert from	Use the unit conversion factor
minutes to seconds	$\frac{60\text{ sec}}{1\text{ min}}$	seconds to minutes	$\frac{1\text{ min}}{60\text{ sec}}$
hours to minutes	$\frac{60\text{ min}}{1\text{ hr}}$	minutes to hours	$\frac{1\text{ hr}}{60\text{ min}}$
days to hours	$\frac{24\text{ hr}}{1\text{ day}}$	hours to days	$\frac{1\text{ day}}{24\text{ hr}}$

9 Convert from one unit of time to another.

EXAMPLE 9 ***Astronomy*** A lunar eclipse occurs when the Earth is between the sun and the moon in such a way that Earth's shadow darkens the moon. (See the figure below, which is not to scale.) A total lunar eclipse can last as long as 105 minutes. Express this time in hours.

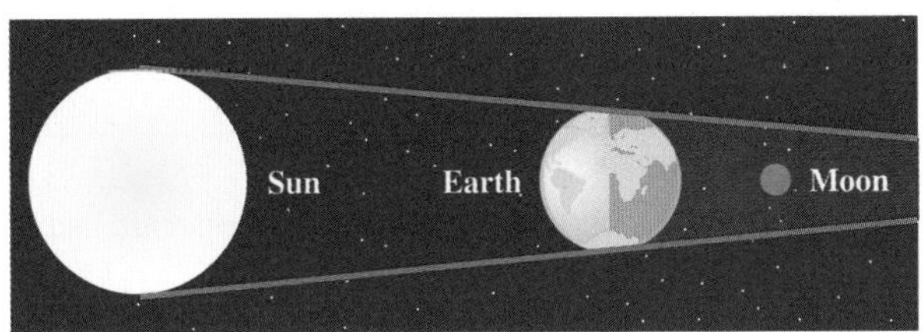

Strategy We will multiply 105 minutes by a carefully chosen unit conversion factor.

WHY If we multiply by the proper unit conversion factor, we can eliminate the unwanted units of minutes and convert to hours.

Solution

To convert from minutes to hours, we must chose a unit conversion factor whose numerator contains the units we want to introduce (hours), and whose denominator contains the units we want to eliminate (minutes). Since there is 1 hour for every 60 minutes, we will use

$$\frac{1\text{ hr}}{60\text{ min}}$$

1 hr ← This is the unit we want to introduce.
60 min ← This is the unit we want to eliminate (the original unit).

To perform the conversion, we multiply.

$105\text{ min} = \frac{105\text{ min}}{1} \cdot \frac{\mathbf{1\text{ hr}}}{\mathbf{60\text{ min}}}$ Write 105 min as a fraction: $105\text{ min} = \frac{105\text{ min}}{1}$. Then multiply by a form of 1: $\frac{1\text{ hr}}{60\text{ min}}$.

$= \frac{105\,\cancel{\text{min}}}{1} \cdot \frac{1\text{ hr}}{60\,\cancel{\text{min}}}$ Remove the common units of minutes in the numerator and denominator. Notice that the units of hours remain.

$= \frac{105}{60}\text{ hr}$ Multiply the fractions.

$= \frac{\overset{1}{\cancel{3}} \cdot \overset{1}{\cancel{5}} \cdot 7}{2 \cdot 2 \cdot \underset{1}{\cancel{3}} \cdot \underset{1}{\cancel{5}}}\text{ hr}$ To simplify the fraction, prime factor 105 and 60. Then remove the common factors 3 and 5 in the numerator and denominator.

$= \frac{7}{4}\text{ hr}$ Multiply the remaining factors in the numerator. Multiply the remaining factors in the denominator.

$= 1\frac{3}{4}\text{ hr}$ Write $\frac{7}{4}$ as a mixed number.

A total lunar eclipse can last as long as $1\frac{3}{4}$ hours.

Self Check 9

THE SUN A solar eclipse (eclipse of the sun) can last as long as 450 seconds. Express this time in minutes.

Now Try **Problem 59**

ANSWERS TO SELF CHECKS

1. $1\frac{7}{8}$ in. **2.** $1\frac{1}{4}$ in. **3.** 27 ft **4.** 18 in. **5.** $\frac{7}{32}$ mi ≈ 0.22 mi **6.** $3\frac{3}{4}$ lb = 3.75 lb **7.** 960 oz **8.** 40 fl oz **9.** $7\frac{1}{2}$ min

SECTION 3.4 STUDY SET

VOCABULARY

Fill in the blanks.

1. A ruler is used for measuring _______.
2. Inches, feet, and miles are examples of American units of _______.
3. $\frac{3\text{ ft}}{1\text{ yd}}, \frac{1\text{ ton}}{2{,}000\text{ lb}}$, and $\frac{4\text{ qt}}{1\text{ gal}}$ are examples of _____ conversion factors.
4. Ounces, pounds, and tons are examples of American units of _______.
5. Some examples of American units of ________ are cups, pints, quarts, and gallons.
6. Some units of ______ are seconds, minutes, hours, and days.

CONCEPTS

Fill in the blanks.

7. **a.** 12 inches = ☐ foot
   b. ☐ feet = 1 yard
   c. 1 yard = ☐ inches
   d. 1 mile = ☐ feet
8. **a.** ☐ ounces = 1 pound
   b. ☐ pounds = 1 ton
9. **a.** 1 cup = ☐ fluid ounces
   b. 1 pint = ☐ cups
   c. 2 pints = ☐ quart
   d. 4 quarts = ☐ gallon
10. **a.** 1 day = ☐ hours
    b. 2 hours = ☐ minutes
11. The value of any unit conversion factor is ☐.
12. In general, a unit conversion factor is a fraction with the following form:

$$\frac{\text{Unit that we want to } \square}{\text{Unit that we want to } \square} \begin{array}{l}\leftarrow \text{Numerator} \\ \leftarrow \text{Denominator}\end{array}$$

13. Consider the work shown below.

$$\frac{48\text{ oz}}{1} \cdot \frac{1\text{ lb}}{16\text{ oz}}$$

    a. What units can be removed?
    b. What units remain?
14. Consider the work shown below.

$$\frac{600\text{ yd}}{1} \cdot \frac{3\text{ ft}}{1\text{ yd}} \cdot \frac{1\text{ mi}}{5{,}280\text{ ft}}$$

    a. What units can be removed?
    b. What units remain?
15. Write a unit conversion factor to convert
    a. pounds to tons
    b. quarts to pints
16. Write the two unit conversion factors used to convert
    a. inches to yards
    b. days to minutes
17. Match each item with its proper measurement.
    a. Length of the U.S. coastline
    b. Height of a Barbie doll
    c. Span of the Golden Gate Bridge
    d. Width of a football field

    i. $11\frac{1}{2}$ in.
    ii. 4,200 ft
    iii. 53.5 yd
    iv. 12,383 mi
18. Match each item with its proper measurement.
    a. Weight of the men's shot put used in track and field
    b. Weight of an African elephant
    c. Amount of gold that is worth $500

    i. $1\frac{1}{2}$ oz
    ii. 16 lb
    iii. 7.2 tons
19. Match each item with its proper measurement.
    a. Amount of blood in an adult
    b. Size of the Exxon Valdez oil spill in 1989
    c. Amount of nail polish in a bottle
    d. Amount of flour to make 3 dozen cookies

    i. $\frac{1}{2}$ fluid oz
    ii. 2 cups
    iii. 5 qt
    iv. 10,080,000 gal
20. Match each item with its proper measurement.
    a. Length of first U.S. manned space flight
    b. A leap year
    c. Time difference between New York and Fairbanks, Alaska
    d. Length of Wright Brothers' first flight

    i. 12 sec
    ii. 15 min
    iii. 4 hr
    iv. 366 days

NOTATION

21. What unit does each abbreviation represent?

a. lb **b.** oz

c. fl oz

22. What unit does each abbreviation represent?

a. qt **b.** c

c. pt

Complete each solution.

23. Convert 2 yards to inches.

$$2 \text{ yd} = \frac{2 \text{ yd}}{1} \cdot \frac{\square \text{ in.}}{1 \text{ yd}}$$
$$= 2 \cdot 36 \square$$
$$= \square \text{ in.}$$

24. Convert 24 pints to quarts.

$$24 \text{ pt} = \frac{24 \text{ pt}}{1} \cdot \frac{1 \text{ qt}}{\square \text{ pt}}$$
$$= \frac{24}{1} \cdot \frac{1}{2} \square$$
$$= \square \text{ qt}$$

25. Convert 1 ton to ounces.

$$1 \text{ ton} = \frac{1 \text{ ton}}{1} \cdot \frac{\square \text{ lb}}{1 \text{ ton}} \cdot \frac{\square \text{ oz}}{1 \text{ lb}}$$
$$= 1 \cdot 2{,}000 \cdot 16 \square$$
$$= \square \text{ oz}$$

26. Convert 37,440 minutes to days.

$$37{,}440 \text{ min} = 37{,}440 \text{ min} \cdot \frac{1 \text{ hr}}{\square \text{ min}} \cdot \frac{1 \text{ day}}{\square \text{ hr}}$$
$$= \frac{37{,}440}{60 \cdot 24} \square$$
$$= \square \text{ days}$$

GUIDED PRACTICE

Refer to the given ruler to answer each question. See Example 1.

27. a. Each inch is divided into how many equal parts?

b. Determine which measurements the arrows point to on the ruler.

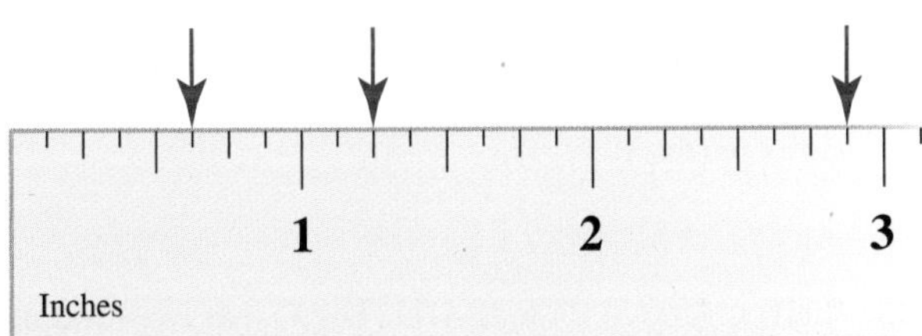

28. Find the length of the needle.

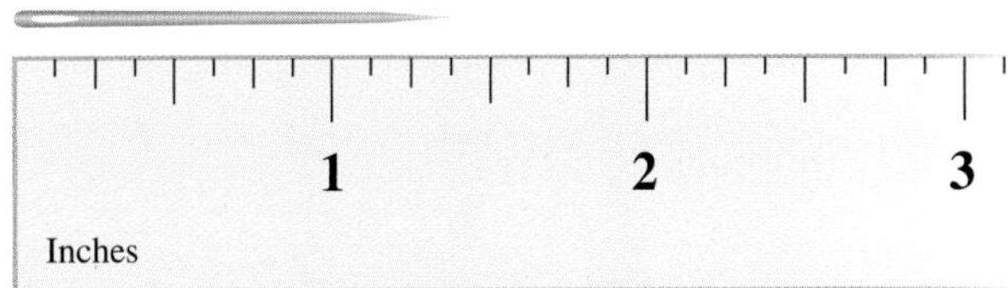

Refer to the given ruler to answer each question. See Example 2.

29. a. Each inch is divided into how many equal parts?

b. Determine which measurements the arrows point to on the ruler.

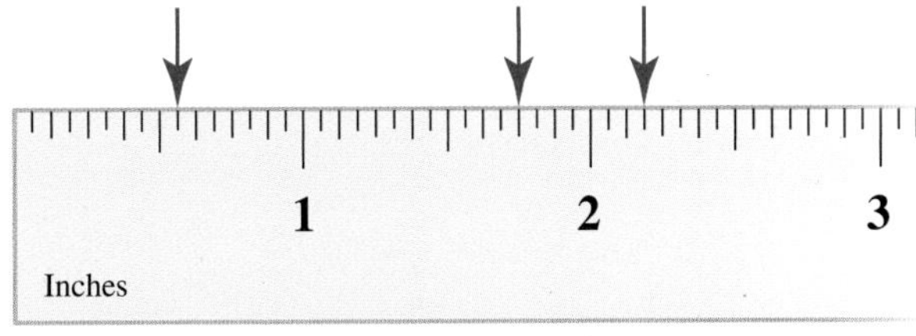

30. Find the length of the bolt.

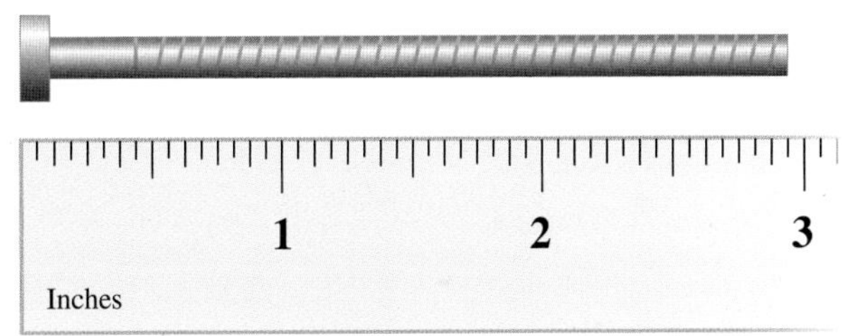

Use a ruler scaled in sixteenths of an inch to measure each object. See Example 2.

31. The width of a dollar bill

32. The length of a dollar bill

33. The length (top to bottom) of this page

34. The length of the word as printed here: supercalifragilisticexpialidocious

Perform each conversion. See Example 3.

35. 4 yards to feet

36. 6 yards to feet

37. 35 yards to feet

38. 33 yards to feet

Perform each conversion. See Example 4.

39. $3\frac{1}{2}$ feet to inches

40. $2\frac{2}{3}$ feet to inches

41. $5\frac{1}{4}$ feet to inches

42. $6\frac{1}{2}$ feet to inches

Use two unit conversion factors to perform each conversion. Give the exact answer and a decimal approximation, rounded to the nearest hundredth, when necessary. See Example 5.

43. 105 yards to miles

44. 198 yards to miles

45. 1,540 yards to miles

46. 1,512 yards to miles

Perform each conversion. See Example 6.

47. Convert 44 ounces to pounds.

48. Convert 24 ounces to pounds.

49. Convert 72 ounces to pounds.

50. Convert 76 ounces to pounds.

Perform each conversion. See Example 7.

51. 50 pounds to ounces
52. 30 pounds to ounces
53. 87 pounds to ounces
54. 79 pounds to ounces

Perform each conversion. See Example 8.

55. 8 pints to fluid ounces
56. 5 pints to fluid ounces
57. 21 pints to fluid ounces
58. 30 pints to fluid ounces

Perform each conversion. See Example 9.

59. 165 minutes to hours

60. 195 minutes to hours

61. 330 minutes to hours

62. 80 minutes to hours

TRY IT YOURSELF

Perform each conversion.

63. 3 quarts to pints **64.** 20 quarts to gallons

65. 7,200 minutes to days **66.** 691,200 seconds to days

67. 56 inches to feet **68.** 44 inches to feet

69. 4 feet to inches **70.** 7 feet to inches

71. 16 pints to gallons **72.** 3 gallons to fluid ounces

73. 80 ounces to pounds **74.** 8 pounds to ounces

75. 240 minutes to hours **76.** 2,400 seconds to hours

77. 8 yards to inches **78.** 324 inches to yards

79. 90 inches to yards **80.** 12 yards to inches

81. 5 yards to feet **82.** 21 feet to yards

83. 12.4 tons to pounds **84.** 48,000 ounces to tons

85. 7 feet to yards **86.** $4\frac{2}{3}$ yards to feet

87. 15,840 feet to miles **88.** 2 miles to feet

89. $\frac{1}{2}$ mile to feet **90.** 1,320 feet to miles

91. 7,000 pounds to tons **92.** 2.5 tons to ounces

93. 32 fluid ounces to pints **94.** 2 quarts to fluid ounces

CONCEPT EXTENSIONS

95. How many feet of a 15-yard long chain are left if 7 feet of chain are removed from it?

96. How many pints of lemonade are left in a 4-gallon igloo cooler if 3 pints of lemonade are dispensed from it?

97. Find the sum: 8 lb 6 oz + 12 lb 15 oz

98. Find the difference: 9 yd 1 ft − 5 yd 2 ft

99. Find the sum:

$$\begin{array}{r} 19 \text{ gal } 2 \text{ qt } 1 \text{ pt } 1 \text{ cup } 4 \text{ oz} \\ + \ 4 \text{ gal } 2 \text{ qt } 1 \text{ pt } 1 \text{ cup } 7 \text{ oz} \\ \hline \end{array}$$

100. Find the sum: 19 hr 54 min 32 sec + 12 hr 17 min 29 sec

101. Write a capacity that is equivalent to 6 gallons using the units pints.

102. Write a length that is equivalent to 2 miles using the units yards.

APPLICATIONS

103. THE GREAT PYRAMID The Great Pyramid in Egypt is about 450 feet high. Express this distance in yards.

104. THE WRIGHT BROTHERS In 1903, Orville Wright made the world's first sustained flight at Kitty Hawk, North Carolina. It lasted 12 seconds, and the plane traveled 120 feet. Express the length of the flight in yards.

Hulton Archive/Getty Images

105. THE GREAT SPHINX The Great Sphinx of Egypt is 240 feet long. Express this in inches.

106. HOOVER DAM The Hoover Dam in Nevada is 726 feet high. Express this distance in inches.

107. THE WILLIS TOWER The Willis Tower in Chicago has 110 stories and is 1,454 feet tall. To the nearest hundredth, express this height in miles.

108. NFL RECORDS Emmit Smith, the former Dallas Cowboys and Arizona Cardinals running back, holds the National Football League record for yards rushing in a career: 18,355. How many miles is this? Round to the nearest tenth of a mile.

109. AMERICA'S FAVORITE DRIVE The Blue Ridge Parkway is 825,440 yards long and connects the Great Smoky Mountains National Park in North Carolina to the Shenandoah National Park in Virginia. What is the length of the Blue Ridge Parkway in miles?

110. LEWIS AND CLARK The trail traveled by the Lewis and Clark expedition is shown below. When the expedition reached the Pacific Ocean, Clark estimated that they had traveled 4,162 miles. (It was later determined that his guess was within 40 miles of the actual distance.) Express Clark's estimate of the distance in feet.

111. WEIGHT OF WATER One gallon of water weighs about 8 pounds. Express this weight in ounces.

112. WEIGHT OF A BABY A newborn baby boy weighed 136 ounces. Express this weight in pounds.

113. HIPPOS An adult hippopotamus can weigh as much as 9,900 pounds. Express this weight in tons.

114. ELEPHANTS An adult elephant can consume as much as 495 pounds of grass and leaves in one day. How many ounces is this?

115. BUYING PAINT A painter estimates that he will need 17 gallons of paint for a job. To take advantage of a closeout sale on quart cans, he decides to buy the paint in quarts. How many cans will he need to buy?

116. CATERING How many cups of apple cider are there in a 10-gallon container of cider?

117. SCHOOL LUNCHES Each student attending Eagle River Elementary School receives 1 pint of milk for lunch each day. If 575 students attend the school, how many gallons of milk are used each day?

118. RADIATORS The radiator capacity of a piece of earth-moving equipment is 39 quarts. If the radiator is drained and new coolant put in, how many gallons of new coolant will be used?

119. CAMPING How many ounces of camping stove fuel will fit in the container shown?

120. HIKING A college student walks 11 miles in 155 minutes. To the nearest tenth, how many hours does he walk?

121. SPACE TRAVEL The astronauts of the Apollo 8 mission, which was launched on December 21, 1968, were in space for 147 hours. How many days did the mission take?

122. AMELIA EARHART In 1935, Amelia Earhart became the first woman to fly across the Atlantic Ocean alone, establishing a new record for the crossing: 13 hours and 30 minutes. How many minutes is this?

WRITING

123. **a.** Explain how to find the unit conversion factor that will convert feet to inches.

b. Explain how to find the unit conversion factor that will convert pints to gallons.

124. Explain why the unit conversion factor $\frac{1 \text{ lb}}{16 \text{ oz}}$ is a form of 1.

Objectives

1 Define metric units of length.

2 Use a metric ruler to measure lengths.

3 Use unit conversion factors to convert metric units of length.

4 Use a conversion chart to convert metric units of length.

5 Define metric units of mass.

6 Convert from one metric unit of mass to another.

7 Define metric units of capacity.

8 Convert from one metric unit of capacity to another.

9 Define a cubic centimeter.

SECTION 3.5
Metric Units of Measurement

ARE YOU READY?

The following problems review some basic skills that are needed when working with metric units of measurement.

1. Multiply: $2.4 \cdot 1{,}000$
2. Multiply: $7.86 \cdot 100$
3. Multiply: $10 \cdot 1{,}000$
4. Divide: $\frac{350}{10}$
5. Divide: $\frac{3.2}{100{,}000}$
6. **a.** Write $\frac{1}{100}$ as a decimal.

   b. Write 0.001 as a fraction.

The metric system is the system of measurement used by most countries in the world. All countries, including the United States, use it for scientific purposes. The metric system, like our decimal numeration system, is based on the number 10. For this reason, converting from one metric unit to another is easier than with the American system.

1 Define metric units of length.

The basic metric unit of length is the **meter** (m). One meter is approximately 39 inches, which is slightly more than 1 yard. The figure below compares the length of a yardstick to a meterstick.

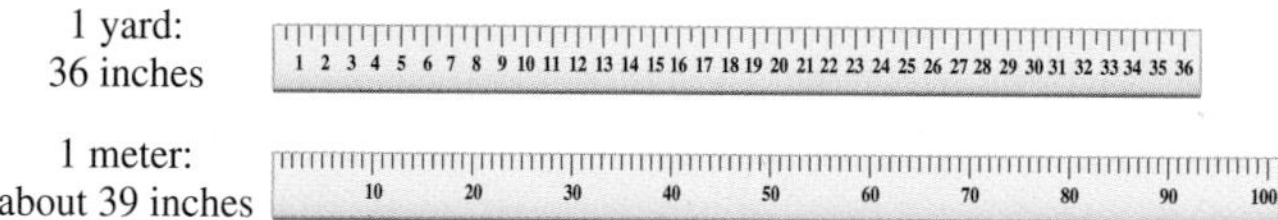

Longer and shorter metric units of length are created by adding **prefixes** to the front of the basic unit, *meter.*

kilo means thousands
hecto means hundreds
deka means tens
deci means tenths
centi means hundredths
milli means thousandths

Metric Units of Length

Prefix	**kilo-meter**	**hecto-meter**	**deka-meter**	**meter**	**deci-meter**	**centi-meter**	**milli-meter**
Meaning	1,000 meters	100 meters	10 meters	1 meter	$\frac{1}{10}$ or 0.1 of a meter	$\frac{1}{100}$ or 0.01 of a meter	$\frac{1}{1{,}000}$ or 0.001 of a meter
Abbreviation	km	hm	dam	m	dm	cm	mm

The Language of Mathematics It is helpful to memorize the prefixes listed above because they are also used with metric units of weight and capacity.

The most often used metric units of length are kilometers, meters, centimeters, and millimeters. It is important that you gain a practical understanding of metric lengths just as you have for the length of an inch, a foot, and a mile. Some examples of metric lengths are shown on the next page.

1 kilometer is about the length of 60 train cars.

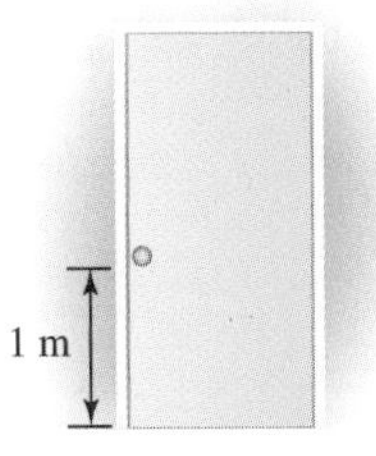

1 meter is about the distance from a doorknob to the floor.

1 centimeter is about as wide as the nail on your little finger.

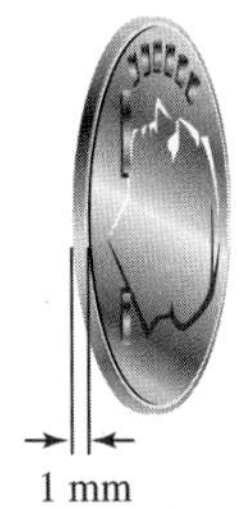

1 millimeter is about the thickness of a dime.

2 Use a metric ruler to measure lengths.

Parts of a metric ruler, scaled in centimeters, and a ruler scaled in inches are shown below. Several lengths on the metric ruler are highlighted.

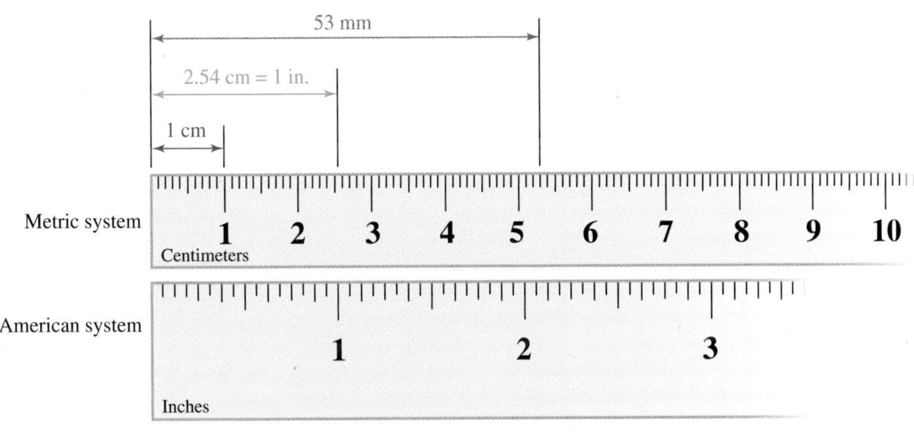

(Actual size)

EXAMPLE 1 Find the length of the nail shown below.

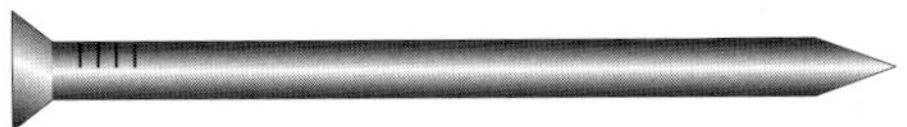

Strategy We will place a metric ruler below the nail, with the left end of the ruler (which could be thought of as 0) directly underneath the head of the nail.

WHY Then we can find the length of the nail by identifying where its pointed end lines up on the tick marks printed in black on the ruler.

Solution

The longest tick marks on the ruler (those labeled with numbers) mark lengths in centimeters. Since the pointed end of the nail lines up on 6, the nail is 6 centimeters long.

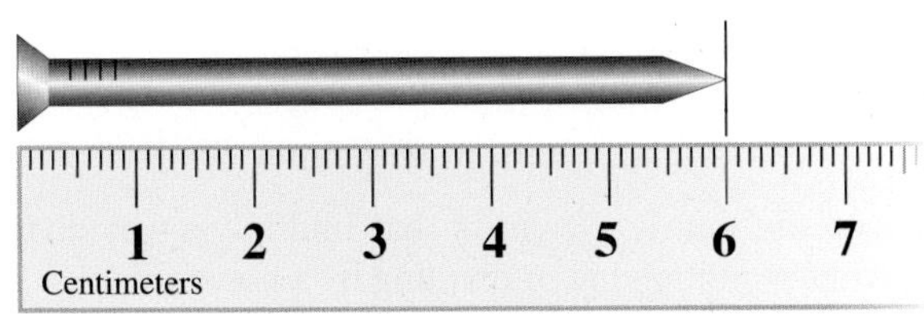

Self Check 1

To the nearest centimeter, find the width of the circle.

Now Try **Problem 23**

Self Check 2

Find the length of the jumbo paper clip.

Now Try **Problem 25**

EXAMPLE 2 Find the length of the paper clip shown below.

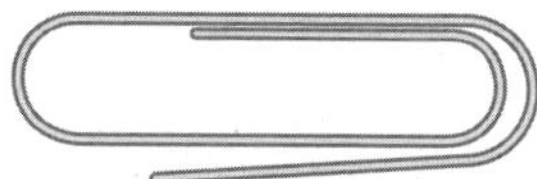

Strategy We will place a metric ruler below the paper clip, with the left end of the ruler (which could be thought of as 0) directly underneath one end of the paper clip.

WHY Then we can find the length of the paper clip by identifying where its other end lines up on the tick marks printed in black on the ruler.

Solution

On the ruler, the shorter tick marks divide each centimeter into 10 millimeters, as shown. If we begin at the left end of the ruler and count by tens as we move right to 3, and then add an additional 6 millimeters to that result, we find that the length of the paper clip is 30 + 6 = 36 millimeters.

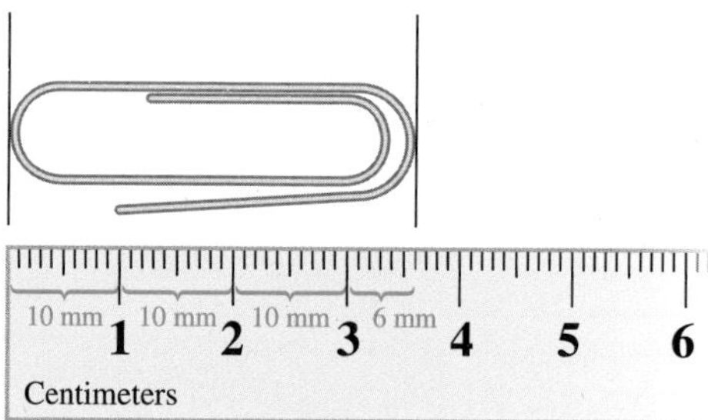

3 Use unit conversion factors to convert metric units of length.

Metric units of length are related as shown in the following table.

Metric Units of Length

1 kilometer (km) = 1,000 meters	1 meter = 10 decimeters (dm)
1 hectometer (hm) = 100 meters	1 meter = 100 centimeters (cm)
1 dekameter (dam) = 10 meters	1 meter = 1,000 millimeters (mm)

The abbreviation for each unit is written within parentheses.

We can use the information in the table to write unit conversion factors that can be used to convert metric units of length. For example, in the table we see that

1 meter = 100 centimeters

From this fact, we can write two unit conversion factors.

$$\frac{1\text{ m}}{100\text{ cm}} = 1 \quad \text{and} \quad \frac{100\text{ cm}}{1\text{ m}} = 1$$

To obtain the first unit conversion factor, divide both sides of the equation 1 m = 100 cm by 100 cm. To obtain the second unit conversion factor, divide both sides by 1 m.

One advantage of the metric system is that multiplying or dividing by a unit conversion factor involves multiplying or dividing by a power of 10.

EXAMPLE 3 Convert 350 centimeters to meters.

Strategy We will multiply 350 centimeters by a carefully chosen unit conversion factor.

WHY If we multiply by the proper unit conversion factor, we can eliminate the unwanted units of centimeters and convert to meters.

Solution

To convert from centimeters to meters, we must choose a unit conversion factor whose numerator contains the units we want to introduce (meters), and whose denominator contains the units we want to eliminate (centimeters). Since there is 1 meter for every 100 centimeters, we will use

$$\frac{1\text{ m}}{100\text{ cm}}$$

← This is the unit we want to introduce. (1 m)
← This is the unit we want to eliminate (the original unit). (100 cm)

To perform the conversion, we multiply 350 centimeters by the unit conversion factor $\frac{1\text{ m}}{100\text{ cm}}$.

$350\text{ cm} = \frac{350\text{ cm}}{1} \cdot \frac{\mathbf{1\text{ m}}}{\mathbf{100\text{ cm}}}$ Write 350 cm as a fraction: $350\text{ cm} = \frac{350\text{ cm}}{1}$. Multiply by a form of 1: $\frac{1\text{ m}}{100\text{ cm}}$.

$= \frac{350\text{ }\cancel{\text{cm}}}{1} \cdot \frac{1\text{ m}}{100\text{ }\cancel{\text{cm}}}$ Remove the common units of centimeters from the numerator and denominator. Notice that the units of meter remain.

$= \frac{350}{100}\text{ m}$ Multiply the fractions.

$= \frac{350.0}{100}\text{ m}$ Write the whole number 350 as a decimal by placing a decimal point immediately to its right and entering a zero: $350 = 350.0$

$= 3.5\text{ m}$ Divide 350.0 by 100 by moving the decimal point 2 places to the left: 3.500.

Thus, 350 centimeters = 3.5 meters.

Self Check 3

Convert 860 centimeters to meters.

Now Try **Problem 31**

4 Use a conversion chart to convert metric units of length.

In Example 3, we converted 350 centimeters to meters using a unit conversion factor. We can also make this conversion by recognizing that all units of length in the metric system are powers of 10 of a meter.

To see this, review the table of metric units of length on page 62. Note that each unit has a value that is $\frac{1}{10}$ of the value of the unit immediately to its left and 10 times the value of the unit immediately to its right. Converting from one unit to another is as easy as multiplying (or dividing) by the correct power of 10 or, simply moving a decimal point the correct number of places to the right (or left). For example, in the **conversion chart** below, we see that to convert from centimeters to meters, we move 2 places to the left.

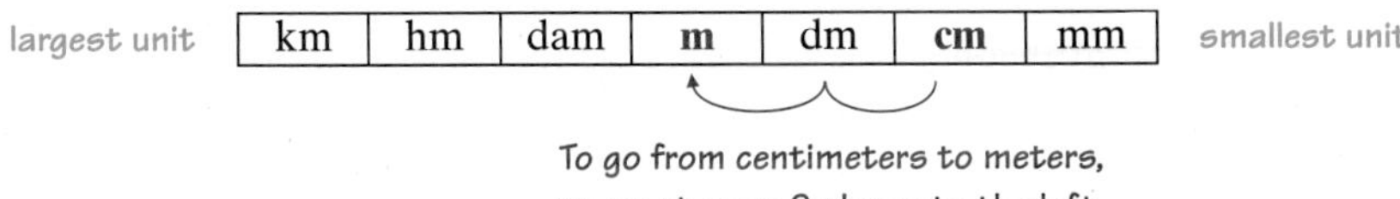

If we write 350 centimeters as 350.0 centimeters, we can convert to meters by moving the decimal point 2 places to the left.

350.0 centimeters = 3.500 meters = 3.5 meters

Move 2 places to the left.

With the unit conversion factor method or the conversion chart method, we get 350 cm = 3.5 m.

Caution! When using a chart to help make a metric conversion, be sure to list the units from *largest to smallest* when reading from left to right.

Self Check 4

Convert 5.3 meters to millimeters.

Now Try **Problem 35**

EXAMPLE 4 Convert 2.4 meters to millimeters.

Strategy On a conversion chart, we will count the places and note the direction as we move from the original units of meters to the conversion units of millimeters.

WHY The decimal point in 2.4 must be moved the same number of places and in that same direction to find the conversion to millimeters.

Solution

To construct a conversion chart, we list the metric units of length from largest (kilometers) to smallest (millimeters), working from left to right. Then we locate the original units of meters and move to the conversion units of millimeters, as shown below.

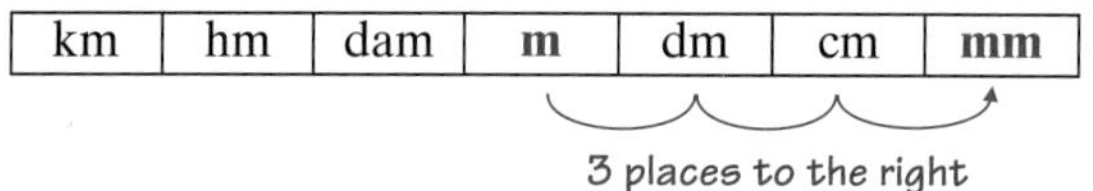

We see that the decimal point in 2.4 should be moved 3 places to the right to convert from meters to millimeters.

2.4 meters = 2 400. millimeters = 2,400 millimeters

Move 3 places to the right.

We can use the unit conversion factor method to confirm this result. Since there are 1,000 millimeters per meter, we multiply 2.4 meters by the unit conversion factor $\frac{1{,}000 \text{ mm}}{1 \text{ m}}$.

$$2.4 \text{ m} = \frac{2.4 \text{ m}}{1} \cdot \frac{\mathbf{1{,}000 \text{ mm}}}{\mathbf{1 \text{ m}}}$$ Write 2.4 m as a fraction: 2.4 m = $\frac{2.4 \text{ m}}{1}$. Multiply by a form 1: $\frac{1{,}000 \text{ mm}}{1 \text{ m}}$.

$$= \frac{2.4 \not{\text{m}}}{1} \cdot \frac{1{,}000 \text{ mm}}{1 \not{\text{m}}}$$ Remove the common units of meters from the numerator and denominator. Notice that the units of millimeters remain.

$$= 2.4 \cdot 1{,}000 \text{ mm}$$ Multiply the fractions and simplify.

$$= 2{,}400 \text{ mm}$$ Multiply 2.4 by 1,000 by moving the decimal point 3 places to the right: 2 400.

Self Check 5

Convert 5.15 centimeters to kilometers.

Now Try **Problem 39**

EXAMPLE 5 Convert 3.2 centimeters to kilometers.

Strategy On a conversion chart, we will count the places and note the direction as we move from the original units of centimeters to the conversion units of kilometers.

WHY The decimal point in 3.2 must be moved the same number of places and in that same direction to find the conversion to kilometers.

Solution

We locate the original units of centimeters on a conversion chart, and then move to the conversion units of kilometers, as shown on the next page.

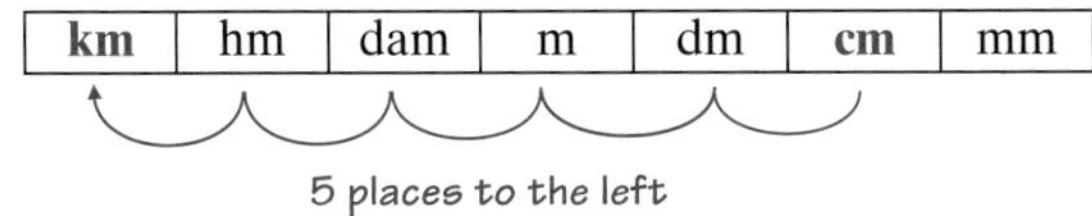

We see that the decimal point in 3.2 should be moved 5 places to the left to convert centimeters to kilometers.

3.2 centimeters = 0.000032 kilometers = 0.000032 kilometers

Move 5 places to the left.

We can use the unit conversion factor method to confirm this result. To convert to kilometers, we must use two unit conversion factors so that the units of centimeters drop out and the units of kilometers remain. Since there is 1 meter for every 100 centimeters and 1 kilometer for every 1,000 meters, we multiply by $\frac{1\text{ m}}{100\text{ cm}}$ and $\frac{1\text{ km}}{1{,}000\text{ m}}$.

$$3.2\text{ cm} = \frac{3.2\text{ cm}}{1} \cdot \frac{1\text{ m}}{100\text{ cm}} \cdot \frac{1\text{ km}}{1{,}000\text{ m}}$$ Remove the common units of centimeters and meters. The units of km remain.

$$= \frac{3.2}{100 \cdot 1{,}000}\text{ km}$$ Multiply the fractions.

$$= 0.000032\text{ km}$$ Divide 3.2 by 1,000 and 100 by moving the decimal point 5 places to the left.

5 Define metric units of mass.

The **mass** of an object is a measure of the amount of material in the object. When an object is moved about in space, its mass does not change. One basic unit of mass in the metric system is the **gram** (g). A gram is defined to be the mass of water contained in a cube having sides 1 centimeter long. (See the figure below.)

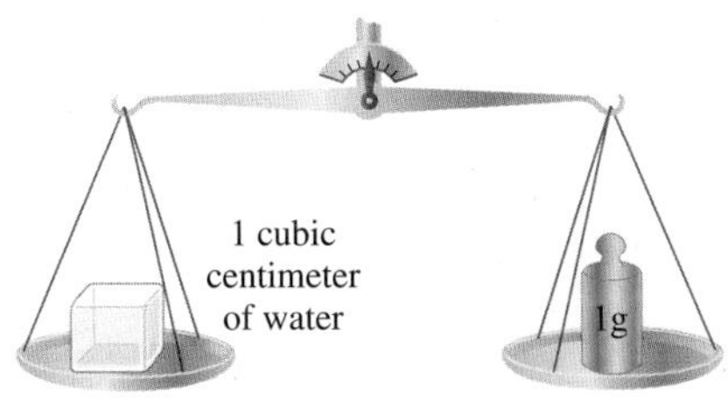

Other units of mass are created by adding prefixes to the front of the basic unit, *gram*.

Metric Units of Mass

Prefix	kilo-gram	hecto-gram	deka-gram	gram	deci-gram	centi-gram	milli-gram
Meaning	1,000 grams	100 grams	10 grams	1 gram	$\frac{1}{10}$ or 0.1 of a gram	$\frac{1}{100}$ or 0.01 of a gram	$\frac{1}{1{,}000}$ or 0.001 of a gram
Abbreviation	kg	hg	dag	g	dg	cg	mg

The most often used metric units of mass are kilograms, grams, and milligrams. Some examples are shown below.

An average bowling ball weighs about 6 kilograms.

A raisin weighs about 1 gram.

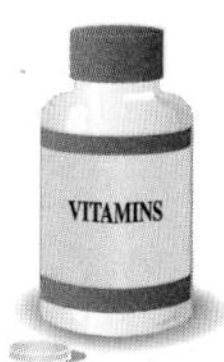

A certain vitamin tablet contains 450 milligrams of calcium.

The **weight** of an object is determined by the Earth's gravitational pull on the object. Since gravitational pull on an object decreases as the object gets farther from Earth, the object weighs less as it gets farther from Earth's surface. This is why astronauts experience weightlessness in space. However, since most of us remain near Earth's surface, we will use the words *mass* and *weight* interchangeably. Thus, a mass of 30 grams is said to weigh 30 grams.

Metric units of mass are related as shown in the following table.

Metric Units of Mass

1 kilogram (kg) = 1,000 grams	1 gram = 10 decigrams (dg)
1 hectogram (hg) = 100 grams	1 gram = 100 centigrams (cg)
1 dekagram (dag) = 10 grams	1 gram = 1,000 milligrams (mg)

The abbreviation for each unit is written within parentheses.

We can use the information in the table to write unit conversion factors that can be used to convert metric units of mass. For example, in the table we see that

1 kilogram = 1,000 grams

From this fact, we can write two unit conversion factors.

$$\frac{1\text{ kg}}{1{,}000\text{ g}} = 1 \quad \text{and} \quad \frac{1{,}000\text{ g}}{1\text{ kg}} = 1$$

To obtain the first unit conversion factor, divide both sides of the equation 1 kg = 1,000 g by 1,000 g. To obtain the second unit conversion factor, divide both sides by 1 kg.

6 Convert from one metric unit of mass to another.

Self Check 6

Convert 5.83 kilograms to grams.

Now Try **Problem 43**

EXAMPLE 6 Convert 7.86 kilograms to grams.

Strategy On a conversion chart, we will count the places and note the direction as we move from the original units of kilograms to the conversion units of grams.

WHY The decimal point in 7.86 must be moved the same number of places and in that same direction to find the conversion to grams.

Solution

To construct a conversion chart, we list the metric units of mass from largest (kilograms) to smallest (milligrams), working from left to right. Then we locate the original units of kilograms and move to the conversion units of grams, as shown below.

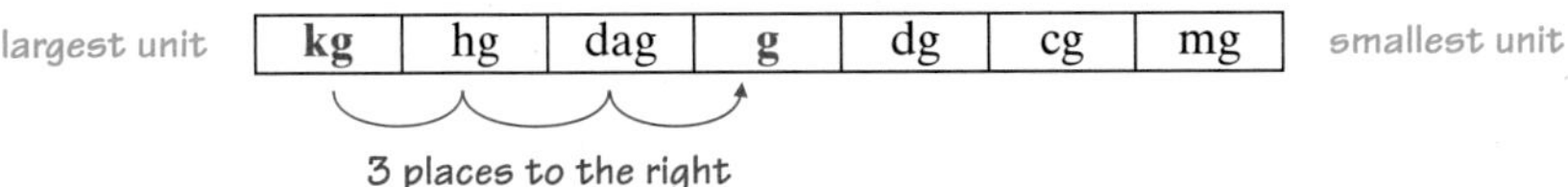

We see that the decimal point in 7.86 should be moved 3 places to the right to change kilograms to grams.

7.86 kilograms = 7 860. grams = 7,860 grams

Move 3 places to the right.

We can use the unit conversion factor method to confirm this result. To convert to grams, we must chose a unit conversion factor such that the units of kilograms drop out and the units of grams remain. Since there are 1,000 grams per 1 kilogram, we multiply 7.86 kilograms by $\frac{1{,}000 \text{ g}}{1 \text{ kg}}$.

$$7.86 \text{ kg} = \frac{7.86 \text{ kg}}{1} \cdot \frac{\mathbf{1{,}000 \text{ g}}}{\mathbf{1 \text{ kg}}}$$ Remove the common units of kilograms in the numerator and denominator. The units of g remain.

$$= 7.86 \cdot 1{,}000 \text{ g}$$ Simplify.

$$= 7{,}860 \text{ g}$$ Multiply 7.86 by 1,000 by moving the decimal point 3 places to the right.

EXAMPLE 7 ***Medications*** A bottle of Verapamil, a drug taken for high blood pressure, contains 30 tablets. If each tablet has 180 mg of active ingredient, how many grams of active ingredient are in the bottle?

Strategy We will multiply the number of tablets in one bottle by the number of milligrams of active ingredient in each tablet.

WHY We need to know the total number of milligrams of active ingredient in one bottle before we can convert that number to grams.

Solution

Since there are 30 tablets, and each one contains 180 mg of active ingredient, there are

$$
\begin{array}{r}
180 \\
\times\ 30 \\
\hline
000 \\
5400 \\
\hline
5{,}400
\end{array}
$$

$$30 \cdot 180 \text{ mg} = 5{,}400 \text{ mg} = 5400.0 \text{ mg}$$

of active ingredient in the bottle. To use a conversion chart to solve this problem, we locate the original units of milligrams and then move to the conversion units of grams, as shown below.

kg	hg	dag	g	dg	cg	mg

3 places to the left

We see that the decimal point in 5,400.0 should be moved 3 places to the left to convert from milligrams to grams.

5,400 milligrams = 5.400 grams

Move 3 places to the left.

There are 5.4 grams of active ingredient in the bottle.

Self Check 7

MEDICATIONS A bottle of Isoptin (a drug taken for high blood pressure) contains 90 tablets, and each has 200 mg of active ingredient, how many grams of active ingredient are in the bottle?

Now Try **Problems 47 and 95**

We can use the unit conversion factor method to confirm this result. To convert milligrams to grams, we multiply 5,400 milligrams by $\frac{1\text{ g}}{1{,}000\text{ mg}}$.

$$5{,}400\text{ mg} = \frac{5{,}400\text{ mg}}{1} \cdot \frac{1\text{ g}}{1{,}000\text{ mg}}$$

Remove the common units of milligrams from the numerator and denominator. The units of g remain.

$$= \frac{5{,}400}{1{,}000}\text{ g}$$

Multiply the fractions.

$$= 5.4\text{ g}$$

Divide 5,400 by 1,000 by moving the understood decimal point in 5,400 three places to the left.

7 Define metric units of capacity.

In the metric system, one basic unit of capacity is the **liter** (L), which is defined to be the capacity of a cube with sides 10 centimeters long. Other units of capacity are created by adding prefixes to the front of the basic unit, liter.

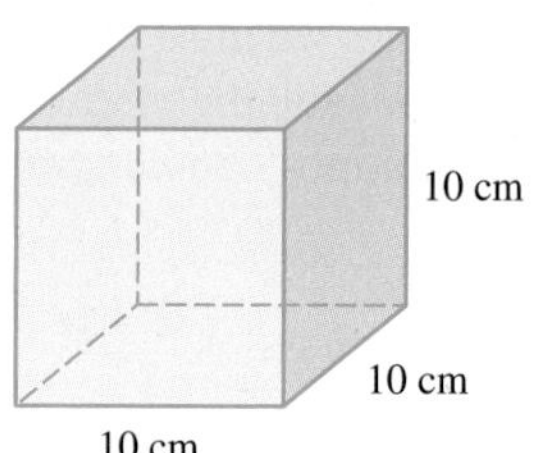

Metric Units of Capacity

Prefix	**kilo-liter**	**hecto-liter**	**deka-liter**	**liter**	**deci-liter**	**centi-liter**	**milli-liter**
Meaning	1,000 liters	100 liters	10 liters	1 liter	$\frac{1}{10}$ or 0.1 of a liter	$\frac{1}{100}$ or 0.01 of a liter	$\frac{1}{1{,}000}$ or 0.001 of a liter
Abbreviation	kL	hL	daL	L	dL	cL	mL

The most often used metric units of capacity are liters and milliliters. Here are some examples.

Soft drinks are sold in 2-liter plastic bottles.

The fuel tank of a minivan can hold about 75 liters of gasoline.

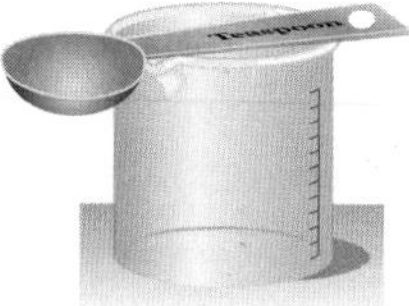

A teaspoon holds about 5 milliliters.

Metric units of capacity are related as shown in the following table.

Metric Units of Capacity

1 kiloliter (kL) = 1,000 liters	1 liter = 10 deciliters (dL)
1 hectoliter (hL) = 100 liters	1 liter = 100 centiliters (cL)
1 dekaliter (daL) = 10 liters	1 liter = 1,000 milliliters (mL)

The abbreviation for each unit is written within parentheses.

We can use the information in the table to write unit conversion factors that can be used to convert metric units of capacity. For example, in the table we see that

1 liter = 1,000 milliliters

From this fact, we can write two unit conversion factors.

$$\frac{1 \text{ L}}{1{,}000 \text{ mL}} = 1 \quad \text{and} \quad \frac{1{,}000 \text{ mL}}{1 \text{ L}} = 1$$

8 Convert from one metric unit of capacity to another.

EXAMPLE 8 ***Soft Drinks*** How many milliliters are in *three* 2-liter bottles of cola?

Strategy We will multiply the number of bottles of cola by the number of liters of cola in each bottle.

WHY We need to know the total number of liters of cola before we can convert that number to milliliters.

Solution

Since there are three bottles, and each contains 2 liters of cola, there are

$$3 \cdot 2 \text{ L} = 6 \text{ L} = 6.0 \text{ L}$$

of cola in the bottles. To construct a conversion chart, we list the metric units of capacity from largest (kiloliters) to smallest (milliliters), working from left to right. Then we locate the original units of liters and move to the conversion units of milliliters, as shown below.

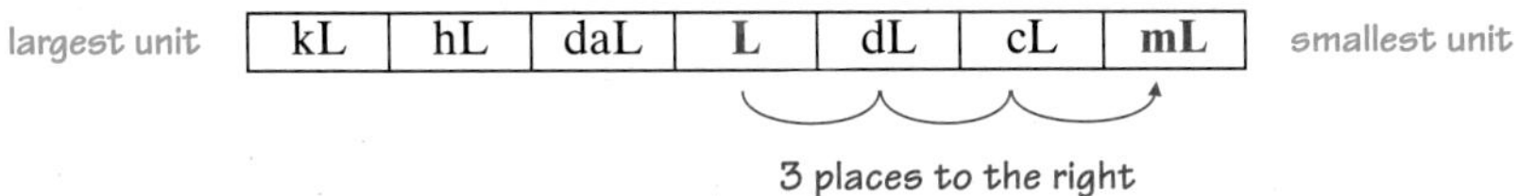

We see that the decimal point in 6.0 should be moved 3 places to the right to convert from liters to milliliters.

6 liters = 6 000. milliliters = 6,000 milliliters

Move 3 places to the right.

Thus, there are 6,000 milliliters in *three* 2-liter bottles of cola.

We can use the unit conversion factor method to confirm this result. To convert to milliliters, we must chose a unit conversion factor such that liters drop out and the units of milliliters remain. Since there are 1,000 milliliters per 1 liter, we multiply 6 liters by the unit conversion factor $\frac{1{,}000 \text{ mL}}{1 \text{ L}}$.

$$6 \text{ L} = \frac{6 \cancel{\text{L}}}{1} \cdot \frac{1{,}000 \text{ mL}}{1 \cancel{\text{L}}}$$ Remove the common units of liters in the numerator and denominator. The units of mL remain.

$$= 6 \cdot 1{,}000 \text{ mL}$$ Simplify.

$$= 6{,}000 \text{ mL}$$ Multiply 6 by 1,000 by moving the understood decimal point in 6 three places to the right.

Self Check 8

SOFT DRINKS How many milliliters are in a case of *twelve* 2-liter bottles of cola?

Now Try **Problems 51 and 105**

9 Define a cubic centimeter.

Another metric unit of capacity is the **cubic centimeter,** which is represented by the notation cm^3 or, more simply, cc. One milliliter and one cubic centimeter represent the same capacity.

$$1 \text{ mL} = 1 \text{ cm}^3 = 1 \text{ cc}$$

The units of cubic centimeters are used frequently in medicine. For example, when a nurse administers an injection containing 5 cc of medication, the dosage can also be expressed using milliliters.

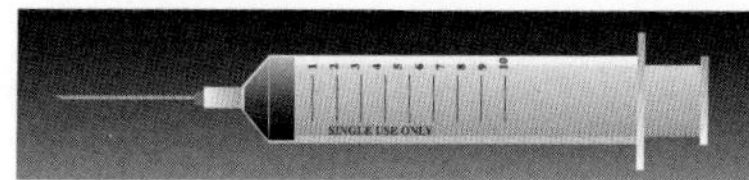

5 cc = 5 mL

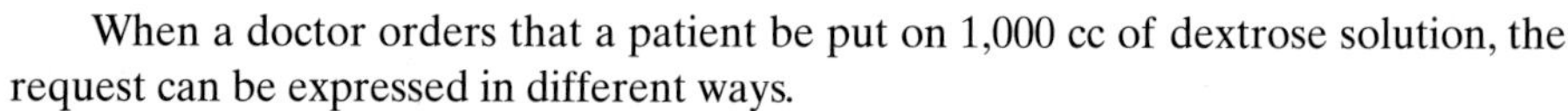

When a doctor orders that a patient be put on 1,000 cc of dextrose solution, the request can be expressed in different ways.

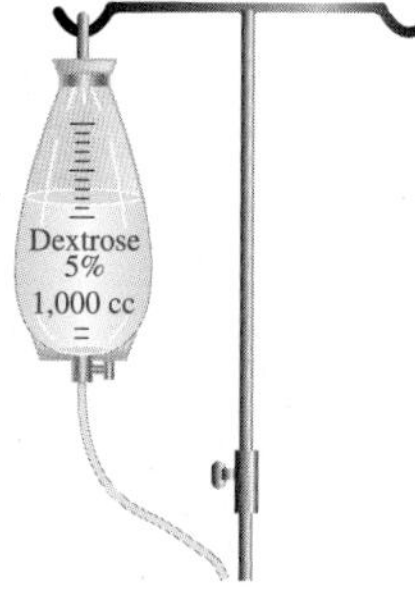

1,000 cc = 1,000 mL = 1 liter

ANSWERS TO SELF CHECKS

1. 3 cm **2.** 47 mm **3.** 8.6 m **4.** 5,300 mm **5.** 0.0000515 km **6.** 5,830 g **7.** 18 g **8.** 24,000 mL

SECTION 3.5 STUDY SET

VOCABULARY

Fill in the blanks.

1. The meter, the gram, and the liter are basic units of measurement in the ______ system.

2. a. The basic unit of length in the metric system is the ______.

b. The basic unit of mass in the metric system is the ______.

c. The basic unit of capacity in the metric system is the ______.

3. a. *Deka* means ______.

b. *Hecto* means ______.

c. *Kilo* means ______.

4. a. *Deci* means ______.

b. *Centi* means ______.

c. *Milli* means ______.

5. We can convert from one unit to another in the metric system using ______ conversion factors or a conversion ______ like that shown below.

km	hm	dam	m	dm	cm	mm

6. The ______ of an object is a measure of the amount of material in the object.

7. The ______ of an object is determined by the Earth's gravitational pull on the object.

8. Another metric unit of capacity is the cubic ______, which is represented by the notation cm^3, or, more simply, cc.

CONCEPTS

Fill in the blanks.

9. a. 1 kilometer = ______ meters

b. ______ centimeters = 1 meter

c. ______ millimeters = 1 meter

10. a. 1 gram = ______ milligrams

b. 1 kilogram = ______ grams

11. a. ______ milliliters = 1 liter

b. 1 dekaliter = ______ liters

12. a. 1 milliliter = ______ cubic centimeter

b. 1 liter = ______ cubic centimeters

13. Write a unit conversion factor to convert

a. meters to kilometers

b. grams to centigrams

c. liters to milliliters

14. Use the chart to determine how many decimal places and in which direction to move the decimal point when converting the following.

a. Kilometers to centimeters

km	hm	dam	m	dm	cm	mm

b. Milligrams to grams

kg	hg	dag	g	dg	cg	mg

c. Hectoliters to centiliters

kL	hL	daL	L	dL	cL	mL

15. Match each item with its proper measurement.

a. Thickness of a phone book **i.** 6,275 km
b. Length of the Amazon River **ii.** 2 m
c. Height of a soccer goal **iii.** 6 cm

16. Match each item with its proper measurement.

a. Weight of a giraffe **i.** 800 kg
b. Weight of a paper clip **ii.** 1 g
c. Active ingredient in an aspirin tablet **iii.** 325 mg

17. Match each item with its proper measurement.

a. Amount of blood in an adult **i.** 290,000 kL
b. Cola in an aluminum can **ii.** 6 L
c. Kuwait's daily production of crude oil **iii.** 355 mL

18. Of the objects shown below, which can be used to measure the following?

a. Millimeters
b. Milligrams
c. Milliliters

Balance

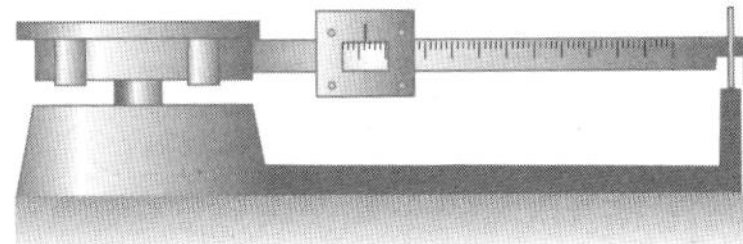

Beaker

Micrometer

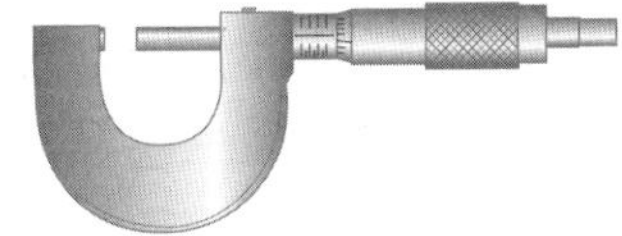

NOTATION

Complete each solution.

19. Convert 20 centimeters to meters.

$$20 \text{ cm} = \frac{20 \text{ cm}}{1} \cdot \frac{\square \text{ m}}{100 \text{ cm}}$$
$$= \frac{20}{\square} \text{ m}$$
$$= \square \text{ m}$$

20. Convert 3,000 milligrams to grams.

$$3{,}000 \text{ mg} = \frac{3{,}000 \text{ mg}}{1} \cdot \frac{1 \text{ g}}{1{,}000 \square}$$
$$= \frac{3{,}000}{1{,}000} \square$$
$$= \square \text{ g}$$

21. Convert 0.2 kilograms to milligrams.

$$0.2 \text{ kg} = \frac{0.2 \text{ kg}}{1} \cdot \frac{\square \text{ g}}{1 \text{ kg}} \cdot \frac{1{,}000 \text{ mg}}{\square \text{ g}}$$
$$= 0.2 \cdot 1{,}000 \cdot 1{,}000 \square$$
$$= \square \text{ mg}$$

22. Convert 400 milliliters to kiloliters.

$$400 \text{ mL} = \frac{400 \text{ mL}}{1} \cdot \frac{1 \text{ L}}{\square \text{ mL}} \cdot \frac{1 \square}{1{,}000 \text{ L}}$$
$$= \frac{\square}{1{,}000 \cdot 1{,}000} \text{ kL}$$
$$= 0.0004 \text{ kL}$$

GUIDED PRACTICE

Refer to the given ruler to answer each question. See Example 1.

23. Determine which measurements the arrows point to on the metric ruler.

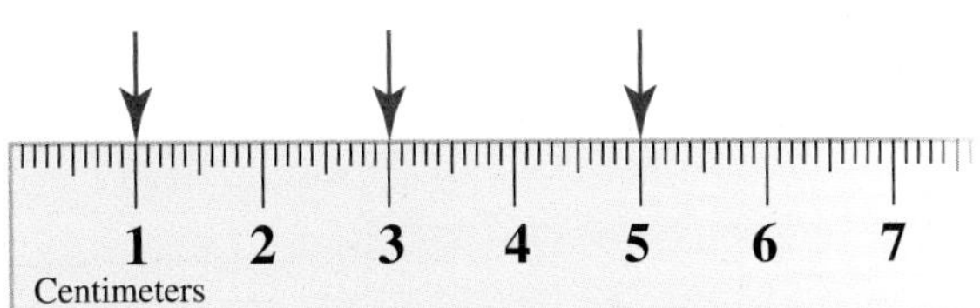

24. Find the length of the birthday candle (including the wick).

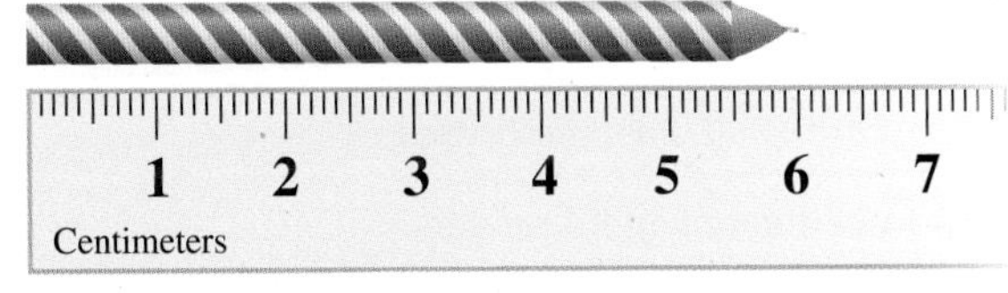

Refer to the given ruler to answer each question. See Example 2.

25. **a.** Refer to the metric ruler below. Each centimeter is divided into how many equal parts? What is the length of one of those parts?

b. Determine which measurements the arrows point to on the ruler.

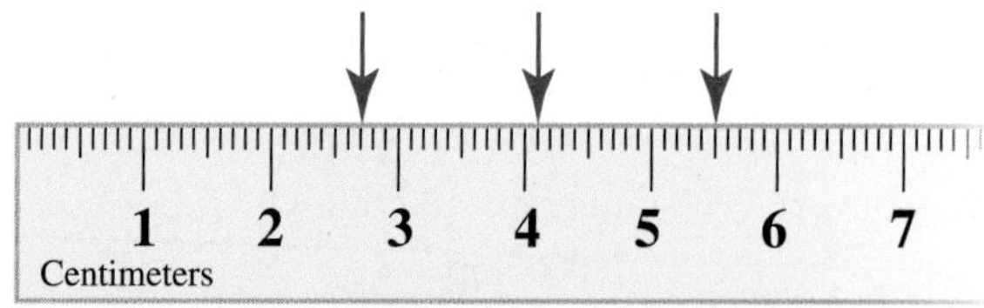

26. Find the length in millimeters of the stick of gum.

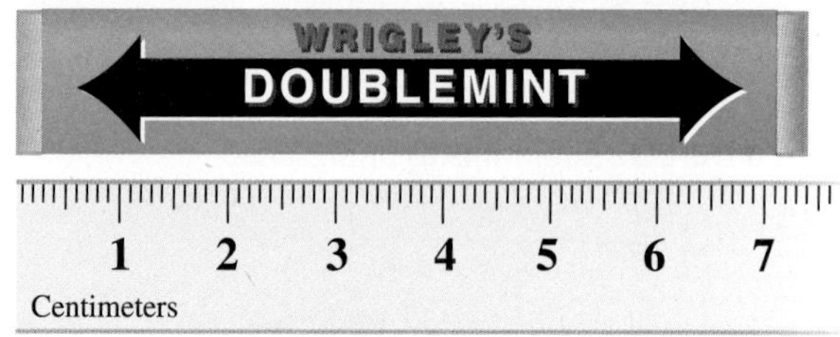

Use a metric ruler scaled in millimeters to measure each object. See Example 2.

27. The length of a dollar bill

28. The width of a dollar bill

29. The length (top to bottom) of this page

30. The length of the word antidisestablishmentarianism as printed here.

Perform each conversion. See Example 3.

31. 380 centimeters to meters

32. 590 centimeters to meters

33. 120 centimeters to meters

34. 640 centimeters to meters

Perform each conversion. See Example 4.

35. 8.7 meters to millimeters

36. 1.3 meters to millimeters

37. 2.89 meters to millimeters

38. 4.06 meters to millimeters

Perform each conversion. See Example 5.

39. 4.5 centimeters to kilometers

40. 6.2 centimeters to kilometers

41. 0.3 centimeters to kilometers

42. 0.4 centimeters to kilometers

Perform each conversion. See Example 6.

43. 1.93 kilograms to grams

44. 8.99 kilograms to grams

45. 4.531 kilograms to grams

46. 6.077 kilograms to grams

Perform each conversion. See Example 7.

47. 6,000 milligrams to grams

48. 9,000 milligrams to grams

49. 3,500 milligrams to grams

50. 7,500 milligrams to grams

Perform each conversion. See Example 8.

51. 3 liters to milliliters

52. 4 liters to milliliters

53. 26.3 liters to milliliters

54. 35.2 liters to milliliters

TRY IT YOURSELF

55. 500 milliliters to liters

56. 500 centiliters to milliliters

57. 2 kilograms to grams

58. 4,000 grams to kilograms

59. 0.074 centimeters to millimeters

60. 0.125 meters to millimeters

61. 1,000 kilograms to grams

62. 2 kilograms to centigrams

63. 658.23 liters to kiloliters

64. 0.0068 hectoliters to kiloliters

65. 4.72 cm to dm

66. 0.593 cm to dam

67. 10 mL = ___ cc

68. 2,000 cc = __ L

69. 500 mg to g

70. 500 mg to cg

71. 5,689 g to kg

72. 0.0579 km to mm

73. 453.2 cm to m

74. 675.3 cm to m

75. 0.325 dL to L

76. 0.0034 mL to L

77. 675 dam = _______ cm

78. 76.8 hm = _______ mm

79. 0.00777 cm = ________ dam

80. 400 liters to hL

81. 134 m to hm

82. 6.77 mm to cm

83. 65.78 km to dam

84. 5 g to cg

CONCEPT EXTENSIONS

85. a. Write a length that is equivalent to 4 meters using kilometers as the unit of measure.

b. Write a length that is equivalent to 4 meters using centimeters as the unit of measure.

86. a. Write a capacity that is equivalent to 9 centiliters using liters as the unit of measure.

b. Write a capacity that is equivalent to 9 centiliters using millimeters as the unit of measure.

87. To use the conversion chart introduced in Objective 4, you need to memorize the order of the six metric prefixes. Some students find that a verse (or rhyme) to aid their memory is helpful. One possibility is the sentence:

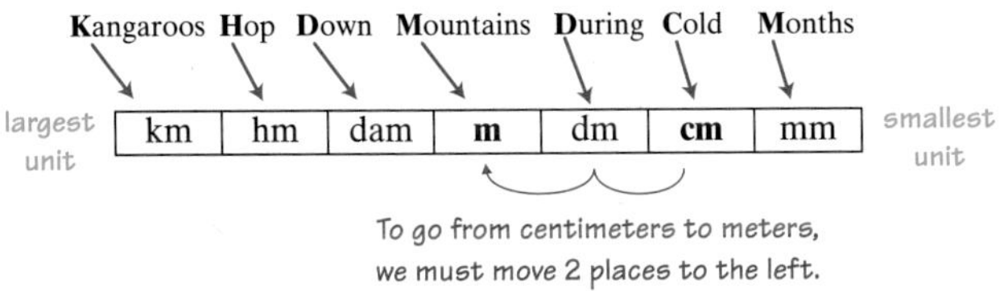

Note that the first letter of each word in the sentence represents one of the metric prefixes. We call such a memory sentence a **mnemonic** (pronounced *knee* · *mon* · *ic*). Write your own mnemonic for the conversion chart.

88. NEW PREFIXES

a. The prefix *mega* means one million. How many meters in one megameter?

b. The prefix *giga* means one billion. How many meters in one gigameter?

c. The prefix *tera* means one trillion. How many meters in one terameter?

89. Each of the following measurements is incorrect because the decimal point is in the wrong place. Correct the mistake by removing the decimal point or by writing it in the proper position.

a. Greatest depth of the Grand Canyon: 182.9 m

b. Maximum allowed weight of a bowling ball: 72.6 kg

c. Average amount of water used during a five-minute shower with unrestricted showerhead: 0.855 L

90. A 250-milliliter serving is poured from a 2-liter bottle of soda.

a. How many milliliters of soda are left in the bottle?

b. How many liters of soda are left in the bottle?

91. AREA How many square centimeters in 1m^2?

92. SCIENCE A very small unit of measurement called an **angstrom** is used in science to express the sizes of atoms and molecules. Its symbol is Å. There are 10,000,000,000 Å in one meter. How many angstroms are in 5 decimeters?

APPLICATIONS

93. SPEED SKATING American Eric Heiden won an unprecedented five gold medals by capturing the men's 500-m, 1,000-m, 1,500-m, 5,000-m, and 10,000-m races at the 1980 Winter Olympic Games in Lake Placid, New York. Convert each race length to kilometers.

94. THE SUEZ CANAL The 163-km-long Suez Canal connects the Mediterranean Sea with the Red Sea. It provides a shortcut for ships operating between European and Asian ports. Convert the length of the Suez Canal to meters.

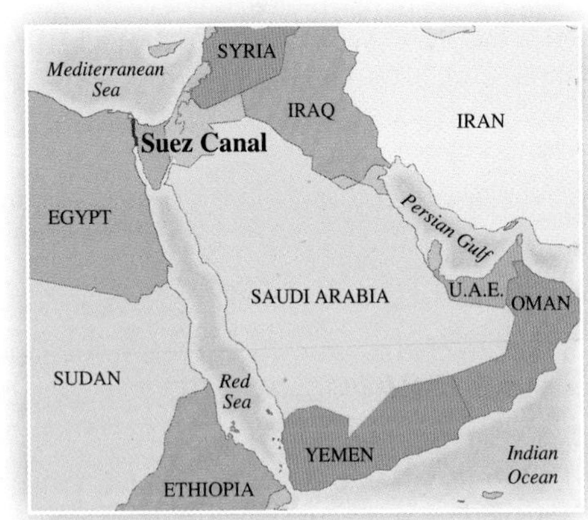

95. SKYSCRAPERS The tallest building in North Carolina is the Bank of America Corporate Center in Charlotte. It is 265 meters tall. Give this height in hectometers.

96. WEIGHT OF A BABY A baby weighs 4 kilograms. Give this weight in centigrams.

97. HEALTH CARE Blood pressure is measured by a sphygmomanometer *(see below)*. The measurement is read at two points and is expressed, for example, as 120/80. This indicates a *systolic* pressure of 120 millimeters of mercury and a *diastolic* pressure of 80 millimeters of mercury. Convert each measurement to centimeters of mercury.

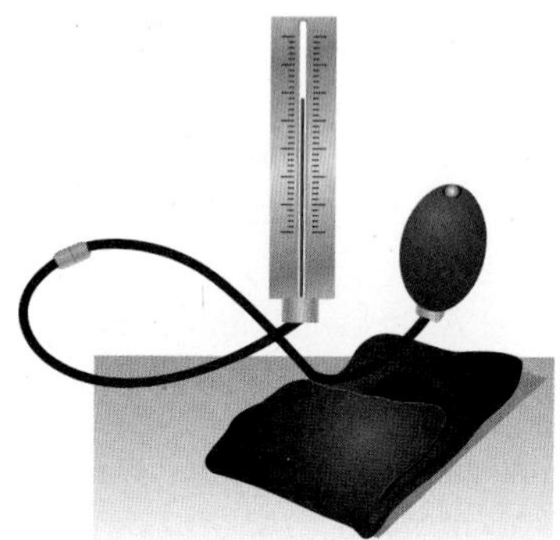

98. JEWELRY A gold chain weighs 1,500 milligrams. Give this weight in grams.

99 EYE DROPPERS One drop from an eye dropper is 0.05 mL. Convert the capacity of one drop to liters.

100. BOTTLING How many liters of wine are in a 750-mL bottle?

101. MEDICINE A bottle of hydrochlorothiazine contains 60 tablets. If each tablet contains 50 milligrams of active ingredient, how many grams of active ingredient are in the bottle?

102. IBUPROFEN What is the total weight, in grams, of all the tablets in the box shown at right?

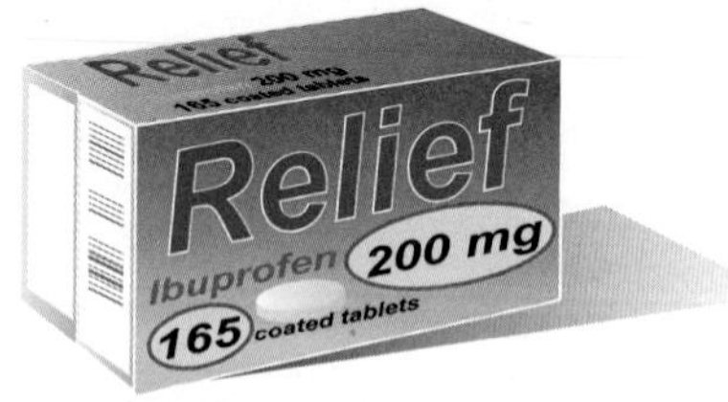

103. SIX PACKS Some stores sell Fanta orange soda in 0.5 liter bottles. How many milliliters are there in a six pack of this size bottle?

104. CONTAINERS How many deciliters of root beer are in *two* 2-liter bottles?

105. OLIVES The net weight of a bottle of olives is 284 grams. Find the smallest number of bottles that must be purchased to have at least 1 kilogram of olives.

106. COFFEE A can of Cafe Vienna has a net weight of 133 grams. Find the smallest number of cans that must be packaged to have at least 1 metric ton of coffee. (*Hint:* 1 metric ton = 1,000 kg.)

107. INJECTIONS The illustration below shows a 3cc syringe. Express its capacity using units of milliliters.

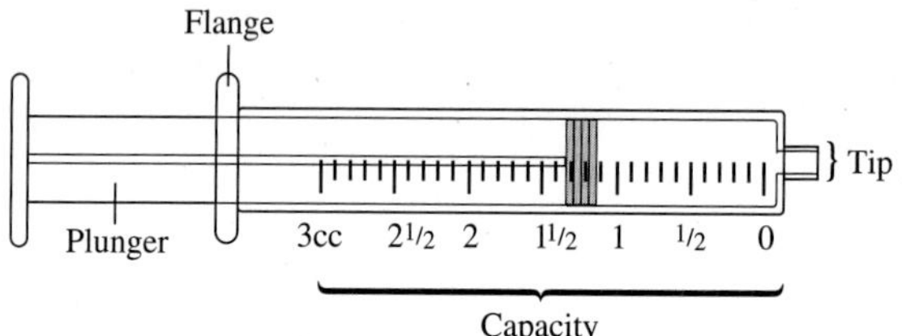

108. MEDICAL SUPPLIES A doctor ordered 2,000 cc of a saline (salt) solution from a pharmacy. How many liters of saline solution is this?

WRITING

109. To change 3.452 kilometers to meters, we can move the decimal point in 3.452 three places to the right to get 3,452 meters. Explain why.

110. To change 7,532 grams to kilograms, we can move the decimal point in 7,532 three places to the left to get 7.532 kilograms. Explain why.

111. A *centimeter* is one hundredth of a meter. Make a list of five other words that begin with the prefix *centi* or *cent* and write a definition for each.

112. List the advantages of the metric system of measurement as compared to the American system. There have been several attempts to bring the metric system into general use in the United States. Why do you think these efforts have been unsuccessful?

SECTION 3.6

Applications Introduction: American and Metric Units Review

Complete the crossworld puzzle below. it will help you prepare for section 3.6 where you will convert between American units and metric units of measure.

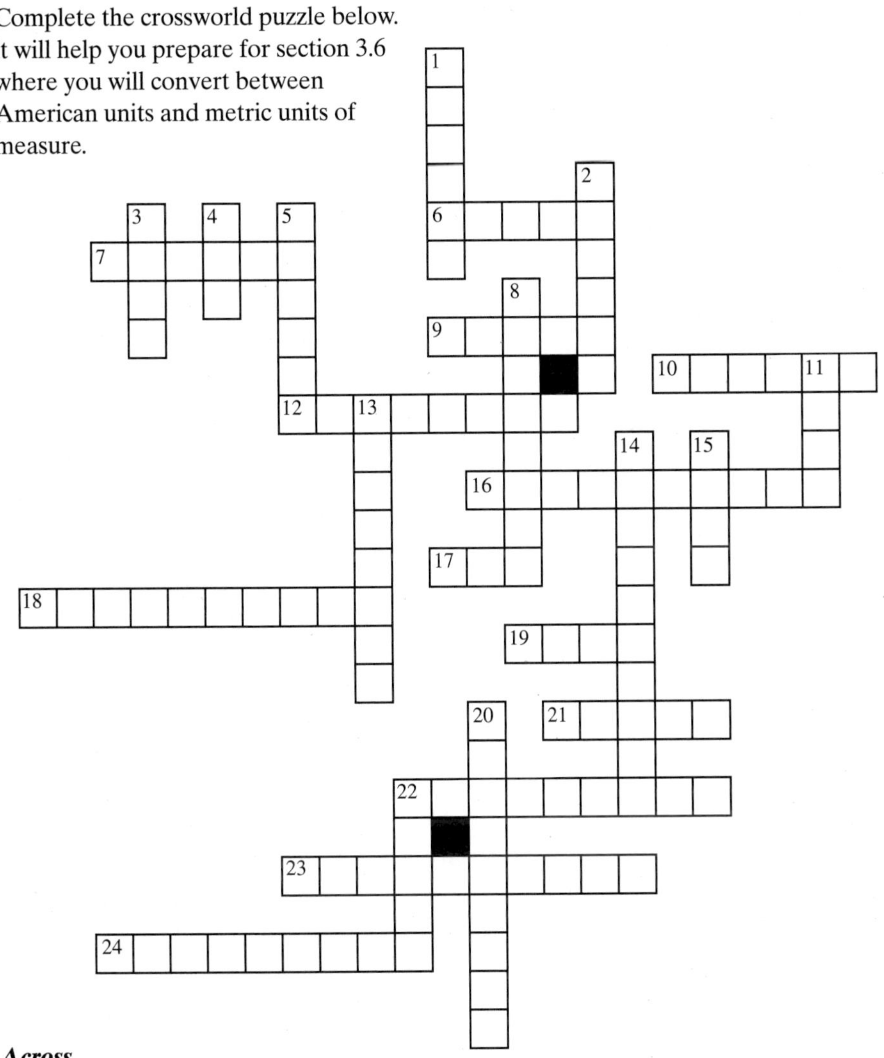

Across

6. 16 of these make one pound
7. 60 seconds
9. 2 pints
10. a measure of the pull of gravity
12. 10 grams
16. 1,000 of these make one liter
17. 24 hours
18. 100 of these make one meter
19. 1,000 of these make one kilogram
21. a basic metric unit of capacity
22. $\frac{1}{1,000}$ of a gram
23. 100 meters
24. $\frac{1}{10}$ of a liter

Down

1. a basic American unit of capacity
2. a measurement from end-to-end
3. 8 of these make one gallon
4. 8 fluid ounces make one of these
5. 60 of these make one minute
8. a measure of the amount a container can hold
11. 24 of these make one day
13. 1,000 grams
14. 1,000 of these make one meter
15. prefix for tenths
20. 1,000 meters
22. a basic metric unit of length

Objectives

1. Use unit conversion factors to convert between American and metric units.
2. Convert between Fahrenheit and Celsius temperatures.

SECTION 3.6 Converting between American and Metric Units

ARE YOU READY?

The following problems review some basic skills that are needed when converting between American and metric units of measurement.

1. Multiply: $14{,}110 \cdot 0.3$
2. Multiply: $50 \cdot 16 \cdot 28.35$
3. Multiply: $1.5 \cdot 2.2$
4. Round 32.222 to the nearest tenth.
5. Evaluate: $\frac{9}{5}(80) + 32$
6. Evaluate $\frac{5}{9}(F - 32)$ for $F = 50$.

It is often necessary to convert between American units and metric units. For example, we must convert units to answer the following questions.

- Which is higher: Pikes Peak (elevation 14,110 feet) or the Matterhorn (elevation 4,478 meters)?
- Does a 2-pound tub of butter weigh more than a 1-kilogram tub?
- Is a quart of soda pop more or less than a liter of soda pop?

In this section, we discuss how to answer such questions.

1 Use unit conversion factors to convert between American and metric units.

The following table shows some conversions between American and metric units of length. In all but one case, the conversions are rounded approximations. An ≈ symbol is used to show this. The one exact conversion in the table is 1 inch = 2.54 centimeters.

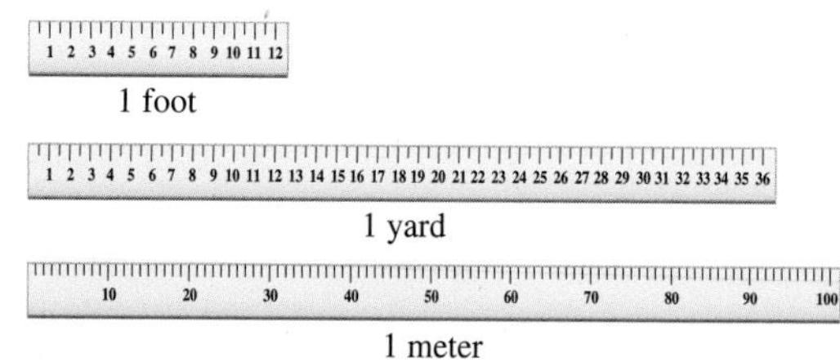

Equivalent Lengths

American to metric	Metric to American
1 in. = 2.54 cm	1 cm ≈ 0.39 in.
1 ft ≈ 0.30 m	1 m ≈ 3.28 ft
1 yd ≈ 0.91 m	1 m ≈ 1.09 yd
1 mi ≈ 1.61 km	1 km ≈ 0.62 mi

Unit conversion factors can be formed from the facts in the table to make specific conversions between American and metric units of length.

Self Check 1

CLOTHING LABELS Refer to the figure in Example 1. What is the inseam length, to the nearest inch?

Now Try **Problem 13**

EXAMPLE 1 *Clothing Labels* The figure shows a label sewn into some pants made in Mexico that are for sale in the United States. Express the waist size to the nearest inch.

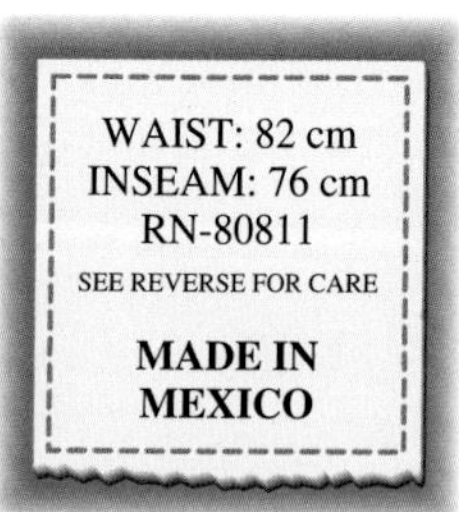

Strategy We will multiply 82 centimeters by a carefully chosen unit conversion factor.

WHY If we multiply by the proper unit conversion factor, we can eliminate the unwanted units of centimeters and convert to inches.

Solution

To convert from centimeters to inches, we must choose a unit conversion factor whose numerator contains the units we want to introduce (inches), and whose denominator contains the units we want to eliminate (centimeters). From the first row of the *Metric to American* column of the table, we see that there is approximately 0.39 inch per centimeter. Thus, we will use the unit conversion factor:

$$\frac{0.39 \text{ in.}}{1 \text{ cm}}$$

← This is the unit we want to introduce.
← This is the unit we want to eliminate (the original unit).

To perform the conversion, we multiply.

$82 \text{ cm} \approx \frac{82 \text{ cm}}{1} \cdot \frac{\mathbf{0.39 \text{ in.}}}{\mathbf{1 \text{ cm}}}$ — Write 82 cm as a fraction: $82 \text{ cm} = \frac{82 \text{ cm}}{1}$. Multiply by a form of 1: $\frac{0.39 \text{ in.}}{1 \text{ cm}}$.

$\approx \frac{82 \cancel{\text{cm}}}{1} \cdot \frac{0.39 \text{ in.}}{1 \cancel{\text{cm}}}$ — Remove the common units of centimeters from the numerator and denominator. The units of inches remain.

$\approx 82 \cdot 0.39 \text{ in.}$ — Simplify.

$\approx 31.98 \text{ in.}$ — Do the multiplication.

$\approx 32 \text{ in.}$ — Round to the nearest inch (ones column).

$$\begin{array}{r} 0.39 \\ \times\ 82 \\ \hline 78 \\ 3120 \\ \hline 31.98 \end{array}$$

To the nearest inch, the waist size is 32 inches.

EXAMPLE 2 ***Mountain Elevations*** Pikes Peak, one of the most famous peaks in the Rocky Mountains, has an elevation of 14,110 feet. The Matterhorn, in the Swiss Alps, rises to an elevation of 4,478 meters. Which mountain is higher?

Strategy We will convert the elevation of Pikes Peak, which given in feet, to meters.

WHY Then we can compare the mountain's elevations in the same units, meters.

Solution

To convert Pikes Peak elevation from feet to meters we must choose a unit conversion factor whose numerator contains the units we want to introduce (meters) and whose denominator contains the units we want to eliminate (feet). From the second row of the *American to metric* column of the table, we see that there is approximately 0.30 meter per foot. Thus, we will use the unit conversion factor:

$$\frac{0.30 \text{ m}}{1 \text{ ft}}$$

← This is the unit we want to introduce.
← This is the unit we want to eliminate (the original unit).

To perform the conversion, we multiply.

$14{,}110 \text{ ft} \approx \frac{14{,}110 \text{ ft}}{1} \cdot \frac{\mathbf{0.30 \text{ m}}}{\mathbf{1 \text{ ft}}}$ — Write 14,110 ft as a fraction: $14{,}110 \text{ ft} = \frac{14{,}110 \text{ ft}}{1}$. Multiply by a form of 1: $\frac{0.30 \text{ m}}{1 \text{ ft}}$.

$\approx \frac{14{,}110 \cancel{\text{ft}}}{1} \cdot \frac{0.30 \text{ m}}{1 \cancel{\text{ft}}}$ — Remove the common units of feet from the numerator and denominator. The units of meters remain.

$\approx 14{,}110 \cdot 0.30 \text{ m}$ — Simplify.

$\approx 4{,}233 \text{ m}$ — Do the multiplication.

$$\begin{array}{r} \overset{1}{1}4{,}110 \\ \times\ 0.30 \\ \hline 000\ 00 \\ 4233\ 00 \\ \hline 4233.00 \end{array}$$

Since the elevation of Pikes Peak is about 4,233 meters, we can conclude that the Matterhorn, with an elevation of 4,478 meters, is higher.

Self Check 2

TRACK AND FIELD Which is longer: a 500-meter race or a 550-yard race?

Now Try **Problem 17**

We can convert between American units of weight and metric units of mass using the rounded approximations in the following table.

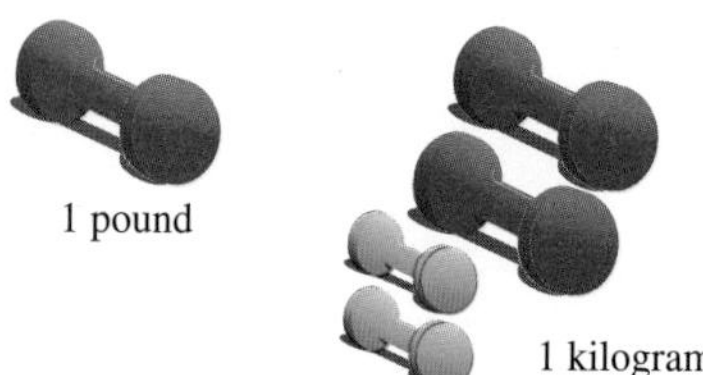

Equivalent Weights and Masses	
American to metric	**Metric to American**
1 oz ≈ 28.35 g	1 g ≈ 0.035 oz
1 lb ≈ 0.45 kg	1 kg ≈ 2.20 lb

Self Check 3

Convert 68 pounds to grams. Round to the nearest gram.

Now Try **Problem 21**

EXAMPLE 3 Convert 50 pounds to grams.

Strategy We will use a two-part multiplication process that converts 50 pounds to ounces, and then converts that result to grams.

WHY We must use a two-part process because the conversion table on page 78 does not contain a single unit conversion factor that converts from pounds to grams.

Solution

Since there are 16 ounces per pound, we can convert 50 pounds to ounces by multiplying by the unit conversion factor $\frac{16\text{ oz}}{1\text{ lb}}$. Since there are approximately 28.35 g per ounce, we can convert that result to grams by multiplying by the unit conversion factor $\frac{28.35\text{ g}}{1\text{ oz}}$.

$50\text{ lb} \approx \frac{50\text{ lb}}{1} \cdot \frac{16\text{ oz}}{1\text{ lb}} \cdot \frac{28.35\text{ g}}{1\text{ oz}}$ Write 50 lb as a fraction: 50 lb = $\frac{50\text{ lb}}{1}$. Multiply by two forms of 1: $\frac{16\text{ oz}}{1\text{ lb}}$ and $\frac{28.35\text{ g}}{1\text{ oz}}$.

$\approx \frac{50\,\cancel{\text{lb}}}{1} \cdot \frac{16\,\cancel{\text{oz}}}{1\,\cancel{\text{lb}}} \cdot \frac{28.35\text{ g}}{1\,\cancel{\text{oz}}}$ Remove the common units of pounds and ounces from the numerator and denominator. The units of grams remain.

$\approx 50 \cdot 16 \cdot 28.35\text{ g}$ Simplify.

$\approx 800 \cdot 28.35\text{ g}$ Multiply: $50 \cdot 16 = 800$.

$\approx 22{,}680\text{ g}$ Do the multiplication.

$$\begin{array}{r} \overset{3}{1}6 \\ \times\ 50 \\ \hline 800 \end{array} \qquad \begin{array}{r} \overset{6\,2\,4}{28.35} \\ \times\ 800 \\ \hline 22680.00 \end{array}$$

Thus, 50 pounds ≈ 22,680 grams.

Self Check 4

BODY WEIGHT Who weighs more, a person who weighs 165 pounds or one who weighs 76 kilograms?

Now Try **Problem 25**

EXAMPLE 4 ***Packaging*** Does a 2.5 pound tub of butter weigh more than a 1.5-kilogram tub?

Strategy We will convert the weight of the 1.5-kilogram tub of butter to pounds.

WHY Then we can compare the weights of the tubs of butter in the same units, pounds.

Solution

To convert 1.5 kilograms to pounds we must choose a unit conversion factor whose numerator contains the units we want to introduce (pounds), and whose denominator contains the units we want to eliminate (kilograms). From the second row of the *Metric to American* column of the table, we see that there are approximately 2.20 pounds per kilogram. Thus, we will use the unit conversion factor:

$\frac{2.20\text{ lb}}{1\text{ kg}}$ ← This is the unit we want to introduce. / ← This is the unit we want to eliminate (the original unit).

To perform the conversion, we multiply.

$1.5 \text{ kg} \approx \frac{1.5 \text{ kg}}{1} \cdot \frac{\mathbf{2.20 \text{ lb}}}{\mathbf{1 \text{ kg}}}$ Write 1.5 kg as a fraction: 1.5 kg = $\frac{1.5 \text{ kg}}{1}$.

Multiply by a form of 1: $\frac{2.20 \text{ lb}}{1 \text{ kg}}$.

$\approx \frac{1.5 \cancel{\text{kg}}}{1} \cdot \frac{2.20 \text{ lb}}{1 \cancel{\text{kg}}}$ Remove the common units of kilograms from the numerator and denominator. The units of pounds remain.

$\approx 1.5 \cdot 2.20 \text{ lb}$ Simplify.

$\approx 3.3 \text{ lb}$ Do the multiplication.

$$\begin{array}{r} 2.20 \\ \times\ 1.5 \\ \hline 1100 \\ 2200 \\ \hline 3.300 \end{array}$$

Since a 1.5-kilogram tub of butter weighs about 3.3 pounds, the 1.5-kilogram tub weighs more.

We can convert between American and metric units of capacity using the rounded approximations in the following table.

Equivalent Capacities	
American to metric	**Metric to American**
1 fl oz ≈ 29.57 mL	1 L ≈ 33.81 fl oz
1 pt ≈ 0.47 L	1 L ≈ 2.11 pt
1 qt ≈ 0.95 L	1 L ≈ 1.06 qt
1 gal ≈ 3.79 L	1 L ≈ 0.264 gal

1 liter 1 quart

THINK IT THROUGH *Studying in Other Countries*

"Over the past decade, the number of U.S. students studying abroad has more than doubled."

From The Open Doors 2008 Report

In 2009/2010, a record number of 270,604 college students received credit for study abroad. Since students traveling to other countries are almost certain to come into contact with the metric system of measurement, they need to have a basic understanding of metric units.

Suppose a student studying overseas needs to purchase the following school supplies. For each item in red, choose the appropriate metric units.

1. $8\frac{1}{2}$ in. × 11 in. notebook paper:

216 meters × 279 meters 216 centimeters × 279 centimeters 216 millimeters × 279 millimeters

2. A backpack that can hold 20 pounds of books:

9 kilograms 9 grams 9 milligrams

3. $\frac{3}{4}$ fluid ounce bottle of Liquid Paper correction fluid:

22.5 hectoliters 2.5 liters 22.2 milliliters

Self Check 5

DRINKING WATER A student bought a 360-mL bottle of water. Convert this measure to quarts. Round to the nearest tenth.

***Now Try* Problem 29**

EXAMPLE 5 ***Cleaning Supplies*** A bottle of window cleaner contains 750 milliliters of solution. Convert this measure to quarts. Round to the nearest tenth.

Strategy We will use a two-part multiplication process that converts 750 milliliters to liters, and then converts that result to quarts.

WHY We must use a two-part process because the conversion table does not contain a single unit conversion factor that converts from milliliters to quarts.

Solution

Since there is 1 liter for every 1,000 mL, we can convert 750 milliliters to liters by multiplying by the unit conversion factor $\frac{1\text{ L}}{1{,}000\text{ mL}}$. Since there are approximately 1.06 qt per liter, we can convert that result to quarts by multiplying by the unit conversion factor $\frac{1.06\text{ qt}}{1\text{ L}}$.

$$750\text{ mL} \approx \frac{750\text{ mL}}{1} \cdot \frac{1\text{ L}}{1{,}000\text{ mL}} \cdot \frac{1.06\text{ qt}}{1\text{ L}}$$

Write 750 mL as a fraction: 750 mL = $\frac{750\text{ mL}}{1}$. Multiply by two forms of 1: $\frac{1\text{ L}}{1{,}000\text{ mL}}$ and $\frac{1.06\text{ qt}}{1\text{ L}}$.

$$\approx \frac{750\,\cancel{\text{mL}}}{1} \cdot \frac{1\,\cancel{\text{L}}}{1{,}000\,\cancel{\text{mL}}} \cdot \frac{1.06\text{ qt}}{1\,\cancel{\text{L}}}$$

Remove the common units of milliliters and liters from the numerator and denominator. The units of quarts remain.

$$\approx \frac{750 \cdot 1.06}{1{,}000}\text{ qt}$$

Multiply the fractions.

$$\approx \frac{795}{1{,}000}\text{ qt}$$

Multiply: 750 · 1.06 = 795.

$$\begin{array}{r} 750 \\ \times\ 1.06 \\ \hline 4500 \\ 0000 \\ 75000 \\ \hline 795.00 \end{array}$$

$$\approx 0.795\text{ qt}$$

Divide 795 by 1,000 by moving the decimal point 3 places to the left.

$$\approx 0.8\text{ qt}$$

Round to the nearest tenth.

The bottle contains approximately 0.8 qt of cleaning solution.

2 Convert between Fahrenheit and Celsius temperatures.

In the American system, we measure temperature using **degrees Fahrenheit** (°F). In the metric system, we measure temperature using **degrees Celsius** (°C). These two scales are shown on the thermometers on the right. From the figures, we can see that

- 212°F ≈ 100°C Water boils
- 32°F ≈ 0°C Water freezes
- 5°F ≈ −15°C A cold winter day
- 95°F ≈ 35°C A hot summer day

There are formulas that enable us to convert from degrees Fahrenheit to degrees Celsius and from degrees Celsius to degrees Fahrenheit.

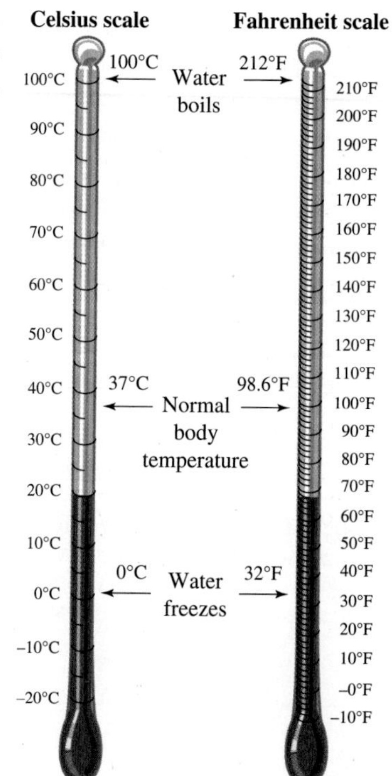

Conversion Formulas for Temperature

If F is the temperature in degrees Fahrenheit and C is the corresponding temperature in degrees Celsius, then

$$C = \frac{5}{9}(F - 32) \quad \text{and} \quad F = \frac{9}{5}C + 32$$

EXAMPLE 6 ***Bathing*** Warm bath water is 90°F. Express this temperature in degrees Celsius. Round to the nearest tenth of a degree.

Strategy We will substitute 90 for F in the formula $C = \frac{5}{9}(F - 32)$.

WHY Then we can use the rule for the order of operations to evaluate the right side of the equation and find the value of C, the temperature in degrees Celsius of the bath water.

Solution

$C = \frac{5}{9}(F - 32)$	This is the formula to find degrees Celsius.
$= \frac{5}{9}(90 - 32)$	Substitute 90 for F.
$= \frac{5}{9}(58)$	Do the subtraction within the parentheses first: $90 - 32 = 58$.
$= \frac{5}{9}\left(\frac{58}{1}\right)$	Write 58 as a fraction: $58 = \frac{58}{1}$.
$= \frac{290}{9}$	Multiply the numerators. Multiply the denominators.
$= 32.222\ldots$	Do the division.
≈ 32.2	Round to the nearest tenth.

$$\begin{array}{r} \overset{4}{58} \\ \times\ 5 \\ \hline 290 \end{array}$$

$$\begin{array}{r} 32.22 \\ 9\overline{)290.00} \\ -\,27 \\ \hline 20 \\ -\,18 \\ \hline 20 \\ -\,18 \\ \hline 20 \\ -\,18 \\ \hline 2 \end{array}$$

To the nearest tenth of a degree, the temperature of the bath water is 32.2°C.

Self Check 6

COFFEE Hot coffee is 110°F. Express this temperature in degrees Celsius. Round to the nearest tenth of a degree.

Now Try **Problem 33**

EXAMPLE 7 ***Dishwashers*** A dishwasher manufacturer recommends that dishes be rinsed in hot water with a temperature of 60°C. Express this temperature in degrees Fahrenheit.

Strategy We will substitute 60 for C in the formula $F = \frac{9}{5}C + 32$.

WHY Then we can use the rule for the order of operations to evaluate the right side of the equation and find the value of F, the temperature in degrees Fahrenheit of the water.

Solution

$F = \frac{9}{5}C + 32$	This is the formula to find degrees Fahrenheit.
$= \frac{9}{5}(60) + 32$	Substitute 60 for C.
$= \frac{540}{5} + 32$	Multiply: $\frac{9}{5}(60) = \frac{9}{5}\left(\frac{60}{1}\right) = \frac{540}{5}$.
$= 108 + 32$	Do the division.
$= 140$	Do the addition.

$$\begin{array}{r} 60 \\ \times\ 9 \\ \hline 540 \end{array}$$

$$\begin{array}{r} 108 \\ 5\overline{)540} \\ -\,5 \\ \hline 4 \\ -\,0 \\ \hline 40 \\ -\,40 \\ \hline 0 \end{array}$$

The manufacturer recommends that dishes be rinsed in 140°F water.

Self Check 7

FEVERS To determine whether a baby has a fever, her mother takes her temperature with a Celsius thermometer. If the reading is 38.8°C, does the baby have a fever? (*Hint:* Normal body temperature is 98.6°F.)

Now Try **Problem 37**

ANSWERS TO SELF CHECKS

1. 30 in. **2.** the 550-yard race **3.** 30, 845 g **4.** the person who weighs 76 kg **5.** 0.4 qt **6.** 43.3°C **7.** yes

SECTION 3.6 STUDY SET

VOCABULARY

Fill in the blanks.

1. In the American system, temperatures are measured in degrees ________. In the metric system, temperatures are measured in degrees ______.

2. a. Inches and centimeters are units used to measure ______.

b. Pounds and grams are used to measure _____ (weight).

c. Gallons and liters are units used to measure _______.

CONCEPTS

3. Which is longer:

a. A yard or a meter?

b. A foot or a meter?

c. An inch or a centimeter?

d. A mile or a kilometer?

4. Which is heavier:

a. An ounce or a gram?

b. A pound or a kilogram?

5. Which is the greater unit of capacity:

a. A pint or a liter?

b. A quart or a liter?

c. A gallon or a liter?

6. a. What formula is used for changing degrees Celsius to degrees Fahrenheit?

b. What formula is used for changing degrees Fahrenheit to degrees Celsius?

7. Write a unit conversion factor to convert

a. feet to meters

b. pounds to kilograms

c. gallons to liters

8. Write a unit conversion factor to convert

a. centimeters to inches

b. grams to ounces

c. liters to fluid ounces

NOTATION

Complete each solution.

9. Convert 4,500 feet to meters.

$$4{,}500\text{ ft} \approx \frac{4{,}500\text{ft}}{1} \cdot \frac{\square}{1\text{ft}}$$

$$\approx 1{,}350\ \square$$

10. Convert 8 liters to gallons.

$$8\text{ L} \approx \frac{8\text{ L}}{1} \cdot \frac{\square\ \text{gal}}{1\text{ L}}$$

$$\approx 2.112\ \square$$

11. Convert 3 kilograms to ounces.

$$3\text{ kg} \approx \frac{3\text{ kg}}{1} \cdot \frac{1{,}000\text{ g}}{1\text{ kg}} \cdot \frac{\square\ \text{oz}}{1\text{ g}}$$

$$\approx 3 \cdot \square \cdot 0.035\text{ oz}$$

$$\approx 105\ \square$$

12. Convert 70°C to degrees Fahrenheit.

$$F = \frac{9}{5}C + 32$$

$$= \frac{9}{5}(\quad) + 32$$

$$= \square + 32$$

$$= 158$$

Thus, 70°C = 158 $\square$

GUIDED PRACTICE

Perform each conversion. Round to the nearest inch. See Example 1.

13. 25 centimeters to inches

14. 35 centimeters to inches

15. 88 centimeters to inches

16. 91 centimeters to inches

Perform each conversion. See Example 2.

17. 8,400 feet to meters

18. 7,300 feet to meters

19. 25,115 feet to meters

20. 36,242 feet to meters

Perform each conversion. See Example 3.

21. 20 pounds to grams
22. 30 pounds to grams
23. 75 pounds to grams
24. 95 pounds to grams

Perform each conversion. See Example 4.

25. 6.5 kilograms to pounds
26. 7.5 kilograms to pounds
27. 300 kilograms to pounds
28. 800 kilograms to pounds

Perform each conversion. Round to the nearest tenth. See Example 5.

29. 650 milliliters to quarts
30. 450 milliliters to quarts
31. 1,200 milliliters to quarts
32. 1,500 milliliters to quarts

Express each temperature in degrees Celsius. Round to the nearest tenth of a degree. See Example 6.

33. 120°F
34. 110°F
35. 35°F
36. 45°F

Express each temperature in degrees Fahrenheit. See Example 7.

37. 75°C
38. 85°C
39. 10°C
40. 20°C

TRY IT YOURSELF

Perform each conversion. If necessary, round answers to the nearest tenth. Since most conversions are approximate, answers will vary slightly depending on the method used.

41. 25 pounds to grams
42. 7.5 ounces to grams
43. 50°C to degrees Fahrenheit
44. 36.2°C to degrees Fahrenheit
45. 0.75 quarts to milliliters
46. 3 pints to milliliters
47. 0.5 kilograms to ounces
48. 35 grams to pounds
49. 3.75 meters to inches
50. 2.4 kilometers to miles
51. 3 fluid ounces to liters
52. 2.5 pints to liters
53. 12 kilometers to feet
54. 3,212 centimeters to feet
55. 37 ounces to kilograms
56. 10 pounds to kilograms
57. −10°C to degrees Fahrenheit
58. −22.5°C to degrees Fahrenheit
59. 17 grams to ounces
60. 100 kilograms to pounds
61. 7.2 liters to fluid ounces
62. 5 liters to quarts
63. 3 feet to centimeters
64. 7.5 yards to meters
65. 500 milliliters to quarts
66. 2,000 milliliters to gallons
67. 50°F to degrees Celsius
68. 67.7°F to degrees Celsius
69. 5,000 inches to meters
70. 25 miles to kilometers
71. − 5°F to degrees Celsius
72. − 10°F to degrees Celsius

CONCEPT EXTENSIONS

Insert the correct symbol, $>$ or $<$, to make a true statement.

73. 75°F 75°C
74. 15 lb 15 kg
75. 8 oz 8 g
76. 6.2 qt 6.2 L
77. 20 gal 20 L
78. 15 in. 15 cm
79. 78 ft 78 m
80. $2\frac{1}{2}$ yd $2\frac{1}{2}$ m

APPLICATIONS

Since most conversions are approximate, answers will vary slightly depending on the method used.

81. THE MIDDLE EAST The distance between Jerusalem and Bethlehem is 8 kilometers. To the nearest mile, give this distance in miles.

82. THE DEAD SEA The Dead Sea is 80 kilometers long. To the nearest mile, give this distance in miles.

83. CHEETAHS A cheetah can run 112 kilometers per hour. Express this speed in mph. Round to the nearest mile.

84. LIONS A lion can run 50 mph. Express this speed in kilometers per hour. Round to the nearest tenth.

85. MOUNT WASHINGTON The highest peak of the White Mountains of New Hampshire is Mount Washington, at 6,288 feet. Give this height in kilometers. Round to the nearest tenth.

86. TRACK AND FIELD Track meets are held on an oval track. One lap around the track is usually 400 meters. However, some older tracks in the United States are 440-yard ovals. Are these two types of tracks the same length? If not, which is longer?

87. HAIR GROWTH When hair is short, its rate of growth averages about $\frac{3}{4}$ inch per month. How many centimeters is this a month? Round to the nearest tenth of a centimeter.

88. WHALES An adult male killer whale can weigh as much as 12,000 pounds and be as long as 25 feet. Change these measurements to kilograms and meters.

89. WEIGHTLIFTING The table lists the personal best bench press records for two of the world's best powerlifters. Change each metric weight to pounds. Round to the nearest pound.

Name	Hometown	Bench press
Liz Willet	Ferndale, Washington	187 kg
Brian Siders	Charleston, W. Virginia	350 kg

90. WORDS OF WISDOM Refer to the wall hanging. Convert the first metric weight to ounces and the second to pounds. What famous saying results?

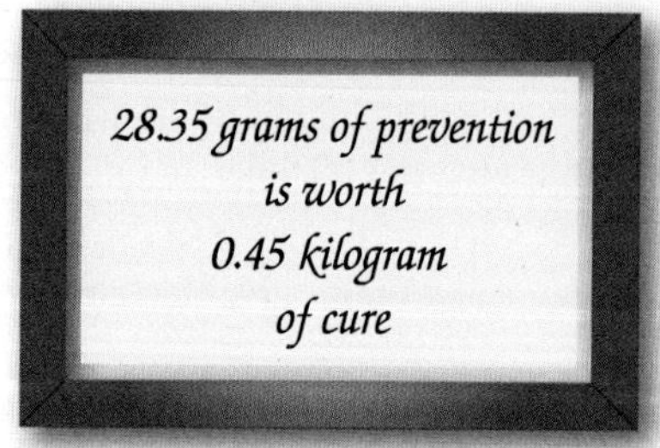

91. OUNCES AND FLUID OUNCES

a. There are 310 calories in 8 ounces of broiled chicken. Convert 8 ounces to grams.

b. There are 112 calories in a glass of fresh Valencia orange juice that holds 8 fluid ounces. Convert 8 fluid ounces to liters. Round to the nearest hundredth.

92. TRACK AND FIELD A shot-put weighs 7.264 kilograms. Convert this weight to pounds. Round to the nearest pound.

93. POSTAL REGULATIONS You can mail a package weighing up to 70 pounds via priority mail. Can you mail a package that weighs 32 kilograms by priority mail?

94. NUTRITION Refer to the nutrition label shown below for a packet of oatmeal. Change each circled weight to ounces.

Nutrition Facts
Serving Size: 1 Packet (46g)
Servings Per Container: 10

Amount Per Serving	
Calories 170	Calories from Fat 20
	% Daily Value
Total fat 2g	3%
Saturated fat (0.5g)	2%
Polyunsaturated Fat 0.5g	
Monounsaturated Fat 1g	
Cholesterol 0mg	0%
Sodium (250mg)	10%
Total carbohydrate 35g	12%
Dietary fiber 3g	12%
Soluble Fiber 1g	
Sugars 16g	
Protein (4g)	

95. HOT SPRINGS WATER TEMPERATURES Hot Springs, North Carolina, is a small mountain town in Madison County. It is best known for the natural hot mineral springs that give the town its name. There are 6 separate springs that vary in temperature from 97°F to 101°F. Change this temperature range to degrees Celsius. Round to the nearest degree.

96. COOKING MEAT Meats must be cooked at temperatures high enough to kill harmful bacteria. According to the USDA and the FDA, the internal temperature for cooked roasts and steaks should be at least 145°F, and whole poultry should be 180°F. Convert these temperatures to degrees Celsius. Round up to the next degree.

97. TAKING A SHOWER When you take a shower, which water temperature would you choose: 15°C, 28°C, or 50°C?

98. DRINKING WATER To get a cold drink of water, which temperature would you choose: −2°C, 10°C, or 25°C?

99. SNOWY WEATHER At which temperatures might it snow: −5°C, 0°C, or 10°C?

100. AIR CONDITIONING At which outside temperature would you be likely to run the air conditioner: 15°, 20°C, or 30°C?

101. COMPARISON SHOPPING Which is the better buy: 3 quarts of root beer for $4.50 or 2 liters of root beer for $3.60?

102. COMPARISON SHOPPING Which is the better buy: 3 gallons of antifreeze for \$10.35 or 12 liters of antifreeze for \$10.50?

WRITING

103. Explain how to change kilometers to miles.

104. Explain how to change 50°C to degrees Fahrenheit.

105. The United States is the only industrialized country in the world that does not officially use the metric system. Some people claim this is costing American businesses money. Do you think so? Why?

106. What is meant by the phrase *a table of equivalent measures*?

SECTION 3.7
Percents, Decimals, and Fractions

Objectives

1. Explain the meaning of percent.
2. Write percents as fractions.
3. Write percents as decimals.
4. Write decimals as percents.
5. Write fractions as percents.

ARE YOU READY?

The following problems review some basic skills that are needed when working with percents.

1. Simplify: $\frac{78}{100}$

2. Simplify: $\frac{10}{10}$

3. Divide: $33\frac{1}{3} \div 100$

4. **a.** Multiply: $0.22 \cdot 100$
b. Divide: $32.86 \div 100$

5. Determine whether each statement is true or false.

a. $1\frac{1}{4} = 1.25$

b. $8\frac{1}{2} = 8.5$

6. Write each fraction as a decimal.

a. $\frac{3}{5}$

b. $\frac{5}{6}$

We see percents everywhere, everyday. Stores use them to advertise discounts, manufacturers use them to describe the contents of their products, and banks use them to list interest rates for loans and savings accounts. Newspapers are full of information presented in percent form. In this section, we introduce percents and show how fractions, decimals, and percents are related.

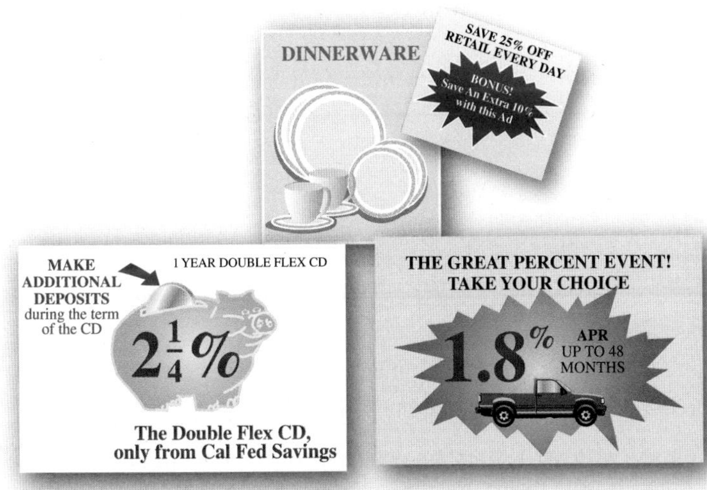

1 Explain the meaning of percent.

A percent tells us the number of parts per one hundred. You can think of a percent as the *numerator* of a fraction (or ratio) that has a denominator of 100.

Percent

Percent means parts per one hundred.

The Language of Mathematics The word *percent* is formed from the prefix *per,* which means ratio, and the suffix *cent,* which comes from the Latin word *centum,* meaning 100.

per • cent

ratio → per; cent ← 100

In the figure below, there are 100 equal-sized square regions, and 93 of them are shaded. Thus, $\frac{93}{100}$ or 93 percent of the figure is shaded. The word *percent* can be written using the symbol %, so we say that 93% of the figure is shaded.

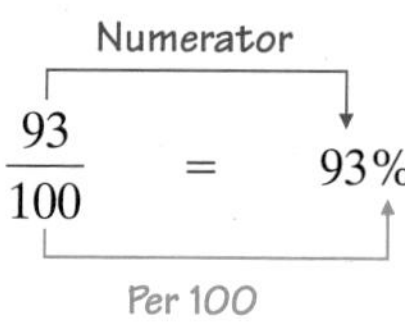

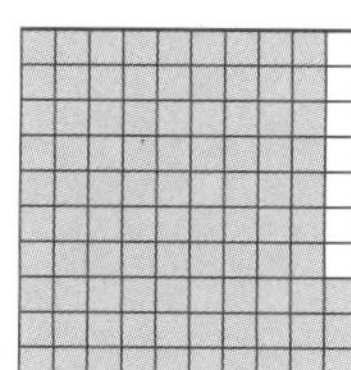

If the entire figure had been shaded, we would say that 100 out of the 100 square regions, or 100%, was shaded. Using this fact, we can determine what percent of the figure is *not* shaded by subtracting the percent of the figure that is shaded from 100%.

$100\% - 93\% = 7\%$

So 7% of the figure is *not* shaded.

To illustrate a percent greater than 100%, say 121%, we would shade one entire figure and 21 of the 100 square regions in a second, equal-sized grid.

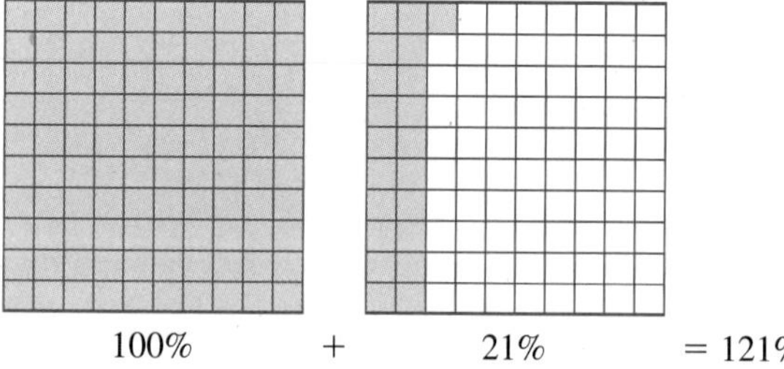

100% + 21% = 121%

Self Check 1

BOARD GAMES A standard Scrabble game contains 100 tiles. There are 42 vowel tiles, 2 blank tiles, and the rest are consonant tiles.

a. What percent of the tiles are vowels?

b. What percent of the letter tiles are consonants?

EXAMPLE 1 ***Tossing a Coin*** A coin was tossed 100 times and it landed heads up 51 times.

a. What percent of the time did the coin land heads up?

b. What percent of the time did it land tails up?

Strategy We will write a fraction that compares the number of times that the coin landed heads up (or tails up) to the total number of tosses.

WHY Since the denominator in each case will be 100, the numerator of the fraction will give the percent.

Solution

a. If a coin landed heads up 51 times after being tossed 100 times, then

$$\frac{51}{100} = 51\%$$

of the time it landed heads up.

b. The number of times the coin landed tails up is $100 - 51 = 49$ times. If a coin landed tails up 49 times after being tossed 100 times, then

$$\frac{49}{100} = 49\%$$

of the time it landed tails up.

Now Try **Problem 13**

2 Write percents as fractions.

We can use the definition of percent to write any percent in an equivalent fraction form.

Writing Percents as Fractions

To write a percent as a fraction, drop the % symbol and write the given number over 100. Then simplify the fraction, if possible.

EXAMPLE 2 ***Earth*** The chemical makeup of Earth's atmosphere is 78% nitrogen, 21% oxygen, and 1% other gases. Write each percent as a fraction in simplest form.

Strategy We will drop the % symbol and write the given number over 100. Then we will simplify the resulting fraction, if possible.

WHY *Percent* means parts per one hundred, and the word *per* indicates a ratio (fraction).

Solution We begin with nitrogen.

$$78\% = \frac{78}{100} \quad \text{Drop the \% symbol and write 78 over 100.}$$

$$= \frac{\overset{1}{\cancel{2}} \cdot 39}{\underset{1}{\cancel{2}} \cdot 50} \quad \text{To simplify the fraction, factor 78 as } 2 \cdot 39 \text{ and 100 as } 2 \cdot 50\text{. Then remove the common factor of 2 from the numerator and denominator.}$$

$$= \frac{39}{50}$$

Nitrogen makes up $\frac{78}{100}$, or $\frac{39}{50}$, of Earth's atmosphere.

Oxygen makes up 21%, or $\frac{21}{100}$, of Earth's atmosphere. Other gases make up 1%, or $\frac{1}{100}$, of the atmosphere.

Self Check 2

WATERMELONS An average watermelon is 92% water. Write this percent as a fraction in simplest form.

Now Try **Problems 17 and 23**

EXAMPLE 3 ***Unions*** In 2010, 11.9% of the U.S. labor force belonged to a union. Write this percent as a fraction in simplest form. (*Source:* Bureau of Labor Statistics)

Strategy We will drop the % symbol and write the given number over 100. Then we will multiply the resulting fraction by a form of 1 and simplify, if possible.

Self Check 3

UNIONS In 2002, 13.3% of the U.S. labor force belonged to a union. Write this percent as a fraction in simplest form.

Now Try **Problems 27 and 31**

WHY When writing a percent as a fraction, the numerator and denominator of the fraction should be whole numbers that have no common factors (other than 1).

Solution

$$11.9\% = \frac{11.9}{100}$$ Drop the % symbol and write 11.9 over 100.

To write this as an equivalent fraction of *whole numbers,* we need to move the decimal point in the numerator one place to the right. (Recall that to find the product of a decimal and 10, we simply move the decimal point one place to the right.) Therefore, it follows that $\frac{10}{10}$ is the form of 1 that we should use to build $\frac{11.9}{100}$.

$$\frac{11.9}{100} = \frac{11.9}{100} \cdot \frac{\mathbf{10}}{\mathbf{10}}$$ Multiply the fraction by a form of 1.

$$= \frac{11.9 \cdot \mathbf{10}}{100 \cdot \mathbf{10}}$$ Multiply the numerators. Multiply the denominators.

$$= \frac{119}{1{,}000}$$ Since 119 and 1,000 do not have any common factors (other than 1), the fraction is in simplest form.

Thus, $11.9\% = \frac{119}{1{,}000}$. This means that 119 out of every 1,000 workers in the U.S. labor force belonged to a union in 2010.

Self Check 4

Write $83\frac{1}{3}\%$ as a fraction in simplest form.

Now Try **Problem 35**

EXAMPLE 4 Write $66\frac{2}{3}\%$ as a fraction in simplest form.

Strategy We will drop the % symbol and write the given number over 100. Then we will perform the division indicated by the fraction bar and simplify, if possible.

WHY When writing a percent as a fraction, the numerator and denominator of the fraction should be whole numbers that have no common factors (other than 1).

Solution

$$66\frac{2}{3}\% = \frac{66\frac{2}{3}}{100}$$ Drop the % symbol and write $66\frac{2}{3}$ over 100.

To write this as a fraction of whole numbers, we will perform the division indicated by the fraction bar.

$$\frac{66\frac{2}{3}}{100} = 66\frac{2}{3} \div 100$$ The fraction bar indicates division.

$$= \frac{200}{3} \cdot \frac{1}{100}$$ Write $66\frac{2}{3}$ as a mixed number and then multiply by the reciprocal of 100.

$$= \frac{200 \cdot 1}{3 \cdot 100}$$ Multiply the numerators. Multiply the denominators.

$$= \frac{2 \cdot \overset{1}{\cancel{100}} \cdot 1}{3 \cdot \underset{1}{\cancel{100}}}$$ To simplify the fraction, factor 200 as $2 \cdot 100$. Then remove the common factor of 100 from the numerator and denominator.

$$= \frac{2}{3}$$

Self Check 5

a. Write 210% as a fraction in simplest form.

b. Write 0.54% as a fraction in simplest form.

Now Try **Problems 39 and 43**

EXAMPLE 5 **a.** Write 175% as a fraction in simplest form.

b. Write 0.22% as a fraction in simplest form.

Strategy We will drop the % symbol and write each given number over 100. Then we will simplify the resulting fraction, if possible.

WHY *Percent* means parts per one hundred and the word *per* indicates a ratio (fraction).

Solution

a. $175\% = \dfrac{175}{100}$ Drop the % symbol and write 175 over 100.

$= \dfrac{\overset{1}{\cancel{5}} \cdot \overset{1}{\cancel{5}} \cdot 7}{2 \cdot 2 \cdot \underset{1}{\cancel{5}} \cdot \underset{1}{\cancel{5}}}$ To simplify the fraction, prime factor 175 and 100. Remove the common factors of 5 from the numerator and denominator.

$= \dfrac{7}{4}$

$$5\,\underline{|175} \quad 5\,\underline{|35} \quad 7 \qquad 2\,\underline{|100} \quad 2\,\underline{|50} \quad 5\,\underline{|25} \quad 5$$

Thus, $175\% = \dfrac{7}{4}$.

b. $0.22\% = \dfrac{0.22}{100}$ Drop the % symbol and write 175 over 100.

To write this as an equivalent fraction of *whole numbers*, we need to move the decimal point in the numerator two places to the right. (Recall that to find the product of a decimal and 100, we simply move the decimal point two places to the right.) Therefore, it follows that $\frac{100}{100}$ is the form of 1 that we should use to build $\frac{0.22}{100}$.

$\dfrac{0.22}{100} = \dfrac{0.22}{100} \cdot \dfrac{\mathbf{100}}{\mathbf{100}}$ Multiply the fraction by a form of 1.

$= \dfrac{0.22 \cdot 100}{100 \cdot 100}$ Multiply the numerators. Multiply the denominators.

$= \dfrac{22}{10{,}000}$

$= \dfrac{\overset{1}{\cancel{2}} \cdot 11}{\underset{1}{\cancel{2}} \cdot 5{,}000}$ To simplify the fraction, factor 22 and 10,000. Remove the common factor of 2 from the numerator and denominator.

$= \dfrac{11}{5{,}000}$

Thus, $0.22\% = \dfrac{11}{5{,}000}$.

> ***Success Tip*** When percents that are greater than 100% are written as fractions, the fractions are greater than 1. When percents that are less than 1% are written as fractions, the fractions are less than $\frac{1}{100}$.

3 Write percents as decimals.

To write a percent as a decimal, recall that a percent can be written as a fraction with denominator 100 and that a denominator of 100 indicates division by 100.

For example, consider 14%, which means 14 parts per 100.

$14\% = \dfrac{14}{100}$ Use the definition of percent: write 14 over 100.

$= 14 \div 100$ The fraction bar indicates division.

$= 14.0 \div 100$ Write the whole number 14 in decimal notation by placing a decimal point immediately to its right and entering a zero to the right of the decimal point.

$= .14\,0$ Since the divisor 100 has two zeros, move the decimal point 2 places to the left.

$= 0.14$ Write a zero to the left of the decimal point.

We have found that $14\% = 0.14$. This example suggests the following procedure.

Writing Percents as Decimals

To write a percent as a decimal, drop the % symbol and divide the given number by 100 by moving the decimal point 2 places to the left.

Self Check 6

a. Write 16.43% as a decimal.

b. Write 2.06% as a decimal.

Now Try **Problems 51 and 57**

EXAMPLE 6 ***The Internet*** The graph below shows the percent of market share for the top 5 search engines.

a. Write the percent of market share for *Google* as a decimal.

b. Write the percent of market share for *Ask* as a decimal.

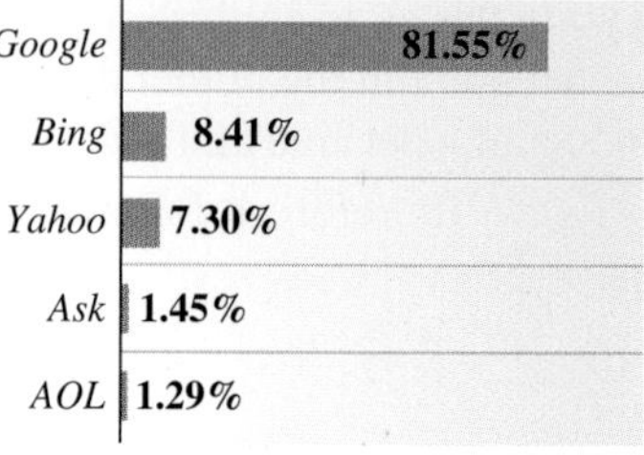

(*Source:* statowl.com)

Strategy We will drop the % symbol and divide each given number by 100 by moving the decimal point 2 places to the left.

WHY To find the quotient of a decimal and 10, 100, 1,000, and so on, move the decimal point to the left the same number of places as there are zeros in the power of 10.

Solution

a. From the graph, we see that the percent market share for the *Google* is 81.55%. To write this percent as a decimal, we proceed as follows.

$81.55\% = .8155$ Drop the % symbol and divide 81.55 by 100 by moving the decimal point 2 places to the left.

$= 0.8155$ Write a zero to the left of the decimal point.

81.55%, written as a decimal, is 0.8155.

b. From the graph, we see that the percent market share for the *Ask* website is 1.45%. To write this percent as a decimal, we proceed as follows.

$1.45\% = .01.45$ Drop the % symbol and divide 1.45 by 100 by moving the decimal point 2 places to the left. This requires that a placeholder zero (shown in blue) be inserted in front of the 1.

$= 0.0145$ Write a zero to the left of the decimal point.

1.45%, written as a decimal, is 0.0145.

Self Check 7

POPULATION The population of the state of Ohio is approximately $3\frac{3}{4}\%$ of the population of the United States. Write this percent as a decimal. (*Source:* U.S. Census Bureau)

Now Try **Problem 59**

EXAMPLE 7 ***Population***

The population of the state of Oregon is approximately $1\frac{1}{4}\%$ of the population of the United States. Write this percent as a decimal. (*Source:* U.S. Census Bureau)

Strategy We will write the mixed number $1\frac{1}{4}$ in decimal notation.

WHY With $1\frac{1}{4}$ in mixed-number form, we cannot apply the rule for writing a percent as a decimal; there is no decimal point to move 2 places to the left.

Solution To change a percent to a decimal, we drop the percent symbol and divide by 100 by moving the decimal point 2 places to the left. In this case, however, there is no decimal point to move in $1\frac{1}{4}\%$. Since $1\frac{1}{4} = 1 + \frac{1}{4}$, and since the decimal equivalent of $\frac{1}{4}$ is 0.25, we can write $1\frac{1}{4}\%$ in an equivalent form as 1.25%.

$1\frac{1}{4}\% = 1.25\%$ Write $1\frac{1}{4}$ as 1.25.

$= .0125$ Drop the % symbol and divide 1.25 by 100 by moving the decimal point 2 places to the left. This requires that a placeholder zero (shown in blue) be inserted in front of the 1.

$= 0.0125$ Write a zero to the left of the decimal point.

$1\frac{1}{4}\%$, written as a decimal, is 0.0125.

EXAMPLE 8

a. Write 310% as a decimal. **b.** Write 0.9% as a decimal.

Strategy We will drop the % symbol and divide each given number by 100 by moving the decimal point two places to the left.

WHY Recall that to find the quotient of a decimal and 100, we move the decimal point to the left the same number of places as there are zeros in 100.

Solution

a. $310\% = 310.0\%$ Write the whole number 310 in decimal notation: 310 = 310.0.

$= 3.100$ Drop the % symbol and divide 310 by 100 by moving the decimal point 2 places to the left.

$= 3.1$ Drop the unnecessary zeros to the right of the 1.

310%, written as a decimal, is 3.1.

b. $0.9\% = .009$ Drop the % symbol and divide 0.9 by 100 by moving the decimal point 2 places to the left. This requires that a placeholder zero (shown in blue) be inserted in front of the 0.

$= 0.009$ Write a zero to the left of the decimal point.

0.9%, written as a decimal, is 0.009.

Self Check 8

a. Write 600% as a decimal.

b. Write 0.8% as a decimal.

Now Try **Problems 63 and 67**

Success Tip When percents that are greater than 100% are written as decimals, the decimals are greater than 1.0. When percents that are less than 1% are written as decimals, the decimals are less than 0.01.

4 Write decimals as percents.

To write a percent as a decimal, we drop the % symbol and move the decimal point 2 places to the left. To write a decimal as a percent, we do the opposite: we move the decimal point 2 places to the right and insert a % symbol.

Writing Decimals as Percents

To write a decimal as a percent, multiply the decimal by 100 by moving the decimal point 2 places to the right, and then insert a % symbol.

Self Check 9

Write 0.5343 as a percent.

Now Try **Problems 71 and 75**

EXAMPLE 9 ***Geography*** Land areas make up 0.291 of Earth's surface. Write this decimal as a percent.

Strategy We will multiply the decimal by 100 by moving the decimal point 2 places to the right, and then insert a % symbol.

WHY To write a *decimal as a percent,* we reverse the steps used to write a *percent as a decimal.*

Solution

$0.291 = 0\,29.1\%$ Multiply 0.291 by 100 by moving the decimal point 2 places to the right, and then insert a % symbol.

$= 29.1\%$

0.291, written as a percent, is 29.1%

5 Write fractions as percents.

We use a two-step process to write a fraction as a percent. First, we write the fraction as a decimal. Then we write that decimal as a percent.

Fraction ⟶ decimal ⟶ percent

Writing Fractions as Percents

To write a fraction as a percent:

1. Write the fraction as a decimal by dividing its numerator by its denominator.
2. Multiply the decimal by 100 by moving the decimal point 2 places to the right, and then insert a % symbol.

Self Check 10

Write 7 out of 8 as a percent.

Now Try **Problem 79**

EXAMPLE 10 ***Television*** The highest-rated television show of all time was a special episode of *M*A*S*H* that aired February 28, 1983. Surveys found that three out of every five American households watched this show. Express the rating as a percent.

Strategy First, we will translate the phrase *three out of every five* to fraction form and write that fraction as a decimal. Then we will write that decimal as a percent.

WHY A fraction-to-decimal-to-percent approach must be used to write a fraction as a percent.

Solution

Step 1 The phrase *three out of every five* can be expressed as $\frac{3}{5}$. To write this fraction as a decimal, we divide the numerator, 3, by the denominator, 5.

$$\begin{array}{r} 0.6 \\ 5\overline{)3.0} \\ -3\,0 \\ \hline 0 \end{array}$$

Write a decimal point and one additional zero to the right of 3.

0 ← The remainder is 0.

The result is a terminating decimal.

Step 2 To write 0.6 as a percent, we proceed as follows.

$$\frac{3}{5} = 0.6$$

$0.6 = 0{.}60.\%$ Write a placeholder 0 to the right of the 6 (shown in blue). Multiply 0.60 by 100 by moving the decimal point 2 places to the right, and then insert a % symbol.

$= 60\%$

60% of American households watched the special episode of *M*A*S*H*.

EXAMPLE 11 Write $\frac{13}{4}$ as a percent.

Strategy We will write the fraction $\frac{13}{4}$ as a decimal. Then we will write that decimal as a percent.

WHY A fraction-to-decimal-to-percent approach must be used to write a fraction as a percent.

Solution

Step 1 To write $\frac{13}{4}$ as a decimal, we divide the numerator, 13, by the denominator, 4.

$$\begin{array}{r} 3.25 \\ 4\overline{)13.00} \\ -12 \\ \hline 1\,0 \\ -8 \\ \hline 20 \\ -20 \\ \hline 0 \end{array}$$

Write a decimal point and two additional zeros to the right of 3.

The remainder is 0.

The result is a terminating decimal.

Step 2 To write 3.25 as a percent, we proceed as follows.

$3.25 = 325\%$ Multiply 3.25 by 100 by moving the decimal point 2 places to the right, and then insert a % symbol.

$= 325\%$

The fraction $\frac{13}{4}$, written as a percent, is 325%.

Self Check 11

Write $\frac{5}{2}$ as a percent.

Now Try **Problem 85**

Success Tip When fractions that are greater than 1 are written as percents, the percents are greater than 100%.

In Examples 10 and 11, the result of the division was a terminating decimal. Sometimes when we write a fraction as a decimal, the result of the division is a repeating decimal.

EXAMPLE 12 Write $\frac{5}{6}$ as a percent. Give the exact answer and an approximation to the nearest tenth of one percent.

Strategy We will write the fraction $\frac{5}{6}$ as a decimal. Then we will write that decimal as a percent.

WHY A fraction-to-decimal-to-percent approach must be used to write a fraction as a percent.

Self Check 12

Write $\frac{2}{3}$ as a percent. Give the exact answer and an approximation to the nearest tenth of one percent.

Now Try **Problem 91**

Solution

Step 1 To write $\frac{5}{6}$ as a decimal, we divide the numerator, 5, by the denominator, 6.

$$\begin{array}{r} 0.8333 \\ 6\overline{)5.0000} \\ -4\,8 \\ 20 \\ -18 \\ 20 \\ -18 \\ 20 \\ -18 \\ 2 \end{array}$$

Write a decimal point and several zeros to the right of 5.

2 ← The repeating pattern is now clear. We can stop the division.

The result is a repeating decimal.

Step 2 To write the decimal as a percent, we proceed as follows.

$$\frac{5}{6} = 0.8333\ldots$$

$$0.833\ldots = 083.33\ldots\% \qquad \text{Multiply } 0.8333\ldots \text{ by 100 by moving the decimal point 2 places to the right, and then insert a \% symbol.}$$

$$= 83.33\ldots\%$$

We must now decide whether we want an exact answer or an approximation. For an exact answer, we can represent *the repeating part of the decimal using an equivalent fraction.* For an approximation, we can round 83.333 . . .% to a specific place value.

Exact answer:

$$\frac{5}{6} = 83.3333\ldots\%$$

$$= 83\frac{1}{3}\% \qquad \text{Use the fraction } \tfrac{1}{3} \text{ to represent } .3333\ldots.$$

Thus,

$$\frac{5}{6} = 83\frac{1}{3}\%$$

Approximation:

$$\frac{5}{6} = 83.33\ldots\%$$

$$\approx 83.3\% \qquad \text{Round to the nearest tenth.}$$

Thus,

$$\frac{5}{6} \approx 83.3\%$$

Some percents occur so frequently that it is useful to memorize their fractional and decimal equivalents.

Percent	Decimal	Fraction
1%	0.01	$\frac{1}{100}$
10%	0.1	$\frac{1}{10}$
$16\frac{2}{3}\%$	0.1666 . . .	$\frac{1}{6}$
20%	0.2	$\frac{1}{5}$
25%	0.25	$\frac{1}{4}$

Percent	Decimal	Fraction
$33\frac{1}{3}\%$	0.3333 . . .	$\frac{1}{3}$
50%	0.5	$\frac{1}{2}$
$66\frac{2}{3}\%$	0.6666 . . .	$\frac{2}{3}$
$83\frac{1}{3}\%$	0.8333 . . .	$\frac{5}{6}$
75%	0.75	$\frac{3}{4}$

ANSWERS TO SELF CHECKS

1. a. 42% **b.** 56% **2.** $\frac{23}{25}$ **3.** $\frac{133}{1,000}$ **4.** $\frac{5}{6}$ **5. a.** $\frac{21}{10}$ **b.** $\frac{27}{5,000}$ **6. a.** 0.1643 **b.** 0.0206 **7.** 0.0375 **8. a.** 6 **b.** 0.008 **9.** 53.43% **10.** 87.5% **11.** 250% **12.** $66\frac{2}{3}\% \approx 66.7\%$

SECTION 3.7 STUDY SET

VOCABULARY

Fill in the blanks.

1. ________ means parts per one hundred.
2. The word *percent* is formed from the prefix *per,* which means ______, and the suffix *cent,* which comes from the Latin word *centum,* meaning _____.

CONCEPTS

Fill in the blanks.

3. To write a percent as a fraction, drop the % symbol and write the given number over _____. Then ________ the fraction, if possible.
4. To write a percent as a decimal, drop the % symbol and divide the given number by 100 by moving the decimal point 2 places to the _____.
5. To write a decimal as a percent, multiply the decimal by 100 by moving the decimal point 2 places to the ______, and then insert a % symbol.
6. To write a fraction as a percent, first write the fraction as a ________. Then multiply the decimal by 100 by moving the decimal point 2 places to the right, and then insert a ____ symbol.

NOTATION

7. What does the symbol % mean?
8. Write the whole number 45 as a decimal.

GUIDED PRACTICE

What percent of the figure is shaded? What percent of the figure is not shaded? See Objective 1.

9.

10. 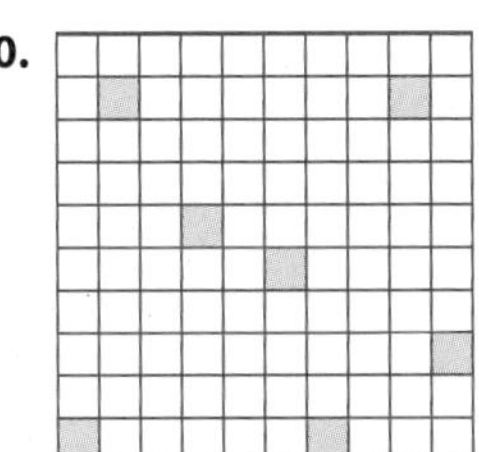

In the following illustrations, each set of 100 square regions represents 100%. What percent is shaded?

11. 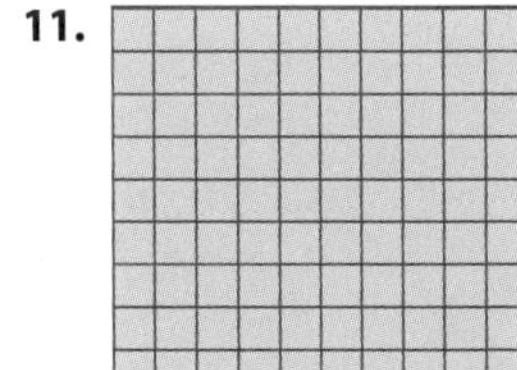 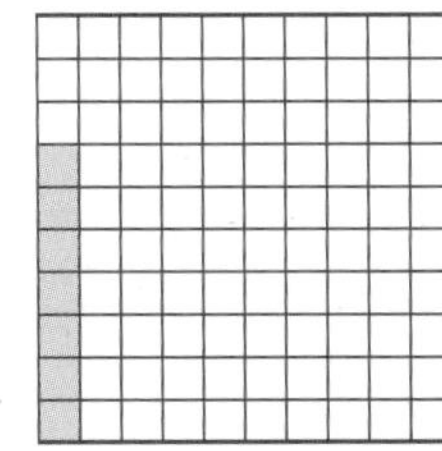

12. 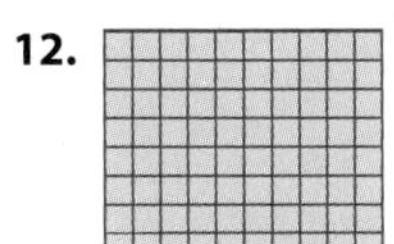 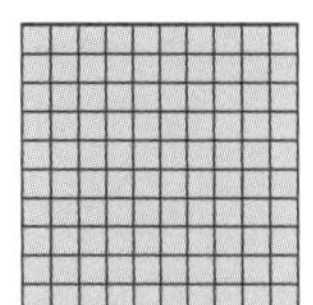 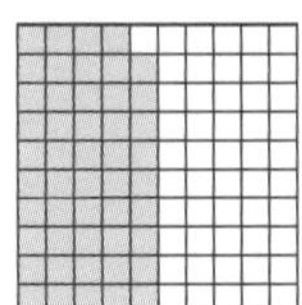

For Problems 13–16, see Example 1.

13. THE INTERNET The following sentence appeared on a technology blog: "Ask Internet users what they want from their service and 99 times out of 100 the answer will be the same: more speed." According to the blog, what percent of the time do Internet users give that answer?
14. BASKETBALL RECORDS In 1962, Wilt Chamberlain of the Philadelphia Warriors scored a total of 100 points in an NBA game. If twenty-eight of his points came from made free throws, what percent of his point total came from free throws?
15. QUILTS A quilt is made from 100 squares of colored cloth.
    a. If fifteen of the squares are blue, what percent of the squares in the quilt are blue?
    b. What percent of the squares are not blue?
16. DIVISIBILITY Of the natural numbers from 1 through 100, only fourteen of them are divisible by 7.
    a. What percent of the numbers are divisible by 7?
    b. What percent of the numbers are not divisible by 7?

Write each percent as a fraction. Simplify, if possible. See Example 2.

17. 17%
18. 31%
19. 91%
20. 89%
21. 4%
22. 5%
23. 60%
24. 40%

Write each percent as a fraction. Simplify, if possible. See Example 3.

25. 1.9%
26. 2.3%
27. 54.7%
28. 97.1%
29. 12.5%
30. 62.5%
31. 6.8%
32. 4.2%

Write each percent as a fraction. Simplify, if possible. See Example 4.

33. $1\frac{1}{3}\%$
34. $3\frac{1}{3}\%$
35. $14\frac{1}{6}\%$
36. $10\frac{5}{6}\%$

Write each percent as a fraction. Simplify, if possible. See Example 5.

37. 130%
38. 160%
39. 220%
40. 240%

41. 0.35% **42.** 0.45%

43. 0.25% **44.** 0.75%

Write each percent as a decimal. See Objective 3.

45. 16% **46.** 11%

47. 81% **48.** 93%

Write each percent as a decimal. See Example 6.

49. 34.12% **50.** 27.21%

51. 50.033% **52.** 40.083%

53. 6.99% **54.** 4.77%

55. 1.3% **56.** 8.6%

Write each percent as a decimal. See Example 7.

57. $7\frac{1}{4}\%$ **58.** $9\frac{3}{4}\%$

59. $18\frac{1}{2}\%$ **60.** $25\frac{1}{2}\%$

Write each percent as a decimal. See Example 8.

61. 460% **62.** 230%

63. 316% **64.** 178%

65. 0.5% **66.** 0.9%

67. 0.03% **68.** 0.06%

Write each decimal or whole number as a percent. See Example 9.

69. 0.362 **70.** 0.245

71. 0.98 **72.** 0.57

73. 1.71 **74.** 4.33

75. 4 **76.** 9

Write each fraction as a percent. See Example 10.

77. $\frac{2}{5}$ **78.** $\frac{1}{5}$

79. $\frac{4}{25}$ **80.** $\frac{9}{25}$

81. $\frac{5}{8}$ **82.** $\frac{3}{8}$

83. $\frac{7}{16}$ **84.** $\frac{9}{16}$

Write each fraction as a percent. See Example 11.

85. $\frac{9}{4}$ **86.** $\frac{11}{4}$

87. $\frac{21}{20}$ **88.** $\frac{33}{20}$

Write each fraction as a percent. Give the exact answer and an approximation to the nearest tenth of one percent. See Example 12.

89. $\frac{1}{6}$ **90.** $\frac{2}{9}$

91. $\frac{5}{3}$ **92.** $\frac{4}{3}$

CONCEPT EXTENSIONS

93. a. Shade 70% of the entire figure below.

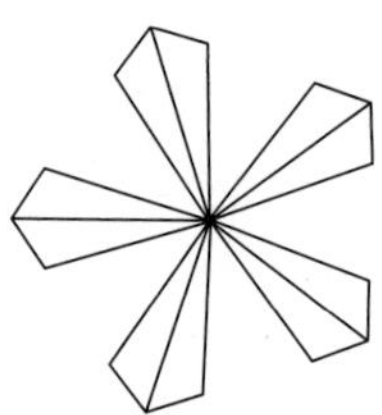

b. Shade 62.5% of the entire figure below.

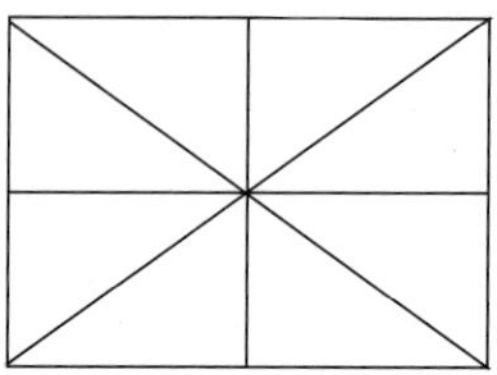

94. a. Shade 37.5% of the figure shown below.

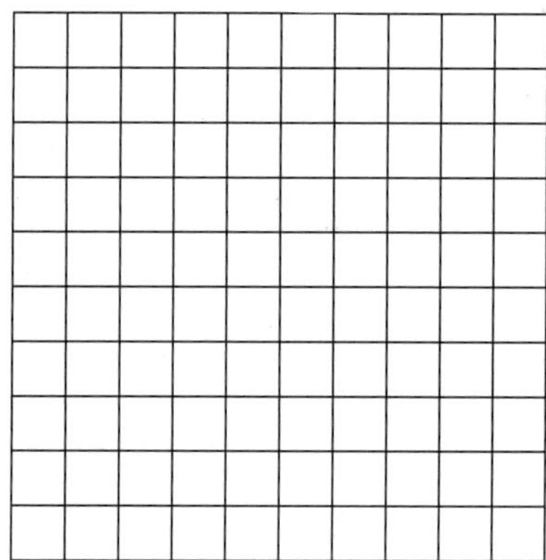

b. Express the shaded portion of the entire figure as a decimal.

c. Fill in the blanks to complete the expanded notation: $0.375 = \frac{3}{} + \frac{7}{} + \frac{5}{}$

d. For your answer to part a, what shaded portion represents $\frac{3}{10}$? What shaded portion represents $\frac{7}{100}$? What shaded portion represents $\frac{5}{1,000}$?

95. Express the shaded portion of the entire figure below as a fraction (in simplified form), adecimal, and a percent.

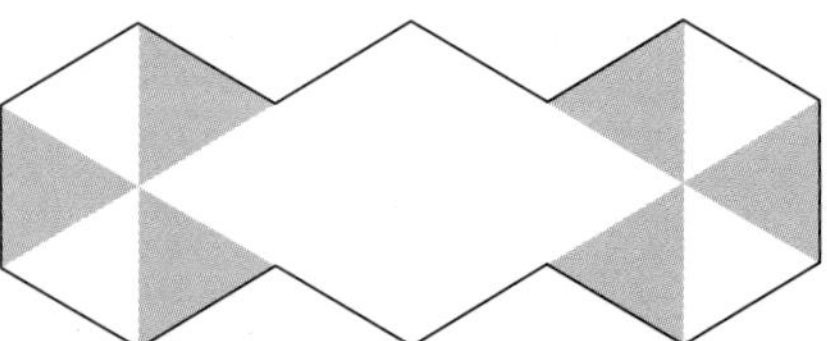

96. Insert the correct symbol, >, <, or =, to make a true statement.

a. $\frac{2}{3}$ ☐ 66%

b. 200% ☐ 2.01

c. 75% ☐ 0.7499

d. 50% ☐ $\frac{1}{2}$%

TRY IT YOURSELF

Complete the table. Give an exact answer and an approximation to the nearest tenth of one percent when necessary. Round decimals to the nearest hundredth when necessary.

	Fraction	Decimal	Percent
97.		0.0314	
98.		0.0021	
99.			40.8%
100.			34.2%
101.			$5\frac{1}{4}$%
102.			$6\frac{3}{4}$%
103.	$\frac{7}{3}$		
104.	$\frac{7}{9}$		

APPLICATIONS

105. THE RED CROSS A fact sheet released by the American Red Cross in 2012 stated, "An average of 91 cents of every dollar donated to the Red Cross is spent on services and programs." What percent of the money donated to the Red Cross went to services and programs?

106. CHARITY GIVING A press release for *The United Way* of Gaston County, North Carolina, states that 86 cents of every dollar collected goes directly to helping people in the community.

a. Express the amount of money that goes directly to help the community as a fraction in simplest form.

b. Write your answer to part a as a percent.

107. REGIONS OF THE COUNTRY The continental United States is divided into seven regions as shown below.

a. What percent of the 50 states are in the Rocky Mountain region?

b. What percent of the 50 states are in the Midwestern region?

c. What percent of the 50 states are not located in any of the seven regions shown here?

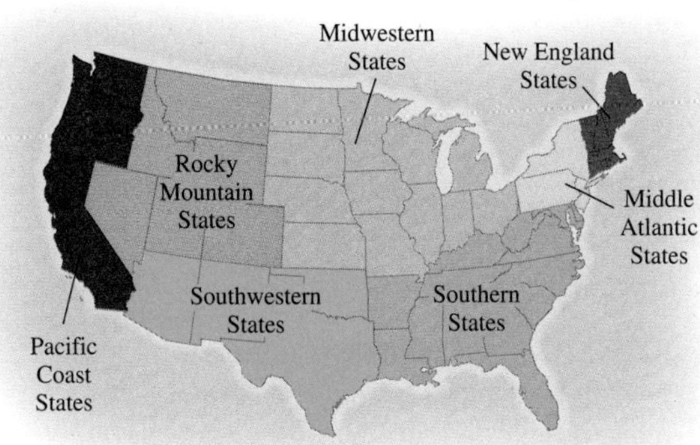

108. ROAD SIGNS Sometimes, signs like that shown below are posted to warn truckers when they are approaching a steep grade on the highway.

a. Write the grade shown on the sign as a fraction.

b. Write the grade shown on the sign as a decimal.

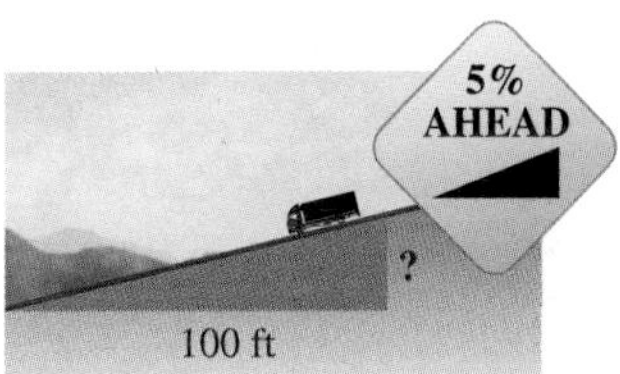

109. INTEREST RATES Write each interest rate for the following accounts as a decimal.

a. Home loan: 7.75%

b. Savings account: 5%

c. Credit card: 14.25%

110. DRUNK DRIVING In most states, it is illegal to drive with a blood alcohol concentration of 0.08% or higher.

a. Write this percent as a fraction. Do not simplify.

b. Use your answer to part a to fill in the blanks: A blood alcohol concentration of 0.08% means ☐ parts alcohol to ☐ parts blood.

111. HUMAN SKIN The illustration below shows what percent of the total skin area that each section of the body covers. Find the missing percent for the torso, and then complete the bar graph. (*Source:* Burn Center at Sherman Oaks Hospital, American Medical Assn. Encyclopedia of Medicine)

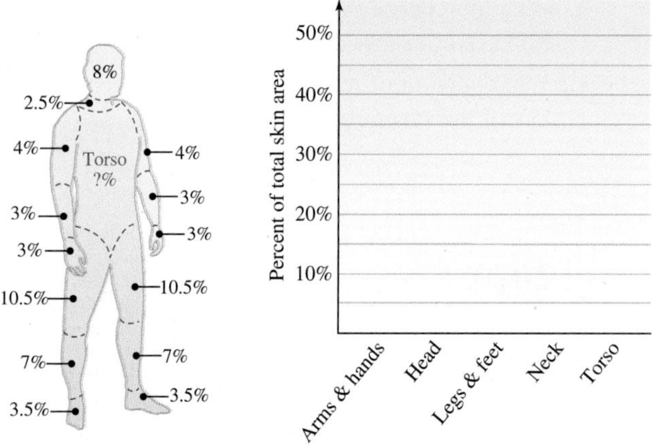

112. RAP MUSIC The table below shows what percent rap/hip-hop music sales were of total U.S. dollar sales of recorded music for the years 2001–2007. Use the data to construct a line graph.

2001	2002	2003	2004	2005	2006	2007	2008
11.4%	13.8%	13.3%	12.1%	13.3%	11.4%	10.8%	10.7%

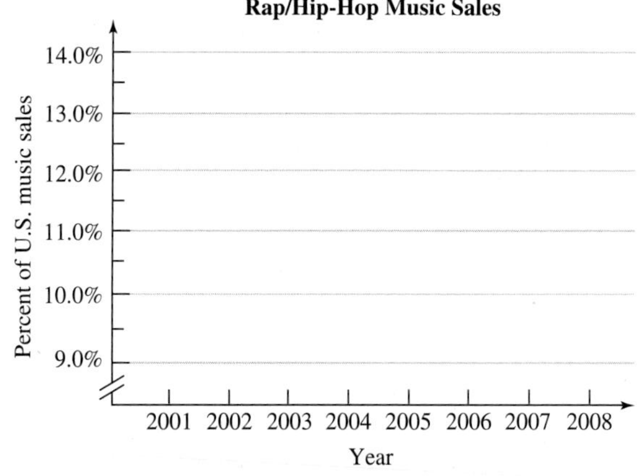

Source: Recording Industry Association of America

113. THE U.N. SECURITY COUNCIL The United Nations has 192 members. The United States, Russia, the United Kingdom, France, and China, along with ten other nations, make up the Security Council. (Source: *The World Almanac and Book of Facts,* 2009)

a. What fraction of the members of the United Nations belong to the Security Council? Write your answer in simplest form.

b. Write your answer to part a as a decimal. (*Hint:* Divide to six decimal places. The result is a terminating decimal.)

c. Write your answer to part b as a percent.

114. SOAP Ivory soap claims to be $99\frac{44}{100}$% pure. Write this percent as a decimal.

115. LOGOS In the illustration, what part of the company's logo is shaded red? Express your answer as a percent (exact), a fraction, and a decimal (using an overbar).

Recycling Industries Inc.

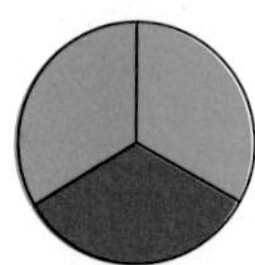

116. THE HUMAN SPINE The human spine consists of a group of bones (vertebrae) as shown.

a. What fraction of the vertebrae are lumbar?

b. What percent of the vertebrae are lumbar? (Round to the nearest one percent.)

c. What percent of the vertebrae are cervical? (Round to the nearest one percent.)

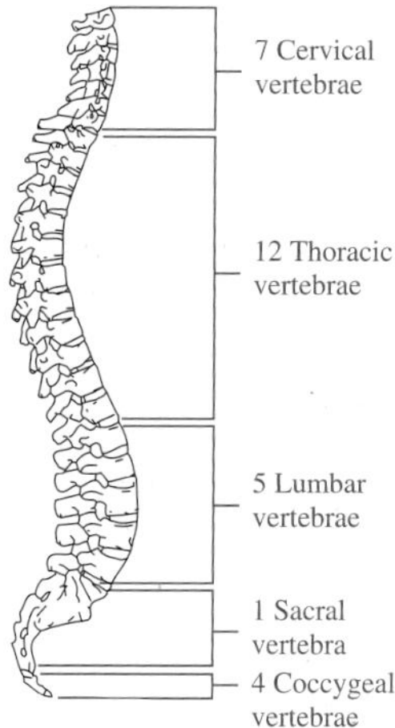

117. BOXING Oscar De La Hoya won 39 out of 45 professional fights.

a. What fraction of his fights did he win?

b. What percent of his fights did he win? Give the exact answer and an approximation to the nearest tenth of one percent.

118. MAJOR LEAGUE BASEBALL In 2011, the St. Louis Cardinals won 90 games and lost 72 during the regular season. (The Cardinals were the wild card entry in the playoffs and eventually upset the Texas Rangers to win the 2011 World Series.)

a. What was the total number of regular season games that the Cardinals played in 2011?

b. What percent of the games played did the Cardinals win in 2011? Give the exact answer and an approximation to the nearest tenth of one percent.

119. ECONOMIC FORECASTS One economic indicator of the national economy is the number of orders placed by manufacturers. One month, the number of orders rose *one-fourth of 1 percent.*

a. Write this using a % symbol.

b. Express it as a fraction.

c. Express it as a decimal.

120. TAXES In August of 2008, Springfield, Missouri, voters approved a *one-eighth of one percent* sales tax to fund transportation projects in the city.

a. Write the percent as a decimal.

b. Write the percent as a fraction.

121. BIRTHDAYS If the day of your birthday represents $\frac{1}{365}$ of a year, what percent of the year is it? Round to the nearest hundredth of a percent.

122. POPULATION As a fraction, each resident of the United States represents approximately $\frac{1}{305{,}000{,}000}$ of the U.S. population. Express this as a percent. Round to one nonzero digit.

WRITING

123. If you were writing advertising, which form do you think would attract more customers: "25% off" or "$\frac{1}{4}$ off"? Explain your reasoning.

124. Many coaches ask their players to give a 110% effort during practices and games. What do you think this means? Is it possible?

125. Explain how an amusement park could have an attendance that is 103% of capacity.

126. WON-LOST RECORDS In sports, when a team wins as many games as it loses, it is said to be playing "500 ball." Suppose in its first 40 games, a team wins 20 games and loses 20 games. Use the concepts in this section to explain why such a record could be called "500 ball."

SECTION 3.8
Applications Introduction Percent on the Internet

PayPal is a very popular online payment service that is used by buyers and sellers to complete secure transactions using the Internet. There is no fee for the buyer, but PayPal does charge the seller a small fee to safely collect and transfer the payment to the seller's account. The fee charged to the seller is based on the seller's total monthly sales, as shown in the table below. The greater the seller's monthly sales, the less the rate that PayPal charges.

Seller's Monthly Sales	Fee charged to the seller by PayPal
\$0.00 to \$3,000.00	2.9% of the selling price plus \$0.30
\$3,000.01 to \$10,000	2.5% of the selling price plus \$0.30
\$10,000.01 to \$100,000	2.2% of the selling price plus \$0.30
Greater than \$100,000	1.9% of the selling price plus \$0.30

We can translate the information given on the first row of the table to obtain a formula to calculate the fee PayPal charges to the seller for an online transaction of any amount.

The seller's fee	is	2.9%	of	the selling price	plus	\$0.30.
F	$=$	2.9%	$\cdot$	p	$+$	0.30

In this case, the word *of* indicates multiplication.

As an example, suppose an online art store has less than $3,000 in monthly sales. The fee PayPal charges to the store to collect the buyer's payment of $550 for an oil painting is given by:

$F = 2.9\% \cdot p + 0.30$

$F = 0.029p + 0.30$ When performing a calculation with a percent, first write it as a decimal (or fraction): 2.9% = 0.029.

$F = 0.029(550) + 0.30$ Substitute 550 for the selling price, p.

$F = 15.95 + 0.30$ Do the multiplication 0.029(550) = 15.95.

$F = 16.25$ Do the addition.

PayPal will charge the online art store $16.25 to collect the payment for the sale of a $550 painting.

Find the fee PayPal charges the online art store to collect a buyer's payment of $550 for an oil painting if the store has the amount of monthly sales shown below.

1. Monthly sales: $6,500
2. Monthly sales: $19,000
3. Monthly sales: $105,000

eBay is a online worldwide marketplace that enables users to buy and sell a wide variety of merchandise. When a seller lists an item on eBay using the fixed price Buy It Now feature, he or she is charged a small **insertion fee** for the listing. If the item sells, there is also a **final value fee** charged to the seller. The basic cost of selling an item on eBay is the insertion fee plus the final value fee.

As an example, suppose a sports memorabilia store lists a Mia Hamm autographed University of North Carolina women's soccer jersey on eBay for $380. The following table gives the insertion fee to be paid by the seller.

Insertion fee for fixed price Buy It Now

But It Now price	Insertion fee
$0.99 or more	$0.50

After listing the jersey on eBay, suppose it is purchased for the Buy It Now price of $380. eBay charges the seller a final value fee as explained in the following table. For a selling price of $380, which is between $50.01 and $1,000, we refer to the third row of the table.

Final value fee for fixed price Buy It Now for clothing, shoes, and accessories

Price to buyer	Final value fee
Item not sold	No fee
$0.99 to $50.00	10% of the price to the buyer
$50.01 to $1,000	10% of the initial $50, plus 8% of the remainder of the price over $50
$1,000.01 or more	10% of the initial $50, plus 8% of the next $950, plus 2% of the remainder of the price over $1,000

We can translate the information on the third row of the table to obtain a formula that calculates the fee eBay charges the seller for a transaction between $50.01 and $1,000.

The seller's fee	is	the insertion fee	plus	10%	of	the initial $50	plus	8%	of	the remainder of the selling price over $50.
F	$=$	0.50	$+$	10%	$\cdot$	50	$+$	8%	$\cdot$	$(p - 50)$

The fee eBay charges to the sports memorabilia store for the listing and sale of the Mia Hamm jersey is given by:

$F = 0.50 + 10\% \cdot 50 + 8\% \cdot (p - 50)$

$F = 0.50 + 0.10(50) + 0.08(p - 50)$ — When performing a calculation with a percent, first write it as a decimal (or fraction): $10\% = 0.10$ and $8\% = 0.08$.

$F = 0.50 + 0.10(50) + 0.08(380 - 50)$ — Substitute 380 for the selling price, p.

$F = 0.50 + 0.10(50) + 0.08(330)$ — Do the subtraction within the parentheses: $380 - 50 = 330$.

$F = 0.50 + 5 + 26.40$ — Do the multiplication.

$F = 31.90$ — Do the addition.

The fee eBay will charge the sports memorabilia store for the sale of a $380 Mia Hamm jersey is $31.90

4. Write a formula that calculates the fee eBay charges the seller when the item's selling price is more than $1,000.
5. COLLECTIBLES Suppose a sports memorabilia store lists a Michael Jordan autographed University of North Carolina basketball jersey on eBay for a fixed Buy It Now price of $1,600 and it sells. Use your answer to problem 4 to find the fee that the store will be charged by eBay.

SECTION 3.8
Solving Percent Problems Using Percent Equations and Proportions

Objectives

PERCENT EQUATIONS

1. Translate percent sentences to percent equations.
2. Solve percent equations to find the amount.
3. Solve percent equations to find the percent.
4. Solve percent equations to find the base.

PERCENT PROPORTIONS

1. Write percent proportions.
2. Solve percent proportions to find the amount.
3. Solve percent proportions to find the percent.
4. Solve percent proportions to find the base.
5. Read circle graphs.

ARE YOU READY?

The following problems review some basic skills that are needed when solving percent problems.

1. Multiply: $1.6 \cdot 15.8$
2. Divide: $\frac{38}{40}$
3. a. Write 75% as a decimal.
   b. Write 125% as a decimal.
4. Divide: $31.5 \div \frac{1}{3}$
5. Solve the proportion: $\frac{x}{500} = \frac{84}{100}$
6. Write $33\frac{1}{3}$ as a mixed number.

The articles on the front page of the newspaper shown below illustrate three types of percent problems.

Type 1 In the labor article, if we want to know how many union members voted to accept the new offer, we would ask:

What number is 84% of 500?

Type 2 In the article on drinking water, if we want to know what percent of the wells are safe, we would ask:

38 is what percent of 40?

Type 3 In the article on new appointees, if we want to know how many members are on the State Board of Examiners, we would ask:

6 is 75% of what number?

This section introduces two methods that can be used to solve the percent problems shown. The first method involves writing and solving *percent equations.* The second method involves writing and solving *percent proportions.* If your instructor only requires you to learn the proportion method, then turn to page xxx and begin reading Objective 1.

METHOD 1: PERCENT EQUATIONS

1 Translate percent sentences to percent equations.

The **percent sentences** highlighted in blue in the introduction have three things in common.

- Each contains the word *is.* Here, *is* can be translated as an = symbol.
- Each contains the word *of.* In this case, *of* means multiply.
- Each contains a phrase such as *what number* or *what percent.* In other words, there is an unknown number that can be represented by a variable.

These observations suggest that each percent sentence contains key words that can be translated to form an equation. The equation, called a **percent equation,** will contain three numbers (two known and one unknown represented by a variable), the operation of multiplication, and, of course, an = symbol.

The Language of Mathematics The key words in a percent sentence translate as follows:

- ***is*** translates to an equal symbol =.
- ***of*** translates to multiplication that is shown with a raised dot ·
- ***what number*** or ***what percent*** translates to an unknown number that is represented by a variable.

Self Check 1

Translate each percent sentence to a percent equation.

a. What number is 33% of 80?

b. What percent of 55 is 6?

c. 172% of what number is 4?

Now Try **Problem 17**

EXAMPLE 1 Translate each percent sentence to a percent equation.

a. What number is 12% of 64?

b. What percent of 88 is 11?

c. 165% of what number is 366?

Strategy We will look for the key words *is, of,* and *what number* (or *what percent*) in each percent sentence.

WHY These key words translate to mathematical symbols that form the percent equation.

Solution In each case, we will let the variable x represent the unknown number. However, any letter can be used.

a. What number is 12% of 64? — This is the given percent sentence.

$$x = 12\% \cdot 64$$ This is the percent equation.

b. What percent of 88 is 11? — This is the given percent sentence.

$$x \cdot 88 = 11$$ This is the percent equation.

c. 165% of what number is 366? — This is the given percent sentence.

$$165\% \cdot x = 366$$ This is the percent equation.

2 Solve percent equations to find the amount.

To solve the labor union percent problem (Type 1 from the newspaper), we translate the percent sentence into a percent equation and then find the unknown number.

EXAMPLE 2 What number is 84% of 500?

Strategy We will look for the key words *is, of,* and *what number* in the percent sentence and translate them to mathematical symbols to form a percent equation.

WHY Then it will be clear what operation should be performed to find the unknown number.

Solution First, we translate.

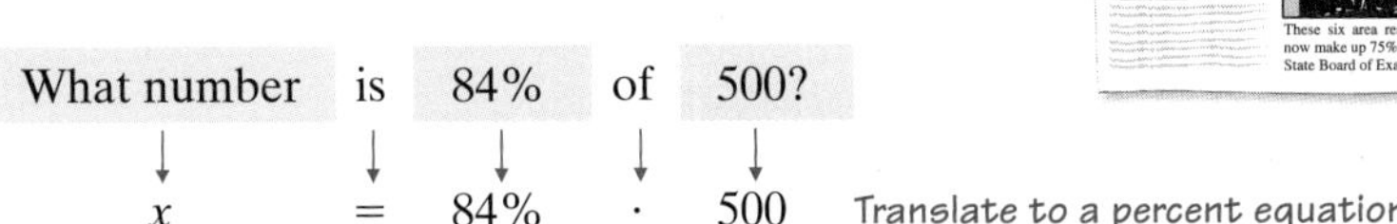

Now we perform the multiplication on the right side of the equation.

$x = 0.84 \cdot 500$ Write 84% as a decimal: 84% = 0.84.

$x = 420$ Do the multiplication.

We have found that 420 is 84% of 500. That is, 420 union members mentioned in the newspaper article voted to accept the new offer.

Self Check 2

What number is 36% of 400?

Now Try **Problems 19 and 75**

The Language of Mathematics When we find the value of the variable that makes a percent equation true, we say that we have **solved the equation.** In Example 2, we *solved* $x = 84\% \cdot 500$ to find that the variable x is 420.

Caution! When solving percent equations, always write the percent as a decimal (or a fraction) before performing any calculations. In Example 2, we wrote 84% as 0.84 before multiplying by 500.

Percent sentences involve a comparison of numbers. In the statement "420 is 84% of 500," the number 420 is called the **amount,** 84% is the **percent,** and 500 is called the **base.** Think of the base as the standard of comparison—it represents the **whole** of some quantity. The amount is a **part** of the base, but it can exceed the base when the percent is more than 100%. The percent, of course, has the % symbol.

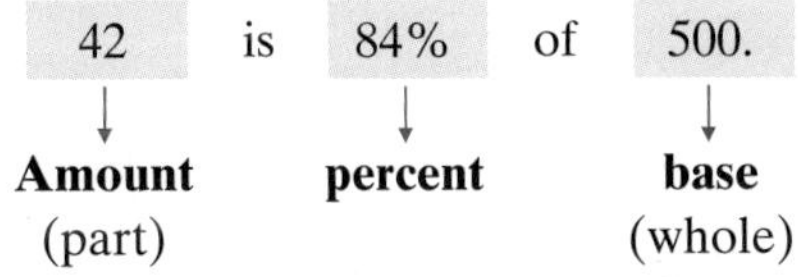

In any percent problem, the relationship between the amount, the percent, and the base is as follows: *Amount is percent of base.* This relationship is shown below as the **percent equation** (also called the **percent formula**).

Percent Equation (Formula)

Any percent sentence can be translated to a percent equation that has the form:

Amount = percent · base or Part = percent · whole

Self Check 3

What number is 240% of 80.3?

Now Try **Problem 23**

EXAMPLE 3 What number is 160% of 15.8?

Strategy We will look for the key words *is, of,* and *what number* in the percent sentence and translate them to mathematical symbols to form a percent equation.

WHY Then it will be clear what operation needs to be performed to find the unknown number.

Solution First, we translate.

What number	is	160%	of	15.8?
↓	↓	↓	↓	↓
x	$=$	160%	$\cdot$	15.8

x is the amount, 160% is the percent, and 15.8 is the base.

Now we solve the equation by performing the multiplication on the right side.

$x = 1.6 \cdot 15.8$ Write 160% as a decimal: 160% = 1.6.

$x = 25.28$ Do the multiplication.

$$\begin{array}{r} 15.8 \\ \times\ 1.6 \\ \hline 948 \\ 1580 \\ \hline 25.28 \end{array}$$

Thus, 25.28 is 160% of 15.8. In this case, the amount exceeds the base because the percent is more than 100%.

3 Solve percent equations to find the percent.

In the drinking water problem (Type 2 from the newspaper), we must find the percent. Once again, we translate the words of the problem into a percent equation and solve it.

> ***The Language of Mathematics*** We solve percent equations by writing a series of steps that result in an equation of the form $x =$ **a number** or **a number** $= x$. We say that the variable x is *isolated* on one side of the equation. *Isolated* means alone or by itself.

Self Check 4

4 is what percent of 80?

Now Try **Problems 27 and 83**

EXAMPLE 4 38 is what percent of 40?

DAILY NEWS

Transit Strike Averted!

Labor: 84% of 500-member union votes to accept new offer

Drinking Water 38 of 40 Wells Declared Safe

New Appointees

These six area residents now make up 75% of the State Board of Examiners

Strategy We will look for the key words *is, of,* and *what percent* in the percent sentence and translate them to mathematical symbols to form a percent equation.

WHY Then we can solve the equation to find the unknown percent.

Solution First, we translate.

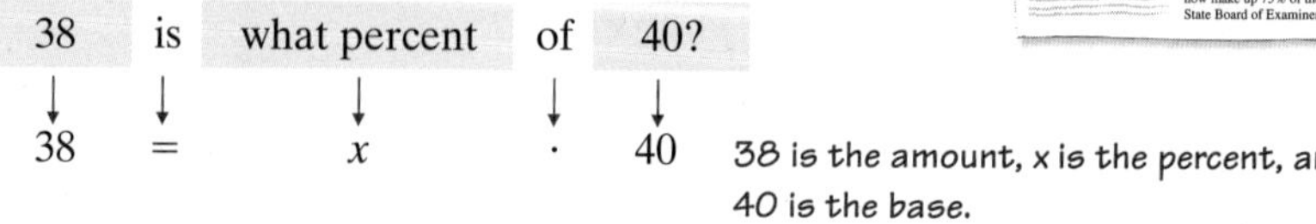

38 is the amount, x is the percent, and 40 is the base.

$38 = x \cdot 40$ This is the equation to solve.

On the right side of the equation, the unknown number x is multiplied by 40. To undo the multiplication by 40 and isolate x, we divide both sides by 40.

$$\frac{38}{\mathbf{40}} = \frac{x \cdot 40}{\mathbf{40}}$$

We can simplify the fraction on the right side of the equation by removing the common factor of 40 from the numerator and denominator. On the left side, we perform the division indicated by the fraction bar.

$$0.95 = \frac{x \cdot \overset{1}{\cancel{40}}}{\underset{1}{\cancel{40}}}$$ To simplify the left side, divide 38 by 40.

$$0.95 = x$$

$$\begin{array}{r} 0.95 \\ 40\overline{)38.00} \\ -36\,0 \\ \hline 2\,00 \\ -2\,00 \\ \hline 0 \end{array}$$

Since we want to find the percent, we need to write the decimal 0.95 as a percent.

$0\,95\% = x$ To write 0.95 as a percent, multiply it by 100 by moving the decimal point two places to the right, and then insert a % symbol.

$95\% = x$

We have found that 38 is 95% of 40. That is, 95% of the wells mentioned in the newspaper article were declared safe.

EXAMPLE 5 14 is what percent of 32?

Strategy We will look for the key words *is, of,* and *what percent* in the percent sentence and translate them to mathematical symbols to form a percent equation.

WHY Then we can solve the equation to find the unknown percent.

Solution First, we translate.

14	is	what percent	of	32?
↓	↓	↓	↓	↓
14	=	x	·	32

14 is the amount, x is the percent, and 32 is the base.

$14 = x \cdot 32$ This is the equation to solve.

$\frac{14}{32} = \frac{x \cdot 32}{32}$ To undo the multiplication by 32 and isolate x on the right side of the equation, divide both sides by 32.

$0.4375 = \frac{x \cdot \overset{1}{\cancel{32}}}{\underset{1}{\cancel{32}}}$ To simplify the fraction on the right side of the equation, remove the common factor of 32 from the numerator and denominator. On the left side, divide 14 by 32.

$0.4375 = x$

$0\,43.75\% = x$ To write the decimal 0.4375 as a percent, multiply it by 100 by moving the decimal point two places to the right, and then insert a % symbol.

$43.75\% = x$

$$\begin{array}{r} 0.4375 \\ 32\overline{)14.0000} \\ -12\,8 \\ \hline 1\,20 \\ -96 \\ \hline 240 \\ -224 \\ \hline 160 \\ -160 \\ \hline 0 \end{array}$$

Thus, 14 is 43.75% of 32.

Self Check 5

9 is what percent of 16?

Now Try **Problem 31**

Using Your CALCULATOR **Cost of an Air Bag**

An air bag is estimated to add an additional $500 to the cost of a car. What percent of the $16,295 sticker price is the cost of the air bag?

First, we translate the words of the problem into a percent equation.

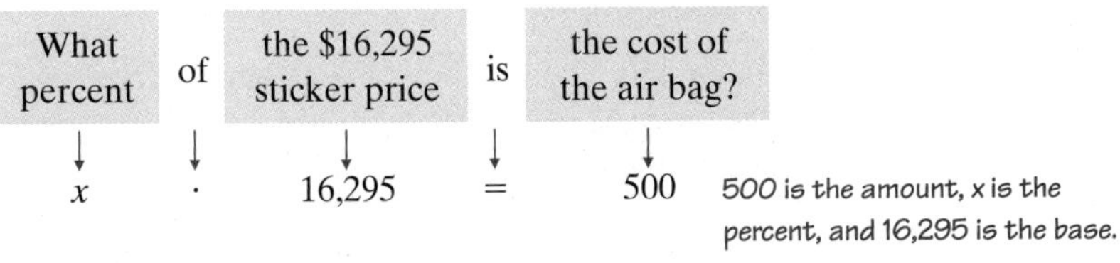

Then we solve the equation.

$$x \cdot 16{,}295 = 500$$

$$\frac{x \cdot 16{,}295}{\mathbf{16{,}295}} = \frac{500}{\mathbf{16{,}295}}$$ To undo the multiplication by 16,295 and isolate *x* on the left side, divide both sides of the equation by 16,295.

$$x = \frac{500}{16{,}295}$$ To simplify the fraction on the left side, remove the common factor of 16,295 from the numerator and denominator.

To perform the division on the right side using a scientific calculator, enter the following:

500 [÷] 16295 [=] **0.030684259**

This display gives the answer in decimal form. To change it to a percent, we multiply the result by 100. This moves the decimal point 2 places to the right. (See the display.) Then we insert a % symbol. If we round to the nearest tenth of a percent, the cost of the air bag is about 3.1% of the sticker price.

3.068425898

Self Check 6

What percent of 5 is 8.5?

Now Try **Problem 35**

EXAMPLE 6 What percent of 6 is 7.5?

Strategy We will look for the key words *is, of,* and *what percent* in the percent sentence and translate them to mathematical symbols to form a percent equation.

WHY Then we can solve the equation to find the unknown percent.

Solution First, we translate.

What percent	of	6	is	7.5
↓	↓	↓	↓	↓
x	$\cdot$	6	=	7.5

$$x \cdot 6 = 7.5$$ This is the equation to solve.

$$\frac{x \cdot 6}{\mathbf{6}} = \frac{7.5}{\mathbf{6}}$$ To undo the multiplication by 6 and isolate *x* on the left side of the equation, divide both sides by 6.

$$\frac{x \cdot \overset{1}{\cancel{6}}}{\underset{1}{\cancel{6}}} = 1.25$$ To simplify the fraction on the left side of the equation, remove the common factor of 6 from the numerator and denominator. On the right side, divide 7.5 by 6.

$$\begin{array}{r} 1.25 \\ 6\overline{)7.50} \\ -6 \\ \hline 1\,5 \\ -1\,2 \\ \hline 30 \\ -30 \\ \hline 0 \end{array}$$

$$x = 1.25$$

$$x = 1\underset{\smile\smile}{25}\%$$ To write the decimal 1.25 as a percent, multiply it by 100 by moving the decimal point two places to the right, and then insert a % symbol.

$$x = 125\%$$

Thus, 7.5 is 125% of 6.

4 Solve percent equations to find the base.

In the percent problem about the State Board of Examiners (Type 3 from the newspaper), we must find the base. As before, we translate the percent sentence into a percent equation and then find the unknown number.

EXAMPLE 7 6 is 75% of what number?

Strategy We will look for the key words *is, of,* and *what number* in the percent sentence and translate them to mathematical symbols to form a percent equation.

WHY Then we can solve the equation to find the unknown number.

DAILY NEWS
Monday, March 23
Transit Strike Averted!
Labor: 84% of 500-member union votes to accept new offer
Drinking Water
38 of 40 Wells Declared Safe
New Appointees
These six area residents now make up 75% of the State Board of Examiners

Solution First, we translate.

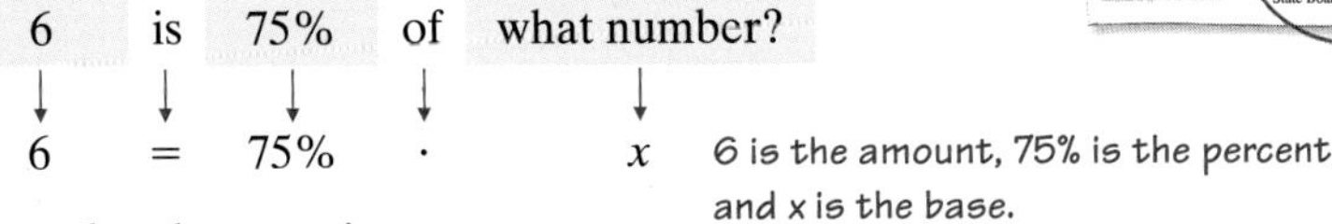

6	is	75%	of	what number?
↓	↓	↓	↓	↓
6	=	75%	·	x

6 is the amount, 75% is the percent, and x is the base.

Now we solve the equation.

$$6 = 0.75 \cdot x$$ *Write 75% as a decimal: 75% = 0.75.*

$$\frac{6}{\mathbf{0.75}} = \frac{0.75 \cdot x}{\mathbf{0.75}}$$ *To undo the multiplication by 0.75 and isolate x on the right side, divide both sides of the equation by 0.75.*

$$8 = \frac{\overset{1}{\cancel{0.75}} \cdot x}{\underset{1}{\cancel{0.75}}}$$ *To simplify the fraction on the right side of the equation, remove the common factor of 0.75. On the left side, divide 6 by 0.75.*

$$\begin{array}{r} 8 \\ 75\overline{)600} \\ -600 \\ \hline 0 \end{array}$$

$$8 = x$$

Thus, 6 is 75% of 8. That is, there are 8 members on the State Board of Examiners mentioned in the newspaper article.

Self Check 7

3 is 5% of what number?

Now Try **Problem 39**

Success Tip Sometimes the calculations to solve a percent problem are made easier if we write the percent as a fraction instead of a decimal. This is the case with percents that have *repeating* decimal equivalents such as $33\frac{1}{3}\%$, $66\frac{2}{3}\%$, and $16\frac{2}{3}\%$. You may want to review the table of percents and their fractional equivalents on page 96.

EXAMPLE 8 31.5 is $33\frac{1}{3}\%$ of what number?

Strategy We will look for the key words *is, of,* and *what number* in the percent sentence and translate them to mathematical symbols to form a percent equation.

WHY Then we can solve the equation to find the unknown number.

Solution First, we translate.

31.5	is	$33\frac{1}{3}\%$	of	what number?
↓	↓	↓	↓	↓
31.5	=	$33\frac{1}{3}\%$	·	x

31.5 is the amount, $33\frac{1}{3}\%$ is the percent, and x is the base.

In this case, the calculations can be made easier by writing $33\frac{1}{3}\%$ as a fraction instead of as a repeating decimal.

$$31.5 = \frac{1}{3} \cdot x$$ *Recall that $33\frac{1}{3}\% = \frac{1}{3}$.*

$$\frac{31.5}{\mathbf{\frac{1}{3}}} = \frac{\frac{1}{3} \cdot x}{\mathbf{\frac{1}{3}}}$$ *To undo the multiplication by $\frac{1}{3}$ and isolate x on the right side of the equation, divide both sides by $\frac{1}{3}$.*

Self Check 8

150 is $66\frac{2}{3}\%$ of what number?

Now Try **Problems 43 and 87**

$$\frac{31.5}{\frac{1}{3}} = \frac{\frac{\overset{1}{\cancel{1}}}{\cancel{3}} \cdot x}{\frac{\cancel{1}}{\underset{1}{\cancel{3}}}}$$ To simplify the fraction on the right side of the equation, remove the common factor of $\frac{1}{3}$ from the numerator and denominator.

$$31.5 \div \frac{1}{3} = x$$ On the left side, the fraction bar indicates division.

$$\frac{31.5}{1} \cdot \frac{3}{1} = x$$ On the left side, write 31.5 as a fraction: $\frac{31.5}{1}$. Then use the rule for dividing fractions: Multiply by the reciprocal of $\frac{1}{3}$, which is $\frac{3}{1}$.

$$94.5 = x$$ Do the multiplication.

$$\begin{array}{r} \overset{1}{31.5} \\ \times\ 3 \\ \hline 94.5 \end{array}$$

Thus, 31.5 is $33\frac{1}{3}\%$ of 94.5.

To solve percent application problems, we often have to rewrite the facts of the problem in percent sentence form before we can translate to an equation.

Self Check 9

CAPACITY OF A GYM A total of 784 people attended a graduation in a high school gymnasium. If this was 98% of capacity, what is the total capacity of the gym?

Now Try **Problem 85**

EXAMPLE 9 ***Rentals*** In an apartment complex, 198 of the units are currently occupied. If this represents an 88% occupancy rate, how many units are in the complex?

Strategy We will carefully read the problem and use the given facts to write them in the form of a percent sentence.

WHY Then we can translate the sentence into a percent equation and solve it to find the unknown number of units in the complex.

Solution An occupancy rate of 88% means that 88% of the units are occupied. Thus, the 198 units that are currently occupied are 88% of some unknown number of units in the complex, and we can write:

198	is	88%	of	what number?
↓	↓	↓	↓	↓
198	=	88%	·	x

198 is the amount, 88% is the percent, and x is the base.

Now we solve the equation.

$$198 = 88\% \cdot x$$

$$198 = 0.88 \cdot x$$ Write 88% as a decimal: 88% = 0.88.

$$\frac{198}{\mathbf{0.88}} = \frac{0.88 \cdot x}{\mathbf{0.88}}$$ To undo the multiplication by 0.88 and isolate x on the right side, divide both sides of the equation by 0.88.

$$\frac{198}{0.88} = \frac{\overset{1}{\cancel{0.88}} \cdot x}{\underset{1}{\cancel{0.88}}}$$ To simplify the fraction on the right side of the equation, remove the common factor of 0.88 from the numerator and denominator. On the left side, divide 198 by 0.88.

$$225 = x$$

$$\begin{array}{r} 225 \\ 88\overline{)19800} \\ -176 \\ \hline 220 \\ -176 \\ \hline 440 \\ -440 \\ \hline 0 \end{array}$$

The apartment complex has 225 units, of which 198, or 88%, are occupied.

If you are only learning the percent equation method for solving percent problems, turn to page 118 and pick up your reading at Objective 5.

METHOD 2: PERCENT PROPORTIONS

1 Write percent proportions.

Another method to solve percent problems involves writing and then solving a proportion. To introduce this method, consider the figure on the right. The vertical line down its middle divides the figure into two equal-sized parts. Since 1 of the 2 parts is shaded red, the shaded portion of the figure can be described by the ratio $\frac{1}{2}$. We call this an **amount-to-base** (or **part-to-whole**) **ratio.**

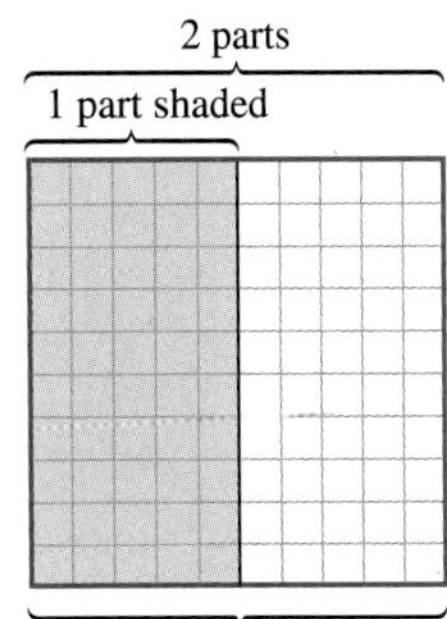

50 of the 100 parts shaded: 50% shaded

Now consider the 100 equal-sized square regions within the figure. Since 50 of them are shaded red, we say that $\frac{50}{100}$, or 50% of the figure is shaded. The ratio $\frac{50}{100}$ is called a **percent ratio.**

Since the amount-to-base ratio, $\frac{1}{2}$, and the percent ratio, $\frac{50}{100}$, represent the same shaded portion of the figure, they must be equal, and we can write

The amount-to-base ratio → $\frac{1}{2} = \frac{50}{100}$ ← The percent ratio

Statements of this type stating that two ratios are equal are called *proportions.* We call $\frac{1}{2} = \frac{50}{100}$ a **percent proportion.** The four terms of a percent proportion are shown below.

Percent Proportion

To translate a percent sentence to a **percent proportion,** use the following form:

Amount is to base as percent is to 100. — *Part is to whole as percent is to 100.*

$$\frac{\text{amount}}{\text{base}} = \frac{\text{percent}}{100} \quad \text{or} \quad \frac{\text{part}}{\text{whole}} = \frac{\text{percent}}{100}$$

↑ This is always 100 because percent means parts per one hundred.

To write a percent proportion, you must identify 3 of the terms as you read the problem. (Remember, the fourth term of the proportion is always 100.) Here are some ways to identify those terms.

- The **percent** is easy to find. Look for the % symbol or the words *what percent.*
- The **base** (or **whole**) usually follows the word *of.*
- The **amount** (or **part**) is compared to the base (or whole).

EXAMPLE 1 Translate each percent sentence to a percent proportion.

a. What number is 12% of 64?

b. What percent of 88 is 11?

c. 165% of what number is 366?

Strategy A percent proportion has the form $\frac{\text{amount}}{\text{base}} = \frac{\text{percent}}{100}$. Since one of the terms of the percent proportion is always 100, we only need to identify three terms to write the proportion. We will begin by identifying the percent and the base in the given sentence.

Self Check 1

Translate each percent sentence to a percent proportion.

a. What number is 33% of 80?

b. What percent of 55 is 6?

c. 172% of what number is 4?

Now Try **Problem 17**

WHY The remaining number (or unknown) must be the amount.

Solution

a. We will identify the terms in this order:

- *First:* the percent (next to the % symbol)
- *Second:* the base (usually after the word *of*)
- *Last:* the amount (the number that remains)

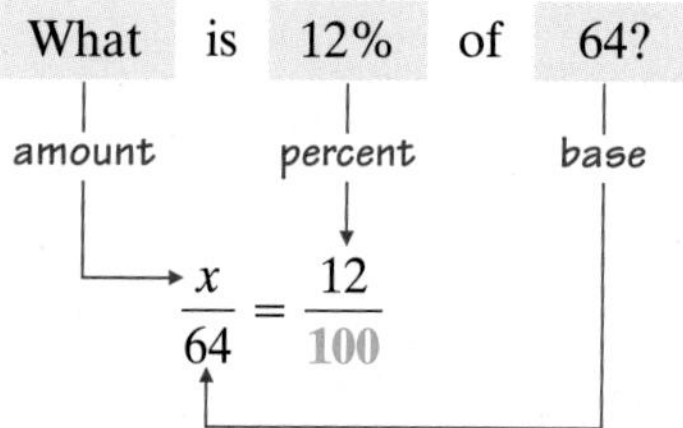

b.

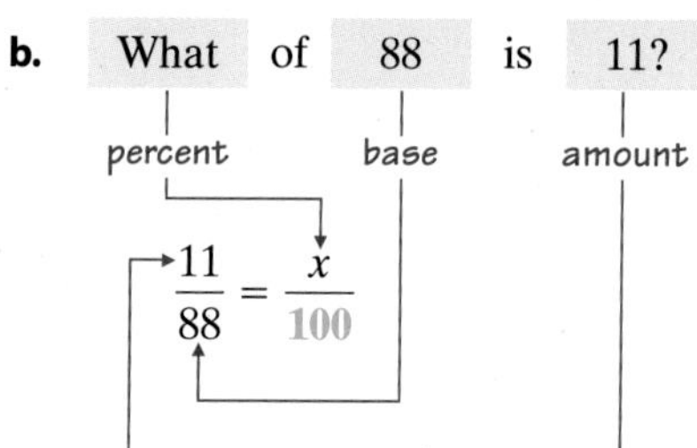

c.

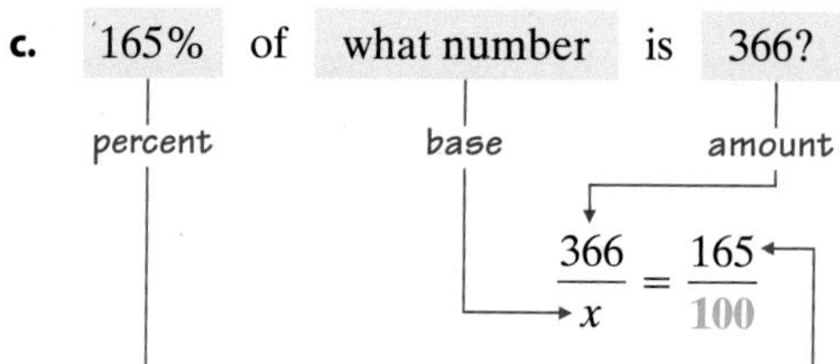

2 Solve percent proportions to find the amount.

Recall the labor union problem from the newspaper example in the introduction to this section. We can write and solve a percent proportion to find the unknown amount.

Self Check 2

What number is 36% of 400?

Now Try **Problems 19 and 75**

EXAMPLE 2 What number is 84% of 500?

Strategy We will identify the percent, the base, and the amount and write a percent proportion of the form $\frac{\text{amount}}{\text{base}} = \frac{\text{percent}}{100}$.

WHY Then we can solve the proportion to find the unknown number.

Solution First, we write the percent proportion.

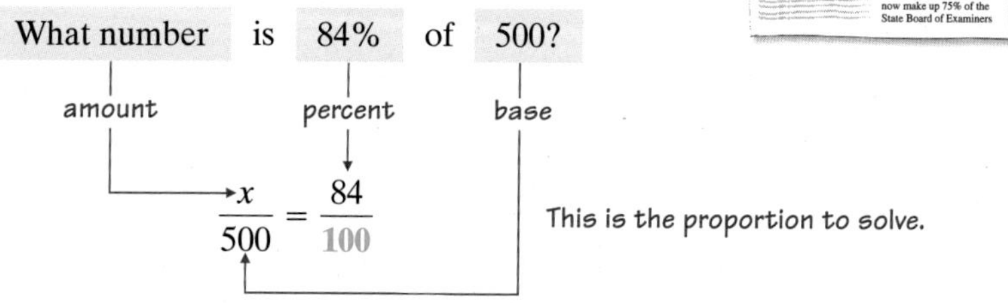

To make the calculations easier, it is helpful to simplify the ratio $\frac{84}{100}$ at this time.

$$\frac{x}{500} = \frac{21}{25}$$ On the right side, simplify: $\frac{84}{100} = \frac{\overset{1}{\cancel{4}} \cdot 21}{\underset{1}{\cancel{4}} \cdot 25} = \frac{21}{25}$.

To solve a proportion we use the cross products.

$x \cdot 25 = 500 \cdot 21$ Find the cross products: $\frac{x}{500} = \frac{21}{25}$. Then set them equal.

$x \cdot 25 = 10{,}500$ To simplify the right side of the equation, do the multiplication: $500 \cdot 21 = 10{,}500$.

$\frac{x \cdot \overset{1}{\cancel{25}}}{\underset{1}{\cancel{25}}} = \frac{10{,}500}{25}$ To undo the multiplication by 25 and isolate x on the left side, divide both sides of the equation by 25. Then remove the common factor of 25 from the numerator and denominator.

$x = 420$ On the right side, divide 10,500 by 25.

$$\begin{array}{r} 500 \\ \times \ 21 \\ \hline 500 \\ 10\,000 \\ \hline 10{,}500 \end{array} \qquad \begin{array}{r} 420 \\ 25\overline{)10{,}500} \\ -10\,0 \\ \hline 50 \\ -50 \\ \hline 00 \\ -0 \\ \hline 0 \end{array}$$

We have found that 420 is 84% of 500. That is, 420 union members mentioned in the newspaper article voted to accept the new offer.

The Language of Mathematics When we find the value of the variable that makes a percent proportion true, we say that we have **solved the proportion.** In Example 2, we *solved* $\frac{x}{500} = \frac{84}{100}$ to find that the variable x is 420.

EXAMPLE 3 What number is 160% of 15.8?

Strategy We will identify the percent, the base, and the amount and write a percent proportion of the form $\frac{\text{amount}}{\text{base}} = \frac{\text{percent}}{100}$.

WHY Then we can solve the proportion to find the unknown number.

Solution First, we write the percent proportion.

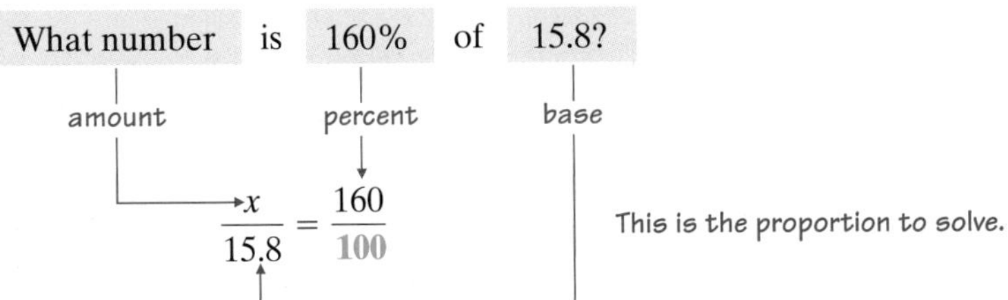

To make the calculations easier, it is helpful to simplify the ratio $\frac{160}{100}$ at this time.

$$\frac{x}{15.8} = \frac{8}{5}$$ On the right side, simplify: $\frac{160}{100} = \frac{8 \cdot \overset{1}{\cancel{20}}}{5 \cdot \underset{1}{\cancel{20}}} = \frac{8}{5}$.

$x \cdot 5 = 15.8 \cdot 8$ Find the cross products: $\frac{x}{15.8} = \frac{8}{5}$. Then set them equal.

$x \cdot 5 = 126.4$ To simplify the right side of the equation, do the multiplication: $15.8 \cdot 8 = 126.4$.

$\frac{x \cdot \overset{1}{\cancel{5}}}{\underset{1}{\cancel{5}}} = \frac{126.4}{5}$ To undo the multiplication by 5 and isolate x on the left side, divide both sides of the equation by 5. Then remove the common factor of 5 from the numerator and denominator.

$x = 25.28$ On the right side, divide 126.4 by 5.

$$\begin{array}{r} {}^{4\,6} \\ 15.8 \\ \times \ 8 \\ \hline 126.4 \end{array} \qquad \begin{array}{r} 25.28 \\ 5\overline{)126.40} \\ -10 \\ \hline 26 \\ -25 \\ \hline 1\,4 \\ -1\,0 \\ \hline 40 \\ -40 \\ \hline 0 \end{array}$$

Thus, 25.28 is 160% of 15.8.

Self Check 3

What number is 240% of 80.3?

Now Try **Problem 23**

3 Solve percent proportions to find the percent.

Recall the drinking water problem from the newspaper example in the introduction to this section. We can write and solve a percent proportion to find the unknown percent.

Self Check 4

4 is what percent of 80?

Now Try **Problems 27 and 83**

EXAMPLE 4 38 is what percent of 40?

DAILY NEWS

Circulation Monday, March 23 50 cents

Transit Strike Averted!

Labor: 84% of 500-member union votes to accept new offer

Drinking Water 38 of 40 Wells Declared Safe

New Appointees

These six area residents now make up 75% of the State Board of Examiners

Strategy We will identify the percent, the base, and the amount and write a percent proportion of the form $\frac{\text{amount}}{\text{base}} = \frac{\text{percent}}{100}$.

WHY Then we can solve the proportion to find the unknown percent.

Solution First, we write the percent proportion.

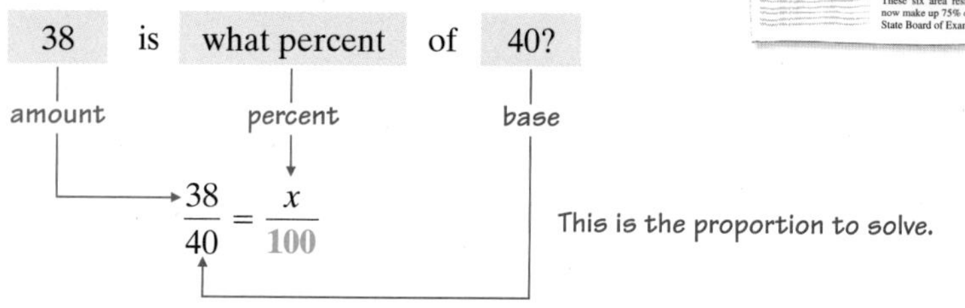

$$\frac{38}{40} = \frac{x}{100}$$ This is the proportion to solve.

To make the calculations easier, it is helpful to simplify the ratio $\frac{38}{40}$ at this time.

$\frac{19}{20} = \frac{x}{100}$ On the left side, simplify: $\frac{38}{40} = \frac{\overset{1}{\cancel{2}} \cdot 19}{\underset{1}{\cancel{2}} \cdot 20} = \frac{19}{20}$.

$19 \cdot 100 = 20 \cdot x$ To solve the proportion, find the cross products: $\frac{19}{20} = \frac{x}{100}$. Then set them equal.

$1{,}900 = 20 \cdot x$ To simplify the left side of the equation, do the multiplication: $19 \cdot 100 = 1{,}900$.

$\frac{1{,}900}{20} = \frac{\overset{1}{\cancel{20}} \cdot x}{\underset{1}{\cancel{20}}}$ To undo the multiplication by 20 and isolate x on the right side, divide both sides of the equation by 20. Then remove the common factor of 20 from the numerator and denominator.

$95 = x$ On the left side, divide 1,900 by 20.

$$\begin{array}{r} 95 \\ 20\overline{)1{,}900} \\ -1\,80 \\ \hline 100 \\ -100 \\ \hline 0 \end{array}$$

We have found that 38 is 95% of 40. That is, 95% of the wells mentioned in the newspaper article were declared safe.

Self Check 5

9 is what percent of 16?

Now Try **Problem 31**

EXAMPLE 5 14 is what percent of 32?

Strategy We will identify the percent, the base, and the amount and write a percent proportion of the form $\frac{\text{amount}}{\text{base}} = \frac{\text{percent}}{100}$.

WHY Then we can solve the proportion to find the unknown percent.

Solution First, we write the percent proportion.

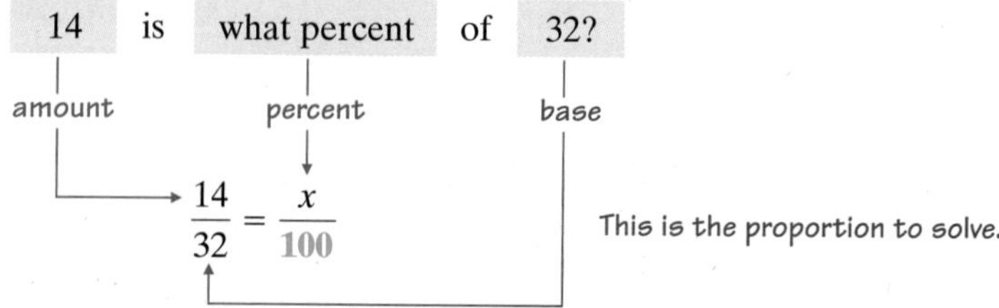

$$\frac{14}{32} = \frac{x}{100}$$ This is the proportion to solve.

To make the calculations easier, it is helpful to simplify the ratio $\frac{14}{32}$ at this time.

$$\frac{7}{16} = \frac{x}{100}$$ On the left side, simplify: $\frac{14}{32} = \frac{\overset{1}{\cancel{2}} \cdot 7}{\underset{1}{\cancel{2}} \cdot 16} = \frac{7}{16}$.

$$7 \cdot 100 = 16 \cdot x$$ To solve the proportion, find the cross products: $\frac{7}{16} = \frac{x}{100}$. Then set them equal.

$$700 = 16 \cdot x$$ To simplify the left side of the equation, do the multiplication: $7 \cdot 100 = 700$.

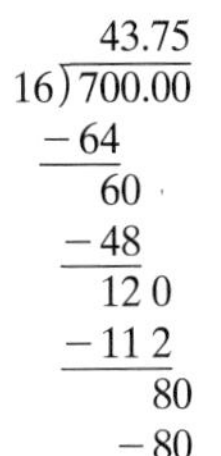

$$\frac{700}{16} = \frac{\overset{1}{\cancel{16}} \cdot x}{\underset{1}{\cancel{16}}}$$ To undo the multiplication by 16 and isolate x on the right side, divide both sides of the equation by 16. Then remove the common factor of 16 from the numerator and denominator.

$$43.75 = x$$ On the left side, divide 700 by 16.

Thus, 14 is 43.75% of 32.

EXAMPLE 6 What percent of 6 is 7.5?

Strategy We will identify the percent, the base, and the amount and write a percent proportion of the form $\frac{\text{amount}}{\text{base}} = \frac{\text{percent}}{100}$.

WHY Then we can solve the proportion to find the unknown percent.

Solution First, we write the percent proportion.

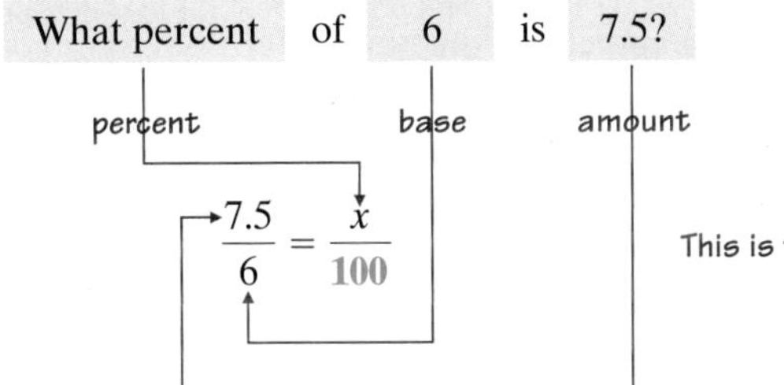

This is the proportion to solve.

$$7.5 \cdot 100 = 6 \cdot x$$ To solve the proportion, find the cross products: $\frac{7.5}{6} = \frac{x}{100}$. Then set them equal.

$$750 = 6 \cdot x$$ To simplify the left side of the equation, do the multiplication: $7.5 \cdot 100 = 750$.

$$\frac{750}{6} = \frac{\overset{1}{\cancel{6}} \cdot x}{\underset{1}{\cancel{6}}}$$ To undo the multiplication by 6 and isolate x on the right side, divide both sides of the equation by 6. Then remove the common factor of 6 from the numerator and denominator.

$$125 = x$$ On the left side, divide 750 by 6.

```
  125
6)750
 -6
  15
 -12
   30
  -30
    0
```

Thus, 7.5 is 125% of 6.

Self Check 6

What percent of 5 is 8.5?

Now Try **Problem 35**

4 Solve percent proportions to find the base.

Recall the State Board of Examiners problem from the newspaper example in the introduction to this section. We can write and solve a percent proportion to find the unknown base.

EXAMPLE 7 6 is 75% of what number?

Strategy We will identify the percent, the base, and the amount and write a percent proportion of the form $\frac{\text{amount}}{\text{base}} = \frac{\text{percent}}{100}$.

Self Check 7

3 is 5% of what number?

Now Try **Problem 39**

WHY Then we can solve the proportion to find the unknown number.

Solution First, we write the percent proportion.

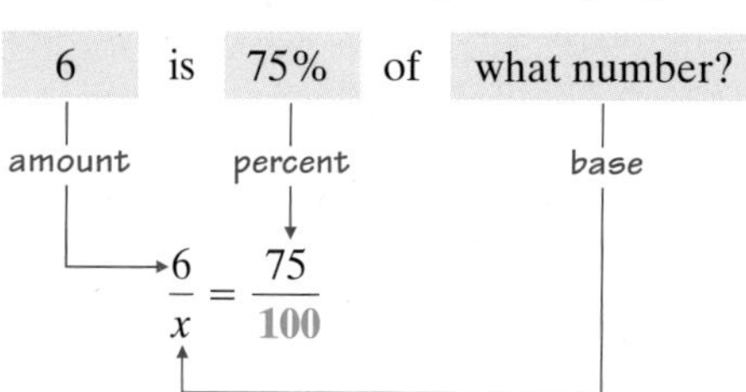

To make the calculations easier, it is helpful to simplify the ratio $\frac{75}{100}$ at this time.

$$\frac{6}{x} = \frac{3}{4}$$ Simplify: $\frac{75}{100} = \frac{3 \cdot \overset{1}{\cancel{25}}}{4 \cdot \underset{1}{\cancel{25}}} = \frac{3}{4}$.

$$6 \cdot 4 = x \cdot 3$$ To solve the proportion, find the cross products: $\frac{6}{x} = \frac{3}{4}$. Then set them equal.

$$24 = x \cdot 3$$ To simplify the left side of the equation, do the multiplication: $6 \cdot 4 = 24$.

$$\frac{24}{3} = \frac{x \cdot \overset{1}{\cancel{3}}}{\underset{1}{\cancel{3}}}$$ To undo the multiplication by 3 and isolate x on the right side, divide both sides of the equation by 3. Then remove the common factor of 3 from the numerator and denominator.

$$8 = x$$ On the left side, divide 24 by 3.

Thus, 6 is 75% of 8. That is, there are 8 members on the State Board of Examiners mentioned in the newspaper article.

Self Check 8

150 is $66\frac{2}{3}\%$ of what number?

Now Try **Problems 43 and 87**

EXAMPLE 8 31.5 is $33\frac{1}{3}\%$ of what number?

Strategy We will identify the percent, the base, and the amount and write a percent proportion of the form $\frac{\text{amount}}{\text{base}} = \frac{\text{percent}}{100}$.

WHY Then we can solve the proportion to find the unknown number.

Solution First, we write the percent proportion.

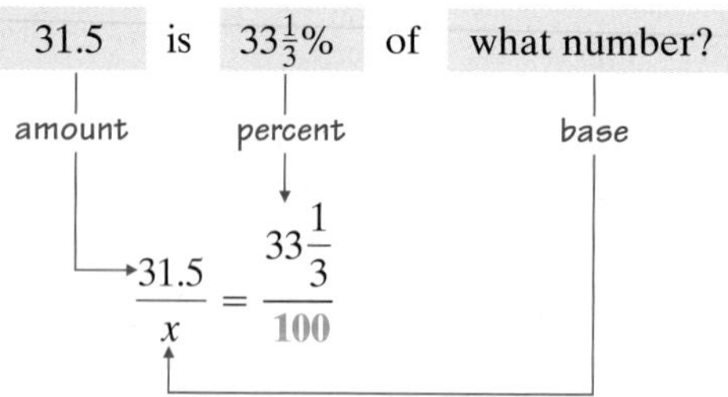

To make the calculations easier, it is helpful to write the mixed number $33\frac{1}{3}$ as the improper fraction $\frac{100}{3}$.

$$\frac{31.5}{x} = \frac{\frac{100}{3}}{100}$$ Write $33\frac{1}{3}$ as $\frac{100}{3}$.

$$31.5 \cdot 100 = x \cdot \frac{100}{3}$$ To solve the proportion, find the cross products: $\frac{31.5}{x} = \frac{\frac{100}{3}}{100}$. Then set them equal.

$$3{,}150 = x \cdot \frac{100}{3}$$ To simplify the left side of the equation, do the multiplication: $31.5 \cdot 100 = 3{,}150$.

$$\frac{3{,}150}{\frac{100}{3}} = \frac{x \cdot \frac{\overset{1}{\cancel{100}}}{\cancel{3}}}{\frac{\cancel{100}}{\underset{1}{\cancel{3}}}}$$ To undo the multiplication by $\frac{100}{3}$ and isolate x on the right side, divide both sides of the equation by $\frac{100}{3}$. Then remove the common factor of $\frac{100}{3}$ from the numerator and denominator.

$$3{,}150 \div \frac{100}{3} = x$$ On the left side, the fraction bar indicates division.

$$\frac{3{,}150}{1} \cdot \frac{3}{100} = x$$ On the left side, write 3,150 as a fraction: $\frac{3{,}150}{1}$. Then use the rule for dividing fractions: Multiply by the reciprocal of $\frac{100}{3}$, which is $\frac{3}{100}$.

$$\frac{9{,}450}{100} = x$$ Multiply the numerators. Multiply the denominators.

$$94.50 = x$$ Divide 9,450 by 100 by moving the understood decimal point in 9,450 two places to the left.

Thus, 31.5 is $33\frac{1}{3}\%$ of 94.5.

To solve percent application problems, we often have to rewrite the facts of the problem in percent sentence form before we can translate to an equation.

EXAMPLE 9 ***Rentals*** In an apartment complex, 198 of the units are currently occupied. If this represents an 88% occupancy rate, how many units are in the complex?

Strategy We will carefully read the problem and use the given facts to write them in the form of a percent sentence.

WHY Then we can write and solve a percent proportion to find the unknown number of units in the complex.

Solution An occupancy rate of 88% means that 88% of the units are occupied. Thus, the 198 units that are currently occupied are 88% of some unknown number of units in the complex, and we can write:

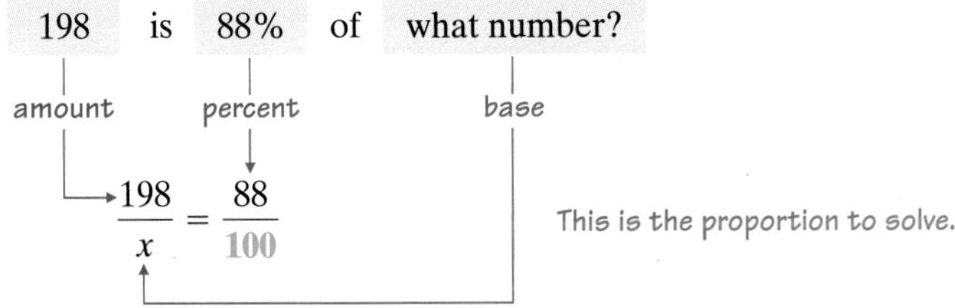

This is the proportion to solve.

To make the calculations easier, it is helpful to simplify the ratio $\frac{88}{100}$ at this time.

$$\frac{198}{x} = \frac{22}{25}$$ On the right side, simplify: $\frac{88}{100} = \frac{\overset{1}{\cancel{4}} \cdot 22}{\underset{1}{\cancel{4}} \cdot 25} = \frac{22}{25}$.

$$198 \cdot 25 = x \cdot 22$$ Find the cross products. Then set them equal.

$$4{,}950 = x \cdot 22$$ To simplify the left side, do the multiplication: $198 \cdot 25 = 4{,}950$.

$$\frac{4{,}950}{22} = \frac{x \cdot \overset{1}{\cancel{22}}}{\underset{1}{\cancel{22}}}$$ To undo the multiplication by 22 and isolate x on the right side, divide both sides of the equation by 22. Then remove the common factor of 22 from the numerator and denominator.

$$225 = x$$ On the left side, divide 4,950 by 22.

$$\begin{array}{r} 198 \\ \times 25 \\ \hline 990 \\ 3960 \\ \hline 4{,}950 \end{array} \qquad \begin{array}{r} 225 \\ 22)\overline{4{,}950} \\ -44 \\ \hline 55 \\ -44 \\ \hline 110 \\ -110 \\ \hline 0 \end{array}$$

The apartment complex has 225 units, of which 198, or 88%, are occupied.

Self Check 9

CAPACITY OF A GYM A total of 784 people attended a graduation in a high school gymnasium. If this was 98% of capacity, what is the total capacity of the gym?

Now Try **Problem 85**

5 Read circle graphs.

Percents are used with **circle graphs,** or **pie charts,** as a way of presenting data for comparison. In the figure below, the entire circle represents the total amount of electricity generated in the United States in 2011. The pie-shaped pieces of the graph show the relative sizes of the energy sources used to generate the electricity. For example, we see that the greatest amount of electricity (42%) was generated from coal. Note that if we add the percents from all categories (42% + 1% + 8% + 25% + 19% + 5%), the sum is 100%.

The 100 tick marks equally spaced around the circle serve as a visual aid when constructing a circle graph. For example, to represent hydropower as 8%, a line was drawn from the center of the circle to a tick mark. Then we counted off 8 ticks and drew a second line from the center to that tick to complete the pie-shaped wedge.

Sources of Electricity in the United States, 2011

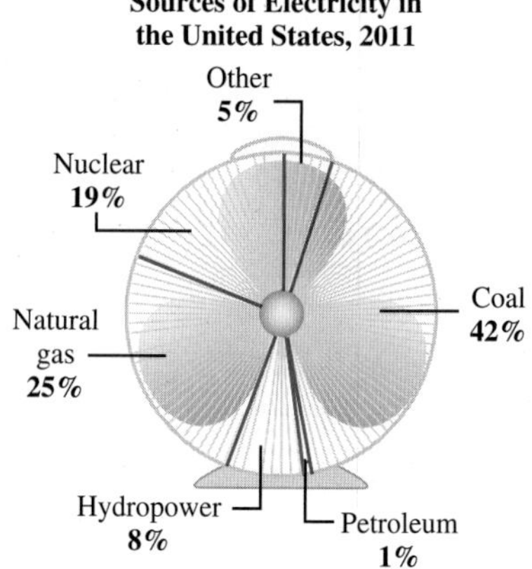

Source: Energy Information Administration

Self Check 10

PRESIDENTIAL ELECTIONS Results from the 2004 U.S. presidential election are shown in the circle graph below. Find the number of states won by President Bush.

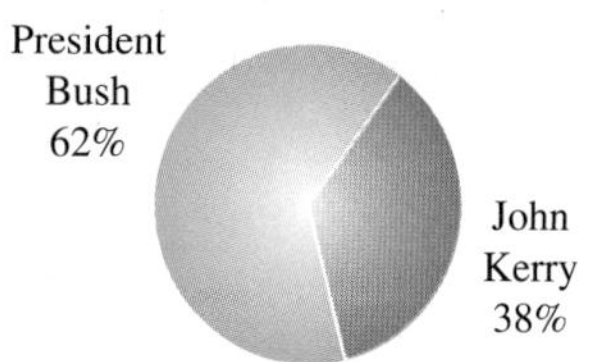

2004 Presidential Election
States won by each candidate

Now Try **Problem 89**

EXAMPLE 10 ***Presidential Elections***

Results from the 2008 U.S. presidential election are shown in the circle graph to the right. Find the number of states won by Barack Obama.

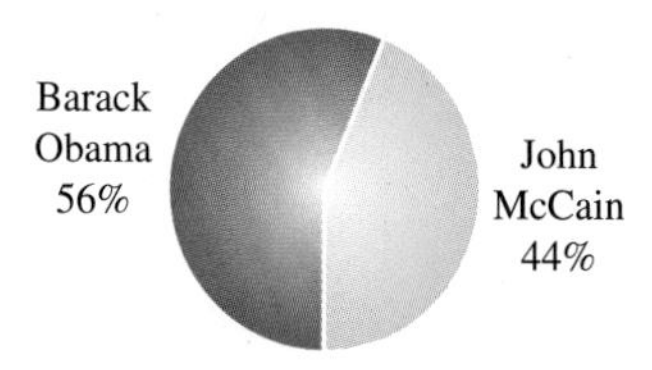

2008 Presidential Election
States won by each candidate

Strategy We will rewrite the facts of the problem in percent sentence form.

WHY Then we can translate the sentence to a percent equation (or percent proportion) to find the number of states won by Barack Obama.

Solution The circle graph shows that Barack Obama won 56% of the 50 states. Thus, the percent is 56% and the base is 50. One way to find the unknown amount is to write and then solve a percent equation.

What number	is	56%	of	50?	
↓	↓	↓	↓	↓	
x	$=$	56%	$\cdot$	50	Translate to a percent equation.

Now we perform the multiplication on the right side of the equation.

$x = 0.56 \cdot 50$ Write 56% as a decimal: 56% = 0.56.

$x = 28$ Do the multiplication.

$$\begin{array}{r} 50 \\ \times 0.56 \\ \hline 3\,00 \\ 25\,00 \\ \hline 28.00 \end{array}$$

Thus, Barack Obama won 28 of the 50 states in the 2008 U.S. presidential election.

Another way to find the unknown amount is to write and then solve a percent proportion.

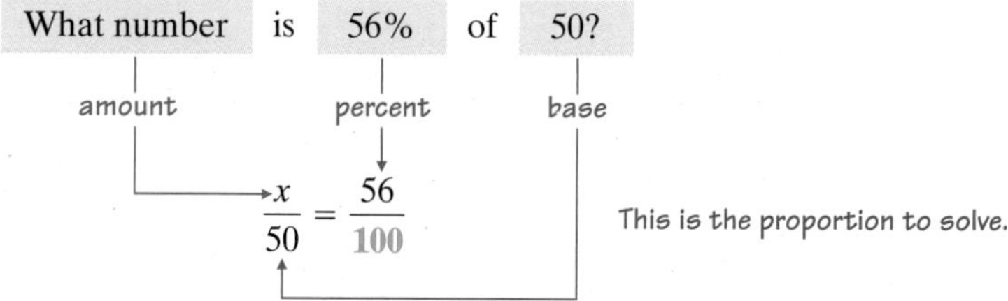

$$\frac{x}{50} = \frac{56}{100}$$ This is the proportion to solve.

To make the calculations easier, it is helpful to simplify the ratio $\frac{56}{100}$ at this time.

$$\frac{x}{50} = \frac{14}{25}$$ On the right side, simplify: $\frac{56}{100} = \frac{\overset{1}{\cancel{4}} \cdot 14}{\underset{1}{\cancel{4}} \cdot 25} = \frac{14}{25}$.

$$x \cdot 25 = 50 \cdot 14$$ Find the cross products: $\frac{x}{50} = \frac{14}{25}$. Then set them equal.

$$x \cdot 25 = 700$$ To simplify the right side, do the multiplication: $50 \cdot 14 = 700$.

$$\frac{x \cdot \overset{1}{\cancel{25}}}{\underset{1}{\cancel{25}}} = \frac{700}{25}$$ To undo the multiplication by 25 and isolate x on the left side, divide both sides of the equation by 25. Then remove the common factor of 25 from the numerator and denominator.

$$x = 28$$ On the right side, divide 700 by 25.

$$\begin{array}{r} 50 \\ \times 14 \\ \hline 200 \\ 500 \\ \hline 700 \end{array}$$

$$\begin{array}{r} 28 \\ 25\overline{)700} \\ -50 \\ \hline 200 \\ -200 \\ \hline 0 \end{array}$$

As we would expect, the percent proportion method gives the same answer as the percent equation method. Barack Obama won 28 of the 50 states in the 2008 U.S. presidential election.

THINK IT THROUGH *Community College Students*

"When the history of American higher education is updated years from now, the story of our current times will highlight the pivotal role community colleges played in developing human capital and bolstering the nation's educational system."

Community College Survey of Student Engagement, 2011

More than 443,000 students responded to the 2011 Community College Survey of Student Engagement. Some results are shown below. Study each circle graph and then complete its legend.

Enrollment in Community Colleges

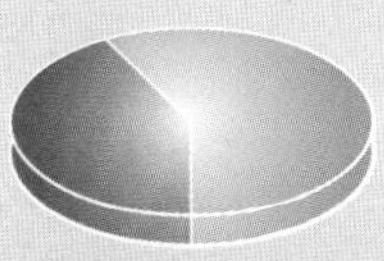

58% are enrolled in college part time.

?

Community College Students Who Work More Than 30 Hours per Week

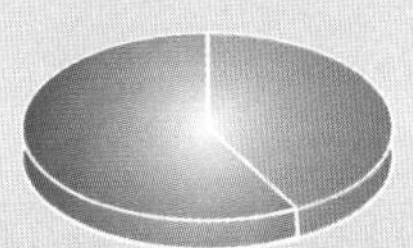

42% of the students work more than 30 hours per week.

?

Community College Students Who Discussed Their Grades or Assignments with an Instructor

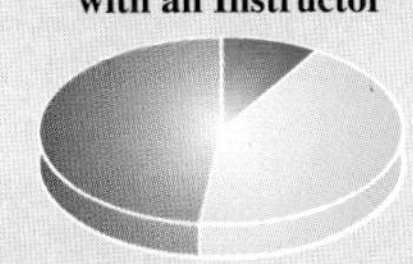

48% often or very often

43% sometimes

?

ANSWERS TO SELF CHECKS

1. a. $x = 33\% \cdot 80$ or $\frac{x}{80} = \frac{33}{100}$ **b.** $x \cdot 55 = 6$ or $\frac{6}{55} = \frac{x}{100}$ **c.** $172\% \cdot x = 4$ or $\frac{4}{x} = \frac{172}{100}$
2. 144 **3.** 192.72 **4.** 5% **5.** 56.25% **6.** 170% **7.** 60 **8.** 225 **9.** 800 people
10. 31 states

SECTION 3.8 STUDY SET

VOCABULARY

Fill in the blanks.

1. We call "What number is 15% of 25?" a percent ________. It translates to the percent ________ $x = 15\% \cdot 25$.

2. The key words in a percent sentence translate as follows:

- ___ translates to an equal symbol =
- ___ translates to multiplication that is shown with a raised dot ·
- _____ *number* or _____ *percent* translates to an unknown number that is represented by a variable.

3. When we find the value of the variable that makes a percent equation true, we say that we have ______ the equation.

4. In the percent sentence "45 is 90% of 50," 45 is the ________, 90% is the percent, and 50 is the _____.

5. The amount is _____ of the base. The base is the standard of comparison—it represents the ______ of some quantity.

6. a. *Amount is to base as percent is to 100:*

$$\frac{\quad}{\text{base}} = \frac{\text{percent}}{\quad}$$

b. *Part is to whole as percent is to 100:*

$$\frac{\text{part}}{\quad} = \frac{\quad}{100}$$

7. The _____ products for the proportion $\frac{24}{x} = \frac{36}{100}$ are $24 \cdot 100$ and $x \cdot 36$.

8. In a ______ graph, pie-shaped wedges are used to show the division of a whole quantity into its component parts.

CONCEPTS

9. Fill in the blanks to complete the percent equation (formula):

$$\quad = \text{percent} \cdot \quad$$

or

$$\text{Part} = \quad \cdot \quad$$

10. a. Without doing the calculation, tell whether 12% of 55 is more than 55 or less than 55.

b. Without doing the calculation, tell whether 120% of 55 is more than 55 or less than 55.

11. CANDY SALES The circle graph shows the percent of the total candy sales for each of four holiday seasons in 2010. What is the sum of all the percents?

Percent of Total Candy Sales, 2010

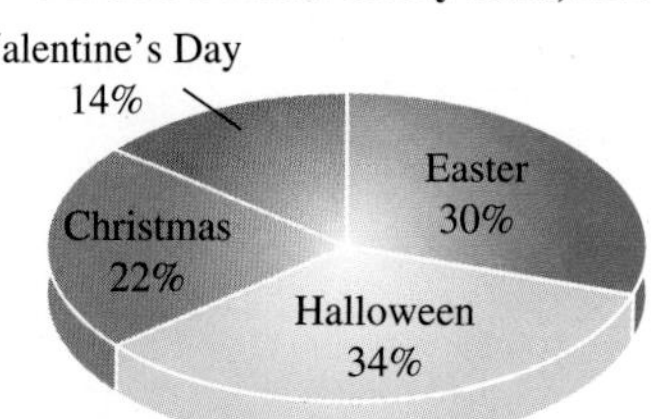

Source: National Confectioners Association, Annual Industry Review, 2011

12. SMARTPHONES The circle graph shows the percent U.S. market share for the leading smartphone companies. What is the sum of all the percents?

U.S. Smartphone Marketshare, 2011

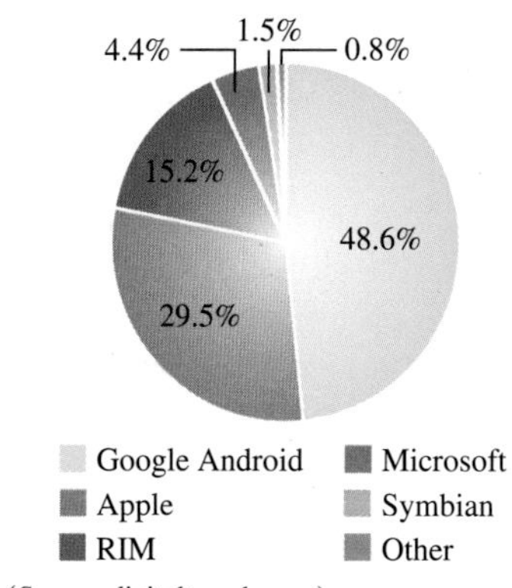

(*Source:* digitaltrends.com)

NOTATION

13. When computing with percents, we must change the percent to a decimal or a fraction. Change each percent to a decimal.

a. 12%

b. 5.6%

c. 125%

d. $\frac{1}{4}\%$

14. When computing with percents, we must change the percent to a decimal or a fraction. Change each percent to a fraction.

a. $33\frac{1}{3}\%$

b. $66\frac{2}{3}\%$

c. $16\frac{2}{3}\%$

d. $83\frac{1}{3}\%$

GUIDED PRACTICE

Translate each percent sentence to a percent equation or percent proportion. Do not solve. See Example 1.

15. **a.** What number is 7% of 16?

b. 125 is what percent of 800?

c. 1 is 94% of what number?

16. **a.** What number is 28% of 372?

b. 9 is what percent of 21?

c. 4 is 17% of what number?

17. **a.** 5.4% of 99 is what number?

b. 75.1% of what number is 15?

c. What percent of 33.8 is 3.8?

18. **a.** 1.5% of 3 is what number?

b. 49.2% of what number is 100?

c. What percent of 100.4 is 50.2?

Translate to a percent equation or percent proportion and then solve to find the unknown number. See Example 2.

19. What is 34% of 200?

20. What is 48% of 600?

21. What is 88% of 150?

22. What number is 52% of 350?

Translate to a percent equation or percent proportion and then solve to find the unknown number. See Example 3.

23. What number is 224% of 7.9?

24. What number is 197% of 6.3?

25. What number is 105% of 23.2?

26. What number is 228% of 34.5?

Translate to a percent equation or percent proportion and then solve to find the unknown number. See Example 4.

27. 8 is what percent of 32?

28. 9 is what percent of 18?

29. 51 is what percent of 60?

30. 52 is what percent of 80?

Translate to a percent equation or percent proportion and then solve to find the unknown number. See Example 5.

31. 5 is what percent of 8?

32. 7 is what percent of 8?

33. 7 is what percent of 16?

34. 11 is what percent of 16?

Translate to a percent equation or percent proportion and then solve to find the unknown number. See Example 6.

35. What percent of 60 is 66?

36. What percent of 50 is 56?

37. What percent of 24 is 84?

38. What percent of 14 is 63?

Translate to a percent equation or percent proportion and then solve to find the unknown number. See Example 7.

39. 9 is 30% of what number?

40. 8 is 40% of what number?

41. 36 is 24% of what number?

42. 24 is 16% of what number?

Translate to a percent equation or percent proportion and then solve to find the unknown number. See Example 8.

43. 19.2 is $33\frac{1}{3}\%$ of what number?

44. 32.8 is $33\frac{1}{3}\%$ of what number?

45. 48.4 is $66\frac{2}{3}\%$ of what number?

46. 56.2 is $16\frac{2}{3}\%$ of what number?

TRY IT YOURSELF

Translate to a percent equation or percent proportion and then solve to find the unknown number.

47. What percent of 40 is 0.5?

48. What percent of 15 is 0.3?

49. 7.8 is 12% of what number?

50. 39.6 is 44% of what number?

51. $33\frac{1}{3}\%$ of what number is 33?

52. $66\frac{2}{3}\%$ of what number is 28?

53. What number is 36% of 250?

54. What number is 82% of 300?

55. 16 is what percent of 20?

56. 13 is what percent of 25?

57. What number is 0.8% of 12?

58. What number is 5.6% of 40?

59. 3.3 is 7.5% of what number?

60. 8.4 is 20% of what number?

61. What percent of 0.05 is 1.25?

62. What percent of 0.06 is 2.46?

63. 102% of 105 is what number?

64. 210% of 66 is what number?

65. $9\frac{1}{2}$% of what number is 5.7?

66. $\frac{1}{2}$% of what number is 5,000?

67. What percent of 8,000 is 2,500?

68. What percent of 3,200 is 1,400?

69. Find $7\frac{1}{4}$% of 600.

70. Find $1\frac{3}{4}$% of 800.

73. Translate each percent equation to a percent sentence.

a. $x = 0.32 \cdot 300$

b. $25.8 = x \cdot 77.4$

c. $18 = 0.815 \cdot x$

74. Translate each proportion to a percent sentence.

a. $\frac{4}{250} = \frac{x}{100}$

b. $\frac{20.8}{x} = \frac{15}{100}$

c. $\frac{x}{16} = \frac{2.5}{100}$

CONCEPT EXTENSIONS

71. FLAGS The official description of the North Carolina state flag requires that "the total length of the flag shall be one half more than its width." This requirement can be stated in another way using a percent. Fill in the blank: The length of the flag should be ______ of its width.

72. Shade figure b so that figure a and figure b have the same percent shaded.

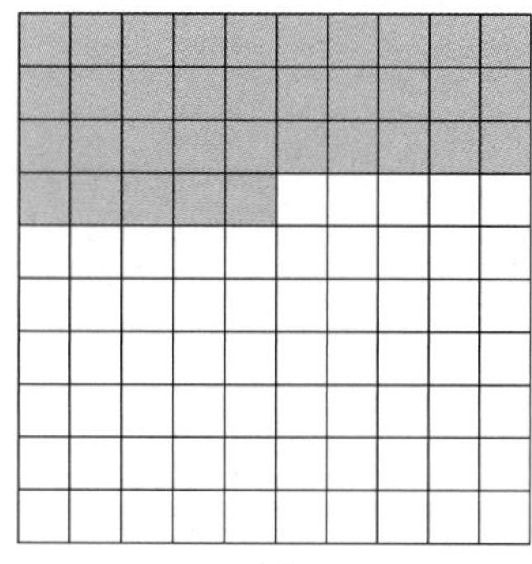

(a)

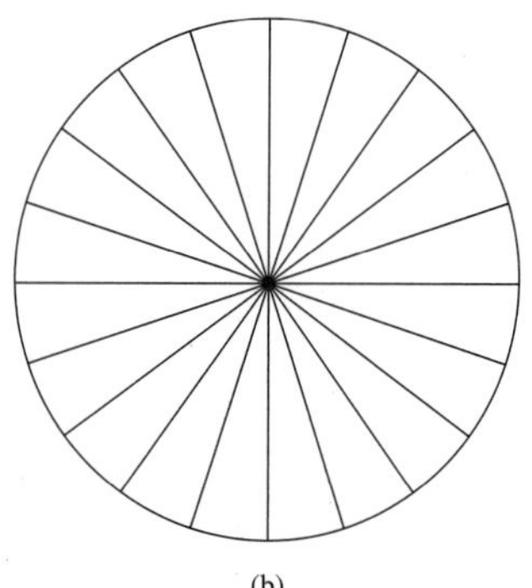

(b)

APPLICATIONS

75. DOWNLOADING The message on the computer monitor screen shown below indicates that 24% of the 50K bytes of information that the user has decided to view have been downloaded to her computer at that time. Find the number of bytes of information that have been downloaded. (50K stands for 50,000.)

76. LUMBER The rate of tree growth for walnut trees is about 3% per year. If a walnut tree has 400 board feet of lumber that can be cut from it, how many more board feet will it produce in a year? (*Source:* Iowa Department of Natural Resources)

77. REBATES A telephone company offered its customers a rebate of 20% of the cost of all long-distance calls made in the month of July. One customer's long-distance calls for July are shown below.

a. Find the total amount of the customer's long-distance charges for July.

b. How much will this customer receive in the form of a rebate for these calls?

Date	Time	Place called	Min.	Amount
Jul 4	3:48 P.M.	Denver	47	$3.80
Jul 9	12:00 P.M.	Detroit	68	$7.50
Jul 20	8:59 A.M.	San Diego	70	$9.45
July Totals			185	?

78. PRICE GUARANTEES To assure its customers of low prices, the Home Club offers a "10% Plus" guarantee. If the customer finds the same item selling for less somewhere else, he or she receives the difference in price, plus 10% of the difference. A woman bought miniblinds at the Home Club for $120 but later saw the same blinds on sale for $98 at another store.

a. What is the difference in the prices of the miniblinds?

b. What is 10% of the difference in price?

c. How much money can the woman expect to receive if she takes advantage of the "10% Plus" guarantee from the Home Club?

79. ENLARGEMENTS The enlarge feature on a copier is set at 180%, and a 1.5-inch wide picture is to be copied. What will be the width of the enlarged picture?

80. COPY MACHINES The reduce feature on a copier is set at 98%, and a 2-inch wide picture is to be copied. What will be the width of the reduced picture?

81. DRIVER'S LICENSE On the written part of his driving test, a man answered 28 out of 40 questions correctly. If 70% correct is passing, did he pass the test?

82. HOUSING A general budget rule of thumb is that your rent or mortgage payment should be less than 30% of your income. Together, a couple earns $4,500 per month and they pay $1,260 in rent. Are they following the budget rule of thumb for housing?

83. INSURANCE The cost to repair a car after a collision was $4,000. The automobile insurance policy paid the entire bill except for a $200 deductible, which the driver paid. What percent of the cost did he pay?

84. FLOOR SPACE A house has 1,200 square feet on the first floor and 800 square feet on the second floor.

a. What is the total square footage of the house?

b. What percent of the square footage of the house is on the first floor?

85. CHILD CARE After the first day of registration, 84 children had been enrolled in a new day care center. That represented 70% of the available slots. What was the maximum number of children the center could enroll?

86. RACING PROGRAMS One month before a stock car race, the sale of ads for the official race program was slow. Only 12 pages, or 60% of the available pages, had been sold. What was the total number of pages devoted to advertising in the program?

87. HEALTHY LAWNS A general guideline when mowing a lawn is to never cut away more than $33\frac{1}{3}\%$ of the grass blade height in any one mowing. If a gardener correctly cut away $1\frac{1}{2}$ inches when moving a lawn, what was the height of the grass before it was mowed?

88. CHRISTMAS TREES According to a forestry web page, the ideal Christmas tree shape is one where the width of the base of the tree is equal to $66\frac{2}{3}\%$ of its height. For a tree with a base 8 feet wide, what would be the ideal height?

89. GOVERNMENT SPENDING The circle graph below shows the breakdown of federal spending for the fiscal year 2010. If the total spending was approximately $3,460 billion, how many dollars were spent on Social Security, Medicare, and other retirement programs?

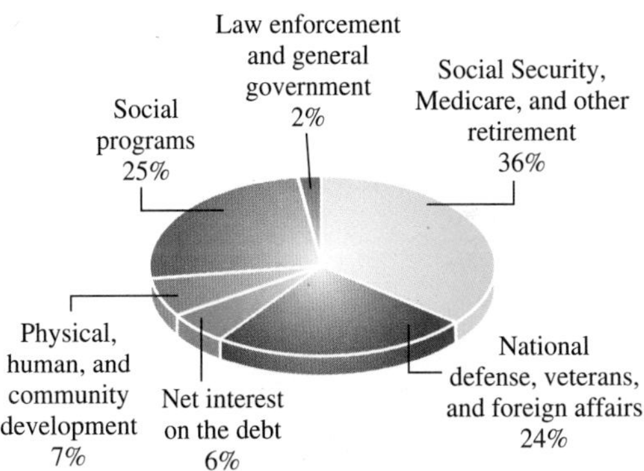

Source: 2011 Federal Income Tax Form 1040

90. WASTE The circle graph below shows the types of trash U.S. residents, businesses, and institutions generated in 2010. If the total amount of trash produced that year was about 250 million tons, how many million tons of yard trimmings was there?

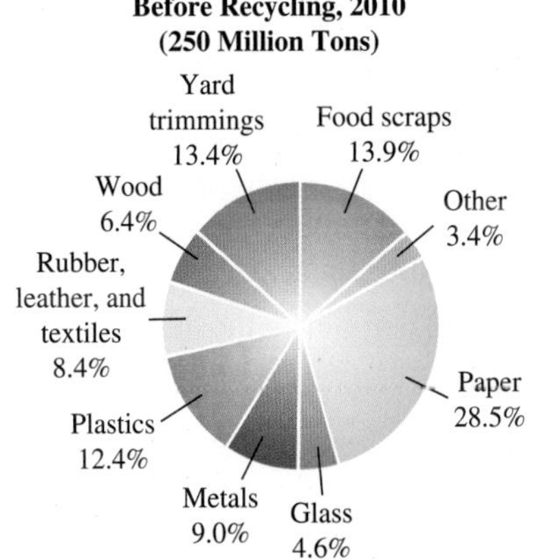

Source: Environmental Protection Agency

91. COMPUTER MEMORY The *My Computer* screen on a student's computer is shown on the next page. What percent of the storage capacity on the hard drive

Local Disk (C:) of his computer is used? What percent is free? (GB stands for gigabytes.)

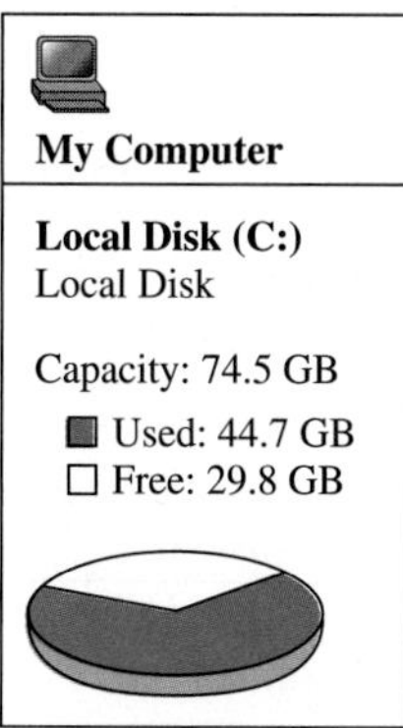

92. IPODs The settings menu screen of an Apple iPod is shown. What percent of the memory capacity is still available? Round to the nearest percent. (GB stands for gigabytes.)

93. TAX TABLES Use the Schedule X table below to compute the amount of federal income tax to be paid on an income of $39,909.

If your income is over—	*But not over—*	Your income tax is—	*of the amount over—*
$0	$8,350	.... 10%	$0
8,350	33,950	$835.00 + 15%	8,350
33,950	82,250	4,675.00 + 25%	33,950

94. GENEALOGY Through an extensive computer search, a genealogist determined that worldwide, 180 out of every 10 million people had his last name. What percent is this?

95. DENTISTRY Refer to the dental record. What percent of the patient's teeth have fillings? Round to the nearest percent.

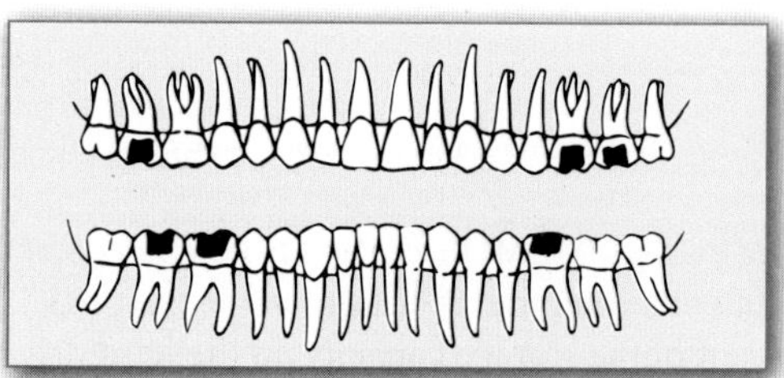

96. ROOM TAXES A guest at the San Antonio Hilton Airport Hotel paid $180 for a room plus a 9% city room tax, a $1\frac{3}{4}$% county room tax, and a 6% state room tax. Find the total amount of tax that the guest paid on the room.

97. TEST SCORES The score 175/200 was written by an algebra instructor at the top of a student's test paper. Write the test score as a percent.

98. COMMERCIALS Jared Fogle credits his tremendous weight loss to exercise and a diet of low-fat Subway sandwiches. His current weight (about 187 pounds) is 44% of his maximum weight (reached in March of 1998). What did he weigh then?

99. PRODUCT PROMOTION To promote sales, a free 6-ounce bottle of shampoo is packaged with every large bottle. Use the information on the package to find how many ounces of shampoo the large bottle contains.

100. NUTRITION FACTS The nutrition label on a package of corn chips is shown.

a. How many milligrams of sodium are in one serving of chips?

b. According to the label, what percent of the daily value of sodium is this?

c. What daily value of sodium intake is considered healthy?

Nutrition Facts
Serving Size: 1 oz. (28g/About 29 chips)
Servings Per Container: About 11

Amount Per Serving	
Calories 160	Calories from Fat 90
	% Daily Value
Total fat 10g	**15%**
Saturated fat 1.5 g	**7%**
Cholesterol 0mg	**0%**
Sodium 240mg	**12%**
Total carbohydrate 15g	**5%**
Dietary fiber 1g	**4%**
Sugars less than 1g	
Protein 2g	

101. MIXTURES Complete the table to find the number of gallons of sulfuric acid in each of two storage tanks.

	Gallons of solution in tank	% Sulfuric acid	Gallons of sulfuric acid in tank
Tank 1	60	50%	
Tank 2	40	30%	

102. THE ALPHABET What percent of the English alphabet do the vowels a, e, i, o, and u make up? (Round to the nearest 1 percent.)

103. TIPS In August of 2006, a customer left Applebee's employee Cindy Kienow of Hutchinson, Kansas, a $10,000 tip for a bill that was approximately $25. What percent tip is this? (*Source:* cbsnews.com)

104. ELECTIONS In Los Angeles City Council races, if no candidate receives more than 50% of the vote, a runoff election is held between the first- and second-place finishers.

a. How many total votes were cast?

b. Determine whether there must be a runoff election for District 10.

City council	District 10
Nate Holden	8,501
Madison T. Shockley	3,614
Scott Suh	2,630
Marsha Brown	2,432

Use a circle graph to illustrate the given data. A circle divided into 100 sections is provided to help in the graphing process.

105. ENERGY Draw a circle graph to show what percent of the total U.S. energy produced in 2010 was provided by each source.

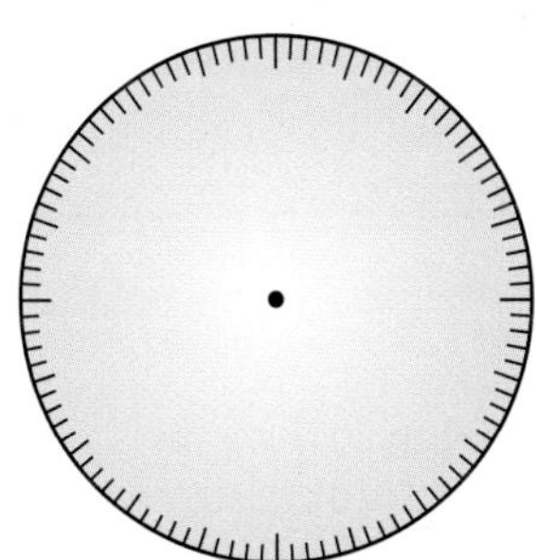

Renewable	15%
Nuclear	11%
Coal	29%
Natural gas	29%
Petroleum	16%

Source: Energy Information Administration

106. GREENHOUSE GASSES Draw a circle graph to show what percent of the total U.S. greenhouse gas emissions in 2009 came from each economic sector.

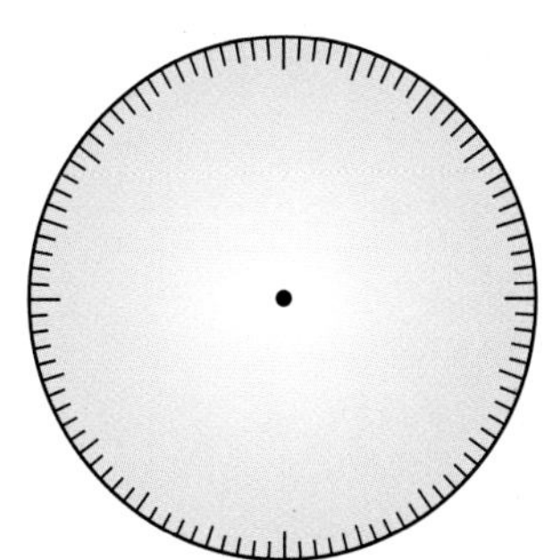

Electric power	34%
Transportation	28%
Industry	20%
Agriculture	7%
Commercial	6%
Residential	5%

Source: Environmental Protection Agency, 2011

107. GOVERNMENT INCOME Complete the following table by finding what percent of total federal government income in 2010 each source provided. Then draw a circle graph for the data.

Total Income, Fiscal Year 2010: $2,160 Billion

Source of income	Amount	Percent of total
Social Security, Medicare, unemployment taxes	$540 billion	
Personal income taxes	$561.6 billion	
Corporate income taxes	$129.6 billion	
Excise, estate, customs taxes	$129.6 billion	
Borrowing to cover deficit	$799.2 billion	

Source: 2011 Federal Income Tax Form

2010 Federal Income Sources

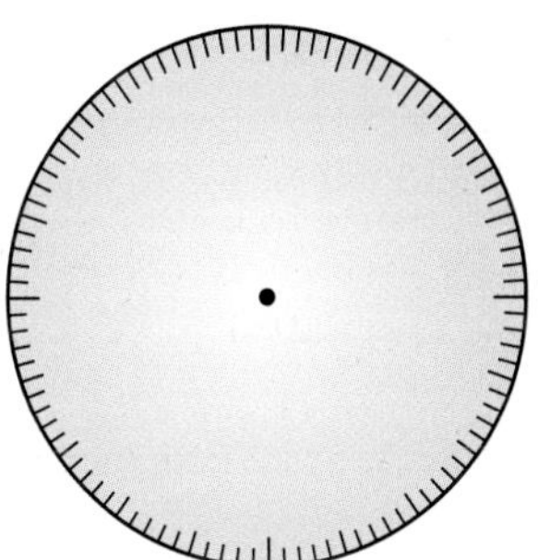

108. WATER USAGE The per-person indoor water use in the typical single family home is about 70 gallons per day. Complete the following table. Then draw a circle graph for the data.

Use	Gallons per person per day	Percent of total daily use
Showers	11.9	
Clothes washer	15.4	
Dishwasher	0.7	
Toilets	18.9	
Baths	1.4	
Leaks	9.8	
Faucets	10.5	
Other	1.4	

Source: American Water Works Association

Daily Water Use per Person

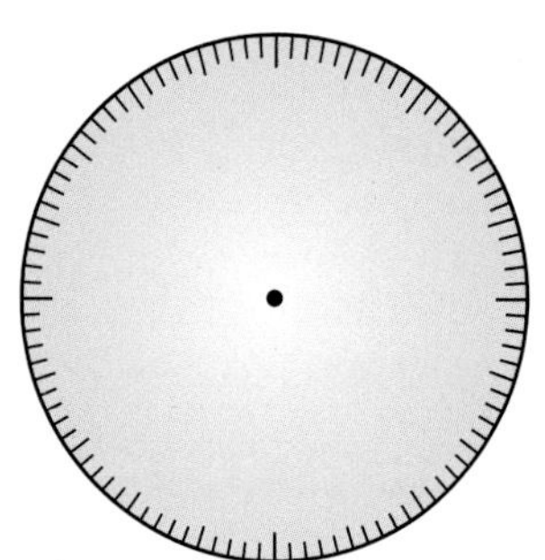

WRITING

109. Write a real-life situation that can be described by "9 is what percent of 20?"

110. Write a real-life situation that can be translated to $15 = 25\% \cdot x$.

111. Explain why 150% of a number is more than the number.

112. Explain why each of the following problems is easy to solve.

a. What is 9% of 100?

b. 16 is 100% of what number?

c. 27 is what percent of 27?

113. When solving percent problems, when is it best to write a given percent as a fraction instead of as a decimal?

114. Explain how to identify the amount, the percent, and the base in a percent problem.

SECTION 3.9
Applications of Percent

Objectives

1. Calculate sales taxes, total cost, and tax rates.
2. Calculate commissions and commission rates.
3. Find the percent of increase or decrease.
4. Calculate the amount of discount, the sale price and the discount rate.

ARE YOU READY?

The following problems review some basic skills that are needed when solving percent application problems.

1. Write each percent as a decimal.

a. 37%

b. 8.4%

2. Solve: $11.04 = x \cdot 240$

3. Solve the proportion: $\frac{1.8}{2.5} = \frac{x}{100}$

4. Round 51.946 to the nearest hundredth.

5. FAST FOOD In 2010, the number of Chipotle restaurants in the United States was 1,084. By 2011, that number had risen to 1,230. What was the amount of increase in stores from 2010 to 2011? (Source: seekingalpha.com)

6. MOVIES The annual movie ticket sales in the U.S. went from 1,330,000,000 in 2010 to 1,290,000,000 in 2011. What was the decrease in the amount of ticket sales from 2010 to 2011?

In this section, we discuss applications of percent. Three of them (taxes, commissions, and discounts) are directly related to purchasing. A solid understanding of these concepts will make you a better shopper and consumer. The fourth uses percent to describe increases or decreases of such things as population and unemployment.

1 Calculate sales taxes, total cost, and tax rates.

The department store sales receipt shown below gives a detailed account of what items were purchased, how many of each were purchased, and the price of each item.

The receipt shows that the $56.35 purchase price (labeled *subtotal*) was taxed at a rate of 5%. Sales tax of $2.82 was charged.

This example illustrates the following sales tax formula. Notice that the formula is based on the percent equation.

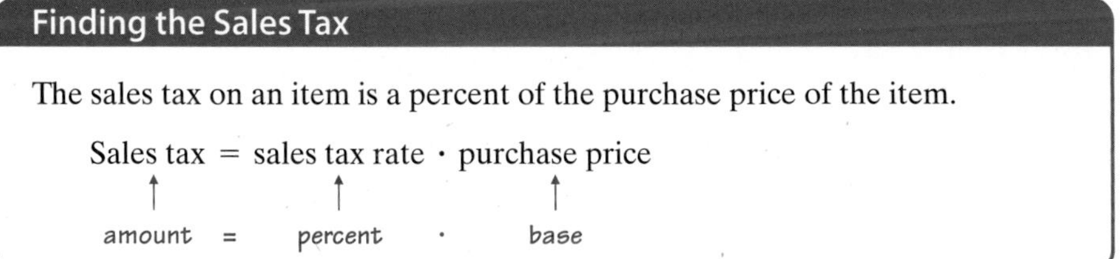

Finding the Sales Tax

The sales tax on an item is a percent of the purchase price of the item.

Sales tax = sales tax rate · purchase price

amount = percent · base

Sales tax rates are usually expressed as a percent and, when necessary, sales tax dollar amounts are rounded to the nearest cent.

EXAMPLE 1 ***Sales Tax*** Find the sales tax on a purchase of $56.35 if the sales tax rate is 5%. (This is the purchase on the sales receipt shown above.)

Strategy We will identify the sales tax rate and the purchase price.

WHY Then we can use the sales tax formula to find the unknown sales tax.

Solution The sales tax rate is 5% and the purchase price is $56.35.

Sales tax = **sales tax rate** · **purchase price**	This is the sales tax formula.	
= 5% · $56.35	Substitute 5% for the sales tax rate and $56.35 for the purchase price.	
= 0.05 · $56.35	Write 5% as a decimal: 5% = 0.05.	$\begin{array}{r} \overset{3\,1\,2}{56.35} \\ \times 0.05 \\ \hline 2.8175 \end{array}$
= $2.8175	Do the multiplication.	

Self Check 1

SALES TAX What would the sales tax be if the $56.35 purchase were made in a state that has a 6.25% state sales tax?

Now Try **Problem 13**

The rounding digit in the hundredths column is 1.

$= \$2.8175$ Prepare to round the sales tax to the nearest cent (hundredth) by identifying the rounding digit and test digit.

The test digit is 7.

$\approx \$2.82$ Since the test digit is 5 or greater, round up.

The sales tax on the $56.35 purchase is $2.82. The sales receipt shown on the previous page is correct.

> ***Success Tip*** It is helpful to see the sales tax problem in Example 1 as a type of percent problem.
>
> | What number | is | 5% | of | $56.35? |
> |---|---|---|---|---|
> | ↓ | ↓ | ↓ | ↓ | ↓ |
> | x | = | 5% | · | $56.35 |

Look at the department store sales receipt once again. Note that the sales tax was added to the purchase price to get the total cost. This example illustrates the following formula for total cost.

Finding the Total Cost

The total cost of an item is the sum of its purchase price and the sales tax on the item.

Total cost = purchase price + sales tax

Self Check 2

TOTAL COST Find the total cost of a $179.95 baby stroller if the sales tax rate on the purchase is 3.2%.

Now Try **Problem 17**

EXAMPLE 2 ***Total Cost*** Find the total cost of the child's car seat shown on the right if the sales tax rate is 7.2%.

Saftey-T First
Child's
Car
Seat
$249.50
Buy today!
Ships next business day

Strategy First, we will find the sales tax on the child's car seat.

WHY Then we can add the purchase price and the sales tax to find the total of the car seat.

Solution The sales tax rate is 7.2% and the purchase price is $249.50.

Sales tax = **sales tax rate** · **purchase price** This is the sales tax formula.

$= 7.2\% \cdot \$249.50$ Substitute 7.2% for the sales tax rate and $249.50 for the purchase price.

$= 0.072 \cdot \$249.50$ Write 7.2% as a decimal: 7.2% = 0.072.

$= \$17.964$ Do the multiplication.

$$\begin{array}{r} 249.50 \\ \times\ 0.072 \\ \hline 49900 \\ 1746500 \\ \hline 17.96400 \end{array}$$

The rounding digit in the hundredths column is 6.

$= \$17.964$ Prepare to round the sales tax to the nearest cent (hundredth) by identifying the rounding digit and test digit.

The test digit is 4.

$\approx \$17.96$ Since the test digit is less than 5, round down.

Thus, the sales tax on the \$249.50 purchase is \$17.96. The total cost of the car seat is the sum of its purchase price and the sales tax.

$\text{Total cost} = \text{purchase price} + \text{sales tax}$ This is the formula for the total cost.

$= \$249.50 + \$17.96$ Substitute \$249.50 for the purchase price and \$17.96 for the sales tax.

$= \$267.46$ Do the addition.

$$\begin{array}{r} \overset{1}{2}49.50 \\ +17.96 \\ \hline 267.46 \end{array}$$

In addition to sales tax, we pay many other taxes in our daily lives. Income tax, gasoline tax, and Social Security tax are just a few.

EXAMPLE 3 ***Withholding Tax*** A waitress found that \$11.04 was deducted from her weekly gross earnings of \$240 for federal income tax. What withholding tax rate was used?

Strategy We will carefully read the problem and use the given facts to write them in the form of a percent sentence.

WHY Then we can translate the sentence into a percent equation (or percent proportion) and solve it to find the unknown withholding tax rate.

Solution There are two methods that can be used to solve this problem.

The percent equation method: Since the withholding tax of \$11.04 is some unknown percent of her weekly gross earnings of \$240, the percent sentence is:

\$11.04 is what percent of \$240?

$11.04 = x \cdot 240$ This is the percent equation to solve.

$\frac{11.04}{\mathbf{240}} = \frac{x \cdot 240}{\mathbf{240}}$ To isolate x on the right side of the equation, divide both sides by 240.

$0.046 = \frac{x \cdot \overset{1}{\cancel{240}}}{\underset{1}{\cancel{240}}}$ To simplify the fraction on the right side of the equation, remove the common factor of 240 from the numerator and denominator. On the left side, divide 11.04 by 240.

$$\begin{array}{r} 0.046 \\ 240\overline{)11.0400} \\ -\ \ 0 \\ \hline 11\ 04 \\ -9\ 60 \\ \hline 1\ 440 \\ -1\ 440 \\ \hline 0 \end{array}$$

$0.046 = x$

$004.6\% = x$ To write the decimal 0.046 as a percent, multiply it by 100 by moving the decimal point two places to the right, and then insert a % symbol.

$4.6\% = x$

The withholding tax rate was 4.6%.

The percent proportion method: Since the withholding tax of \$11.04 is some unknown percent of her weekly gross earnings of \$240, the percent sentence is:

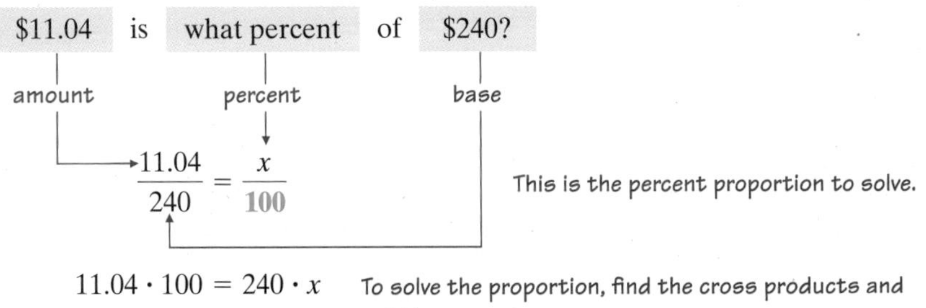

$11.04 \cdot 100 = 240 \cdot x$ To solve the proportion, find the cross products and set them equal.

Self Check 3

INHERITANCE TAX A tax of \$5,250 was paid on an inheritance of \$15,000. What was the inheritance tax rate?

Now Try **Problem 21**

$1{,}104 = 240 \cdot x$ To simplify the left side of the equation, do the multiplication: $11.04 \cdot 100 = 1{,}104$.

$\frac{1{,}104}{240} = \frac{\overset{1}{\cancel{240}} \cdot x}{\underset{1}{\cancel{240}}}$ To isolate x on the right side, divide both sides of the equation by 240. Then remove the common factor of 240 from the numerator and denominator.

$4.6 = x$ On the left side, divide 1,104 by 240.

$$\begin{array}{r} 4.6 \\ 240\overline{)1{,}104.0} \\ -960 \\ \hline 144\ 0 \\ -144\ 0 \\ \hline 0 \end{array}$$

The withholding tax rate was 4.6%.

2 Calculate commissions and commission rates.

Instead of working for a salary or getting paid at an hourly rate, many salespeople are paid on **commission.** They earn a certain percent of the total dollar amount of the goods or services that they sell. The following formula to calculate a commission is based on the percent equation.

Finding the Commission

The amount of commission paid is a percent of the total dollar sales of goods or services.

Commission = commission rate · sales

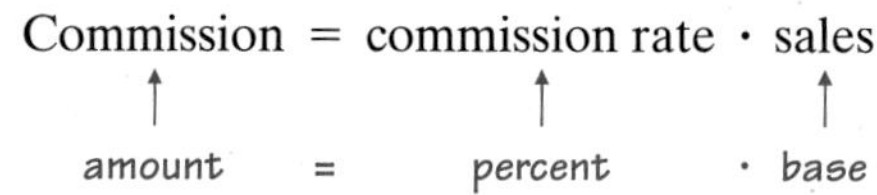

amount = percent · base

Self Check 4

SELLING INSURANCE An insurance salesperson receives a 4.1% commission on each \$120 premium paid by a client. What is the amount of the commission on this premium?

Now Try **Problem 25**

EXAMPLE 4 ***Appliance Sales*** The commission rate for a salesperson at an appliance store is 16.5%. Find his commission from the sale of a refrigerator that costs \$500.

Strategy We will identify the commission rate and the dollar amount of the sale.

WHY Then we can use the commission formula to find the unknown amount of the commission.

Solution The commission rate is 16.5% and the dollar amount of the sale is \$500.

Commission = **commission rate** · **sales** This is the commission formula.

= **16.5%** · **\$500** Substitute 16.5% for the commission rate and \$500 for the sales.

= 0.165 · \$500 Write 16.5% as a decimal: 16.5% = 0.165.

= \$82.50 Do the multiplication.

$$\begin{array}{r} \overset{3\,2}{0.165} \\ \times\ 500 \\ \hline 82.500 \end{array}$$

The commission earned on the sale of the \$500 refrigerator is \$82.50.

EXAMPLE 5 ***Jewelry Sales*** A jewelry salesperson earned a commission of \$448 for selling a diamond ring priced at \$5,600. Find the commission rate.

Strategy We will identify the commission and the dollar amount of the sale.

WHY Then we can use the commission formula to find the unknown commission rate.

Solution The commission is \$448 and the dollar amount of the sale is \$5,600.

Commission = commission rate · **sales**		This is the commission formula.
\$448 = x · **\$5,600**		Substitute \$448 for the commission and \$5,600 for the sales. Let x represent the unknown commission rate.

$$\frac{448}{5{,}600} = \frac{x \cdot 5{,}600}{5{,}600}$$ We can drop the dollar signs. To undo the multiplication by 5,600 and isolate x on the right side of the equation, divide both sides by 5,600.

$$0.08 = \frac{x \cdot \overset{1}{\cancel{5{,}600}}}{\underset{1}{\cancel{5{,}600}}}$$ On the right side, remove the common factor of 5,600 from the numerator and denominator. On the left side, divide 448 by 5,600.

$$\begin{array}{r} 0.08 \\ 5{,}600\overline{)448.00} \\ -448\ 00 \\ \hline 0 \end{array}$$

$008\% = x$ To write the decimal 0.08 as a percent, multiply it by 100 by moving the decimal point two places to the right, and then insert a % symbol.

$8\% = x$

The commission rate paid the salesperson on the sale of the diamond ring was 8%.

Self Check 5

SELLING ELECTRONICS If the commission on a \$430 digital camcorder is \$21.50, what is the commission rate?

Now Try **Problem 29**

3 Find the percent of increase or decrease.

Percents can be used to describe how a quantity has changed. For example, consider the table on the right, which shows the number of television channels that the average U.S. home received in 2007 and 2010.

From the table, we see that the number of television channels received increased considerably from 2007 to 2010. To describe this increase using a percent, we first subtract to find the **amount of increase.**

Year	Number of television channels that the average U.S. home received
2007	119
2010	135

Source: TV Dimensions, 2011

$135 - 119 = 16$ Subtract the number of TV channels received in 2007 from the number received in 2010.

Thus, the number of channels received increased by 16 from 2007 to 2010.

Next, we find what percent of the *original* 119 channels received in 2007 that the 16 channel increase represents. To do this, we translate the problem into a percent equation (or percent proportion) and solve it.

The percent equation method:

16	is	what percent	of	119?	
↓	↓	↓	↓	↓	
16	=	x	·	119	Translate.

$16 = x \cdot 119$ This is the equation to solve.

$$\frac{16}{119} = \frac{x \cdot \overset{1}{\cancel{119}}}{\underset{1}{\cancel{119}}}$$ To isolate x on the right side, divide both sides of the equation by 119. Then remove the common factor of 119 from the numerator and denominator.

$$\frac{16}{119} = x$$

$0.1344 \approx x$ On the left side of the equation, divide 16 by 119. The division does not terminate.

$13.44\% \approx x$ To write the decimal as a percent, multiply it by 100 by moving the decimal point two places to the right, and then insert a % symbol.

$13\% \approx x$ Round to the nearest one percent.

$$\begin{array}{r} 0.1344 \\ 119\overline{)16.0000} \\ -11\,9 \\ \hline 4\,10 \\ -3\,57 \\ \hline 530 \\ -476 \\ \hline 540 \\ 476 \\ \hline 64 \end{array}$$

The percent proportion method:

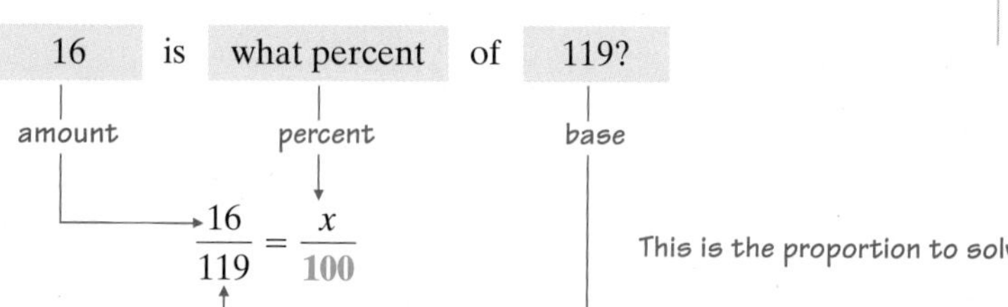

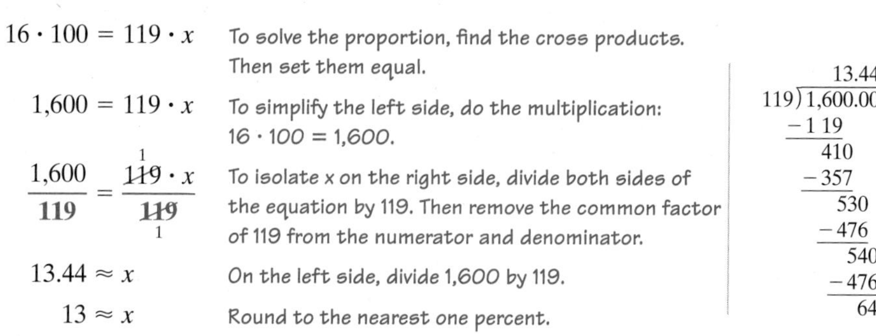

$16 \cdot 100 = 119 \cdot x$ To solve the proportion, find the cross products. Then set them equal.

$1{,}600 = 119 \cdot x$ To simplify the left side, do the multiplication: $16 \cdot 100 = 1{,}600$.

$\frac{1{,}600}{119} = \frac{\overset{1}{\cancel{119}} \cdot x}{\underset{1}{\cancel{119}}}$ To isolate x on the right side, divide both sides of the equation by 119. Then remove the common factor of 119 from the numerator and denominator.

$13.44 \approx x$ On the left side, divide 1,600 by 119.

$13 \approx x$ Round to the nearest one percent.

$$\begin{array}{r} 13.44 \\ 119\overline{)1{,}600.00} \\ -1\,19 \\ \hline 410 \\ -357 \\ \hline 530 \\ -476 \\ \hline 540 \\ -476 \\ \hline 64 \end{array}$$

With either method, we see that there was a 13% increase in the number of television channels received by the average American home from 2007 to 2010.

Self Check 6

HOME SCHOOLING In one school district, the number of home-schooled children increased from 15 to 150 in 4 years. Find the percent of increase.

Now Try **Problem 33**

EXAMPLE 6 ***JFK*** A 1996 auction included an oak rocking chair used by President John F. Kennedy in the Oval Office. The chair, originally valued at $5,000, sold for $453,500. Find the percent of increase in the value of the rocking chair.

Paul Schutzer/Time & Life Pictures/Getty Images

Strategy We will begin by finding the amount of increase in the value of the rocking chair.

WHY Then we can calculate what percent of the original $5,000 value of the chair that the increase represents.

Solution First, we find the amount of increase in the value of the rocking chair.

$453{,}500 - 5{,}000 = 448{,}500$ Subtract the original value from the price paid at auction.

The rocking chair increased in value by $448,500. Next, we find what percent of the original $5,000 value of the rocking chair the $448,500 increase represents by translating the problem into a percent equation (or percent proportion) and solving it.

The percent equation method:

$448,500 is what percent of $5,000?

$448{,}500 = x \cdot 5{,}000$ Translate.

$448{,}500 = x \cdot 5{,}000$ This is the equation to solve.

$$\frac{448{,}500}{5{,}000} = \frac{x \cdot \overset{1}{\cancel{5{,}000}}}{\underset{1}{\cancel{5{,}000}}}$$ To isolate x on the right side, divide both sides of the equation by 5,000. Then remove the common factor of 5,000 from the numerator and denominator.

$$\frac{4{,}485}{50} = x$$ Before performing the division on the left side of the equation, recall that there is a shortcut for dividing a dividend by a divisor when both end with zeros. Remove two of the ending zeros in the divisor 5,000 and remove the same number of ending zeros in the dividend 448,500.

$$89.7 = x$$ Divide 4,485 by 50.

$$8970\% = x$$ To write the decimal 89.7 as a percent, multiply it by 100 by moving the decimal point two places to the right, and then insert a % symbol.

$$8{,}970\% = x$$

$$\begin{array}{r} 89.7 \\ 50\overline{)4{,}485.0} \\ -4\,00 \\ \hline 485 \\ -450 \\ \hline 35\,0 \\ -35\,0 \\ \hline 0 \end{array}$$

The percent proportion method:

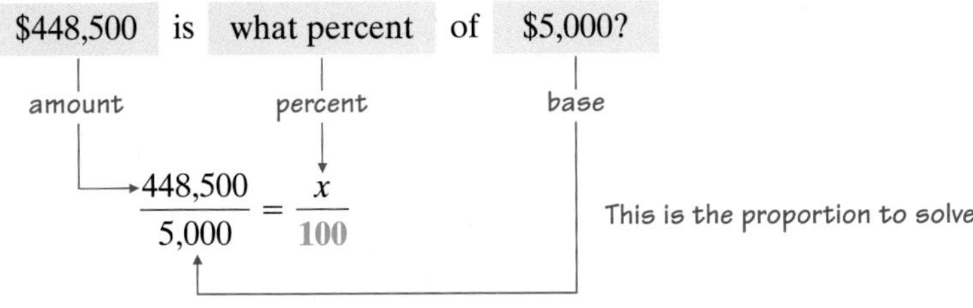

$$\frac{448{,}500}{5{,}000} = \frac{x}{100}$$ This is the proportion to solve.

$$448{,}500 \cdot 100 = 5{,}000 \cdot x$$ To solve the proportion, find the cross products. Then set them equal.

$$44{,}850{,}000 = 5{,}000 \cdot x$$ To simplify the left side of the equation, do the multiplication: $448{,}500 \cdot 100 = 44{,}850{,}000$.

$$\frac{44{,}850{,}000}{5{,}000} = \frac{\overset{1}{\cancel{5{,}000}} \cdot x}{\underset{1}{\cancel{5{,}000}}}$$ To isolate x on the right side, divide both sides of the equation by 5,000. Then remove the common factor of 5,000 from the numerator and denominator.

$$\frac{44{,}850{,}000}{5{,}000} = x$$

$$\begin{array}{r} 8970 \\ 5\overline{)44{,}850} \\ -40 \\ \hline 4\,8 \\ -4\,5 \\ \hline 35 \\ -35 \\ \hline 0 \\ -0 \\ \hline 0 \end{array}$$

Before performing the division on the left side of the equation, recall that there is a shortcut for dividing a dividend by a divisor when both end with zeros.

$$\frac{44{,}850}{5} = x$$ Remove the three ending zeros in the divisor 5,000 and remove the same number of ending zeros in the dividend 44,850,000.

$$8{,}970 = x$$ Divide 44,850 by 5.

With either method, we see that there was an amazing 8,970% increase in the value of the Kennedy rocking chair.

Caution! The percent of increase (or decrease) is a percent of the *original number,* that is, the number before the change occurred. Thus, in Example 6, it would be incorrect to write a percent sentence that compares the increase to the *new value* of the Kennedy rocking chair.

$448,500 is what percent of ~~$453,500?~~

Finding the Percent of Increase or Decrease

To find the percent of increase or decrease:

1. Subtract the smaller number from the larger to find the amount of increase or decrease.
2. Find what percent the amount of increase or decrease is of the original amount.

Self Check 7

REDUCING FAT INTAKE One serving of the original *Jif* peanut butter has 16 grams of fat per serving. The new *Jif Reduced Fat* product contains 12 grams of fat per serving. What is the percent decrease in the number of grams of fat per serving?

Now Try **Problem 37**

EXAMPLE 7 ***Commercials*** Jared Fogle credits his tremendous weight loss to exercise and a diet of low-fat Subway sandwiches. His maximum weight (reached in March of 1998) was 425 pounds. His current weight is about 187 pounds. Find the percent of decrease in his weight.

Zack Seckler/Getty Images

Strategy We will begin by finding the amount of decrease in Jared Fogle's weight.

WHY Then we can calculate what percent of his original 425-pound weight that the decrease represents.

Solution First, we find the amount of decrease in his weight.

$425 - 187 = 238$ Subtract his new weight from his weight before going on the weight-loss program.

His weight decreased by 238 pounds.

Next, we find what percent of his original 425 weight the 238-pound decrease represents by translating the problem into a percent equation (or percent proportion) and solving it.

The percent equation method:

238 is what percent of 425?

$238 = x \cdot 425$ Translate.

$238 = x \cdot 425$ This is the equation to solve.

$\frac{238}{425} = \frac{x \cdot \overset{1}{\cancel{425}}}{\underset{1}{\cancel{425}}}$ To isolate x on the right side, divide both sides of the equation by 425. Then remove the common factor of 425 from the numerator and denominator.

$0.56 = x$ Divide 238 by 425.

$$\begin{array}{r} 0.56 \\ 425\overline{)238.00} \\ -212\,5 \\ \hline 25\,50 \\ -25\,50 \\ \hline 0 \end{array}$$

$056\% = x$ To write the decimal 0.56 as a percent, multiply it by 100 by moving the decimal point two places to the right, and then insert a % symbol.

$56\% = x$

The percent proportion method:

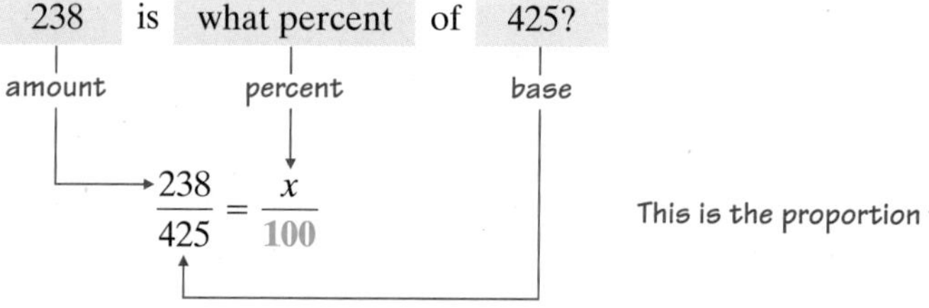

$\frac{238}{425} = \frac{x}{100}$ This is the proportion to solve.

$238 \cdot 100 = 425 \cdot x$ To solve the proportion, find the cross products. Then set them equal.

$23{,}800 = 425 \cdot x$	To simplify the left side of the equation, do the multiplication: $238 \cdot 100 = 23{,}800$.	
$\dfrac{23{,}800}{425} = \dfrac{\overset{1}{\cancel{425}} \cdot x}{\underset{1}{\cancel{425}}}$	To isolate x on the right side, divide both sides of the equation by 425. Then remove the common factor of 425 from the numerator and denominator.	$\begin{array}{r} 56 \\ 425\overline{)23{,}800} \\ -21\,25 \\ \hline 2\,550 \\ -2\,550 \\ \hline 0 \end{array}$
$56 = x$	Divide 23,800 by 425.	

With either method, we see that there was a 56% decrease in Jared Fogle's weight.

4 Calculate the amount of discount, the sale price, and the discount rate.

While shopping, you have probably noticed that many stores display signs advertising sales. Store managers have found that offering discounts attracts more customers. To be a smart shopper, it is important to know the vocabulary of discount sales.

The difference between the **original price** and the **sale price** of an item is called the **amount of discount,** or simply the **discount.** If the discount is expressed as a percent of the selling price, it is called the **discount rate.**

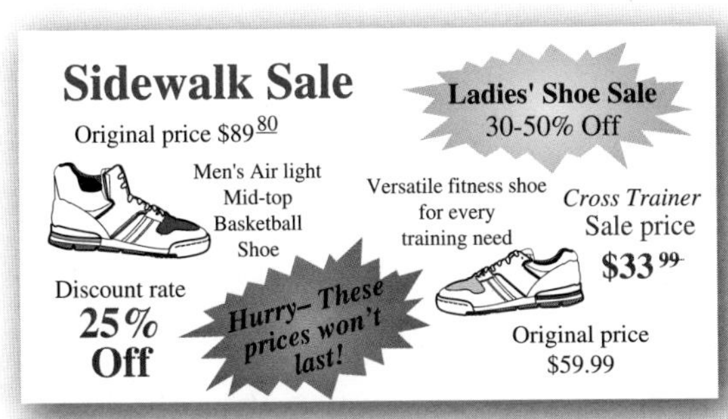

If we know the original price and the sale price of an item, we can use the following formula to find the amount of discount.

Finding the Discount

The amount of discount is the difference between the original price and the sale price.

Amount of discount = original price − sale price

If we know the original price of an item and the discount rate, we can use the following formula to find the amount of discount. Like several other formulas in this section, it is based on the percent equation.

Finding the Discount

The amount of discount is a percent of the original price.

Amount of discount	=	discount rate	·	original price
↑		↑		↑
amount	=	percent	·	base

We can use the following formula to find the sale price of an item that is being discounted.

Finding the Sale Price

To find the sale price of an item, subtract the discount from the original price.

Sale price = original price − discount

Self Check 8

SUNGLASSES SALES Sunglasses, regularly selling for $15.40, are discounted 15%. Find the amount of the discount. Then find the sale price.

Now Try **Problem 41**

EXAMPLE 8 ***Shoe Sales*** Use the information in the advertisement shown on the previous page to find the amount of the discount on the pair of men's basketball shoes. Then find the sale price.

Strategy We will identify the discount rate and the original price of the shoes and use a formula to find the amount of the discount.

WHY Then we can subtract the discount from the original price to find the sale price of the shoes.

Solution From the advertisement, we see that the discount rate on the men's shoes is 25% and the original price is $89.80.

Amount of discount = **discount rate** · **original price** This is the amount of discount formula.

= 25% · $89.80 Substitute 25% for the discount rate and $89.80 for the original price.

= 0.25 · $89.80 Write 25% as a decimal: 25% = 0.25.

= $22.45 Do the multiplication.

$$\begin{array}{r} 89.80 \\ \times 0.25 \\ \hline 44900 \\ 179600 \\ \hline 22.4500 \end{array}$$

The discount on the men's shoes is $22.45. To find the sale price, we use subtraction.

Sale price = **original price** − **discount** This is the sale price formula.

= $89.80 − $22.45 Substitute $89.80 for the original price and $22.45 for the discount.

= $67.35 Do the subtraction.

$$\begin{array}{r} {}^{7\,10} \\ 89.8\not{0} \\ -22.45 \\ \hline 67.35 \end{array}$$

The sale price of the men's basketball shoes is $67.35.

Self Check 9

DINING OUT An early-bird special at a restaurant offers a $10.99 prime rib dinner for only $7.95 if it is ordered before 6 P.M. Find the rate of discount. Round to the nearest one percent.

Now Try **Problem 45**

EXAMPLE 9 ***Discounts*** Find the discount rate on the ladies' cross trainer shoes shown in the advertisement on the previous page. Round to the nearest one percent.

Strategy We will think of this as a percent-of-decrease problem.

WHY We want to find what percent of the $59.99 original price the amount of discount represents.

Solution From the advertisement, we see that the original price of the women's shoes is $59.99 and the sale price is $33.99. The discount (decrease in price) is found using subtraction.

$59.99 − $33.99 = $26 Use the formula: Amount of discount = original price − sale price.

The shoes are discounted \$26. Now we find what percent of the original price the \$26 discount represents.

Amount of discount = discount rate · **original price** — This is the amount of discount formula.

$26 = x \cdot \$59.99$ — Substitute 26 for the amount of discount and \$59.99 for the original price. Let x represent the unkown discount rate.

$\frac{26}{59.99} = \frac{x \cdot 59.99}{59.99}$ — We can drop the dollar signs. To undo the multiplication by 59.99 and isolate x on the right side of the equation, divide both sides by 59.99.

$0.433 \approx \frac{x \cdot \cancel{59.99}^{1}}{\cancel{59.99}_{1}}$ — To simplify the fraction on the right side of the equation, remove the common factor of 59.99 from the numerator and denominator. On the left side, divide 26 by 59.99.

```
         0.433
5999)2600.000
    -2399 6
      200 40
     -179 97
       20 430
      -17 997
        2 433
```

$043.3\% \approx x$ — To write the decimal 0.433 as a percent, multiply it by 100 by moving the decimal point two places to the right, and then insert a % symbol.

$43\% \approx x$ — Round to the nearest one percent.

To the nearest one percent, the discount rate on the women's shoes is 43%.

ANSWERS TO SELF CHECKS

1. \$3.52 **2.** \$185.71 **3.** 35% **4.** \$4.92 **5.** 5% **6.** 900% **7.** 25% **8.** \$2.31, \$13.09 **9.** 28%

SECTION 3.9 STUDY SET

VOCABULARY

Fill in the blanks.

1. Instead of working for a salary or getting paid at an hourly rate, some salespeople are paid on __________. They earn a certain percent of the total dollar amount of the goods or services they sell.
2. Sales tax _____ are usually expressed as a percent.
3. **a.** When we use percent to describe how a quantity has increased compared to its original value, we are finding the percent of _______.

   b. When we use percent to describe how a quantity has decreased compared to its _______ value, we are finding the percent of decrease.
4. Refer to the advertisement below for a ceiling fan on sale.

   a. The _______ price of the ceiling fan was \$199.99.

   b. The amount of the _______ is \$40.00.

   c. The discount _____ is 20%.

   d. The _____ price of the ceiling fan is \$159.00.

CONCEPTS

Fill in the blanks in each of the following formulas.

5. Sales tax = sales tax rate · ________
6. Total cost = ________ + sales tax
7. Commission = commission rate · ________

8. a. Amount of discount = original price − ______

b. Amount of discount = ______ · original price

c. Sale price = ______ − discount

9. a. The sales tax on an item priced at $59.32 is $4.75. What is the total cost of the item?

b. The original price of an item is $150.99. The amout of discount is $15.99. What is the sale price of the item?

10. Round each dollar amount to the nearest cent.

a. $168.257

b. $57.234

c. $3.396

11. Fill in the blanks: To find the percent decrease, ______ the smaller number from the larger number to find the amount of decrease. Then find what percent that difference is of the ______ amount.

12. POPULATION CHANGES The table below shows how the populations of two North Carolina cities changed from 2000 to 2012.

Population	Goldsboro	Durham
2000	40,709	190,069
2012	36,437	228,330

Source: bestplaces.net

a. What was the *amount of decrease* in population for Goldsboro?

b. What was the *amount of increase* in population for Durham?

GUIDED PRACTICE

Solve each problem to find the sales tax. See Example 1.

13. Find the sales tax on a purchase of $92.70 if the sales tax rate is 4%.

14. Find the sales tax on a purchase of $33.60 if the sales tax rate is 8%.

15. Find the sales tax on a purchase of $83.90 if the sales tax rate is 5%.

16. Find the sales tax on a purchase of $234.80 if the sales tax rate is 2%.

Solve each problem to find the total cost. See Example 2.

17. Find the total cost of a $68.24 purchase if the sales tax rate is 3.8%.

18. Find the total cost of a $86.56 purchase if the sales tax rate is 4.3%.

19. Find the total cost of a $60.18 purchase if the sales tax rate is 6.4%.

20. Find the total cost of a $70.73 purchase if the sales tax rate is 5.9%.

Solve each problem to find the tax rate. See Example 3.

21. SALES TAX The purchase price for a blender is $140. If the sales tax is $7.28, what is the sales tax rate?

22. SALES TAX The purchase price for a camping tent is $180. If the sales tax is $8.64, what is the sales tax rate?

23. SELF-EMPLOYED TAXES A business owner paid self-employment taxes of $4,590 on a taxable income of $30,000. What is the self-employment tax rate?

24. CAPITAL GAINS TAXES A couple paid $3,000 in capital gains tax on a profit of $20,000 made from the sale of some shares of stock. What is the capital gains tax rate?

Solve each problem to find the commission. See Example 4.

25. SELLING SHOES A shoe salesperson earns a 12% commission on all sales. Find her commission if she sells a pair of dress shoes for $95.

26. SELLING CARS A used car salesperson earns an 11% commission on all sales. Find his commission if he sells a 2001 Chevy Malibu for $4,800.

27. EMPLOYMENT AGENCIES An employment counselor receives a 35% commission on the first week's salary of anyone that she places in a new job. Find her commission if one of her clients is hired as a secretary at $480 per week.

28. PHARMACEUTICAL SALES A medical sales representative is paid an 18% commission on all sales. Find her commission if she sells $75,000 of Coumadin, a blood-thinning drug, to a pharmacy chain.

Solve each problem to find the commission rate. See Example 5.

29. AUCTIONS An auctioneer earned a $15 commission on the sale of an antique chair for $750. What is the commission rate?

30. SELLING TIRES A tire salesman was paid a $28 commission after one of his customers purchased a set of new tires for $560. What is the commission rate?

31. SELLING ELECTRONICS If the commission on a $500 laptop computer is $20, what is the commission rate?

32. SELLING CLOCKS If the commission on a $600 grandfather clock is $54, what is the commission rate?

Solve each problem to find the percent of increase. See Example 6.

33. CLUBS The number of members of a service club increased from 80 to 88. What was the percent of increase in club membership?

34. SAVINGS ACCOUNTS The amount of money in a savings account increased from $2,500 to $3,000. What was the percent of increase in the amount of money saved?

35. RAISES After receiving a raise, the salary of a secretary increased from $300 to $345 dollars per week. What was the percent of increase in her salary?

36. TUITION The tuition at a community college increased from $2,500 to $2,650 per semester. What was the percent of increase in the tuition?

Solve each problem to find the percent of decrease. See Example 7.

37. TRAVEL TIME After a new freeway was completed, a commuter's travel time to work decreased from 30 minutes to 24 minutes. What was the percent of decrease in travel time?

38. LAYOFFS A printing company reduced the number of employees from 300 to 246. What was the percent of decrease in the number of employees?

39. ENROLLMENT Thirty-six of the 40 students originally enrolled in an algebra class completed the course. What was the percent of decrease in the number of students in the class?

40. DECLINING SALES One year, a pumpkin patch sold 1,200 pumpkins. The next year, they only sold 900 pumpkins. What was the percent of decrease in the number of pumpkins sold?

Solve each problem to find the amount of the discount and the sale price. See Example 8.

41. DINNERWARE SALES Find the amount of the discount on a six-place dinnerware set if it regularly sells for $90, but is on sale for 33% off. Then find the sale price of the dinnerware set.

42. BEDDING SALES Find the amount of the discount on a $130 bedspread that is now selling for 20% off. Then find the sale price of the bedspread.

43. MEN'S CLOTHING SALES 501 Levi jeans that regularly sell for $58 are now discounted 15%. Find the amount of the discount. Then find the sale price of the jeans.

44. BOOK SALES At a bookstore, the list price of $23.50 for the *Merriam-Webster's Collegiate Dictionary* is crossed out, and a 30% discount sticker is pasted on the cover. Find the amount of the discount. Then find the sale price of the dictionary.

Solve each problem to find the discount rate. See Example 9.

45. LADDER SALES Find the discount rate on an aluminum ladder regularly priced at $79.95 that is on sale for $64.95. Round to the nearest one percent.

46. OFFICE SUPPLIES SALES Find the discount rate on an electric pencil sharpener regularly priced at $49.99 that is on sale for $45.99. Round to the nearest one percent.

47. DISCOUNT TICKETS The price of a one-way airline ticket from Atlanta to New York City was reduced from $209 to $179. Find the discount rate. Round to the nearest one percent.

48. DISCOUNT HOTELS The cost of a one-night stay at a hotel was reduced from $245 to $200. Find the discount rate. Round to the nearest one percent.

CONCEPT EXTENSIONS

49. POPULATION GROWTH
   a. Suppose the population of a city doubles. What percent increase is that?
   b. Suppose the population of a city triples. What percent increase is that?

50. TIPPING To quickly determine the amount of a 15% tip for a restaurant bill of $80,a customer mentally added $8.00 and one-half of $8.00 (which is $4.00) to get $12. Explain the mathematics that the customer performed to find the amount of the 15% tip so easily.

51. WEIGHT TRAINING After a six-week workout program, a defensive back increased his maximum bench press from 200 to 240 pounds. After the same program, an offensive lineman increased his maximum bench press from 300 to 340 pounds. Both athletes had an increase of 40 pounds. Did they have the same percent increase? Explain why or why not?

52. RAISES A construction worker received a salary raise of 5%, followed by another raise of 10%, followed by a third raise of 4%. By what percent did his original salary increase after receiving the three raises?

APPLICATIONS

53. SALES TAX The North Carolina state sales tax rate is 4.75%. However, Buncombe, Durham, Montgomery and Orange counties added an additional 2.25% as of April 1, 2012. Find the sales tax on a dining room set that sells for $980 if it is purchased in one of those counties.

54. SALES TAX Find the sales tax on a pair of jeans costing $40 if they are purchased in Missouri, which has a state sales tax rate of 4.225%.

55. SALES RECEIPTS Complete the sales receipt below by finding the subtotal, the sales tax, and the total cost of the purchase.

NURSERY CENTER

Your one-stop garden supply

3 @ 2.99	PLANTING MIX	$ 8.97
1 @ 9.87	GROUND COVER	$ 9.87
2 @ 14.25	SHRUBS	$28.50
	SUBTOTAL	$
	SALES TAX @ 6.00%	$
	TOTAL	$

56. SALES RECEIPTS Complete the sales receipt below by finding all three prices, the subtotal, the sales tax, and the total cost of the purchase.

McCOY'S FURNITURE

1 @ 450.00	SOFA	$
2 @ 90.00	END TABLES	$
1 @ 350.00	LOVE SEAT	$
	SUBTOTAL	$
	SALES TAX @ 4.20%	$
	TOTAL	$

57. ROOM TAX After checking out of a hotel, a man noticed that the hotel bill included an additional charge labeled *room tax.* If the price of the room was $129 plus a room tax of $10.32, find the room tax rate.

58. EXCISE TAX While examining her monthly telephone bill, a woman noticed an additional charge of $1.24 labeled *federal excise tax.* If the basic service charges for that billing period were $42, what is the federal excise tax rate? Round to the nearest one percent.

59. GAMBLING For state authorized wagers (bets) placed with legal bookmakers and lottery operators, there is a federal excise tax on the wager. What is the excise tax rate if there is an excise tax of $5 on a $2,000 bet?

60. BUYING FISHING EQUIPMENT There are federal exercise taxes on the retail price when purchasing fishing equipment. The taxes are intended to help pay for parks and conservation. What is the federal excise tax rate if there is an excise tax of $17.50 on a fishing rod and reel that has a retail price of $175?

61. TAX HIKES In order to raise more revenue, some states raise the sales tax rate. How much additional money will be collected on the sale of a $15,000 car if the sales tax rate is raised 1%?

62. FOREIGN TRAVEL Value-added tax (VAT) is a consumer tax on goods and services. Currently, VAT systems are in place all around the world. (The United States is one of the few nations not using a value-added tax system.) Complete the table by determining the VAT a traveler would pay in each country on a dinner that cost $25. Round to the nearest cent.

Country	VAT rate	Tax on a $25 dinner
Mexico	16%	
Germany	19%	
France	19.6%	
Sweden	25%	

Source: www.worldwide-tax.com

63. PAYCHECKS Use the information on the paycheck stub to find the tax rate for the federal withholding, worker's compensation, Medicare, and Social Security taxes that were deducted from the gross pay.

6286244

Issue date: 03-27-10

GROSS PAY	$360.00
TAXES	
FED. TAX	$ 28.80
WORK. COMP.	$ 13.50
MEDICARE	$ 4.32
SOCIAL SECURITY	$ 22.32
NET PAY	$291.06

64. GASOLINE TAX In North Carolina a gallon of unleaded gasoline sells for approximately $3.55. This price includes federal and state taxes that total about $0.59. Therefore, the price of a gallon of gasoline, before taxes, is $2.96. What is the tax rate on gasoline? Round to the nearest one percent.

65. POLICE FORCE A police department plans to increase its 80-person force to 84 persons. Find the percent increase in the size of the police force.

66. COST-OF-LIVING INCREASES A woman making $32,000 a year receives a cost-of-living increase that raises her salary to $32,768 per year. Find the percent of increase in her yearly salary.

67. LAKE SHORELINES Because of a heavy spring runoff, the shoreline of a lake increased from 5.8 miles to 7.6 miles. What was the percent of increase in the length of the shoreline? Round to the nearest one percent.

68. CROP DAMAGE After flooding damaged much of the crop, the cost of a head of lettuce jumped from \$0.99 to \$2.20. What percent of increase is this? Round to the nearest one percent.

69. OVERTIME From May to June, the number of overtime hours for employees at a printing company increased from 42 to 106. What is the percent of increase in the number of overtime hours? Round to the nearest percent.

70. TOURISM The graph below shows the number of international visitors (travelers) to the United States each year from 2002 to 2008.

a. The greatest percent of increase in the number of travelers was between 2003 and 2004. Find the percent increase. Round to the nearest one percent.

b. The only decrease in the number of travelers was between 2002 and 2003. Find the percent decrease. Round to the nearest one percent.

Source: U.S. Department of Commerce

71. REDUCED CALORIES A company advertised its new, improved chips as having 96 calories per serving. The original style contained 150 calories. What percent of decrease in the number of calories per serving is this?

72. CAR INSURANCE A student paid a car insurance premium of \$420 every three months. Then the premium dropped to \$370, because she qualified for a good-student discount. What was the percent of decrease in the premium? Round to the nearest percent.

73. BUS PASSES To increase the number of riders, a bus company reduced the price of a monthly pass from \$112 to \$98. What was the percent of decrease in the cost of a bus pass?

74. BASEBALL The illustration in the next column shows the path of a baseball hit 110 mph, with a launch angle of 35 degrees, at sea level and at Coors Field, home of the Colorado Rockies. What is the percent of increase in the distance the ball travels at Coors Field?

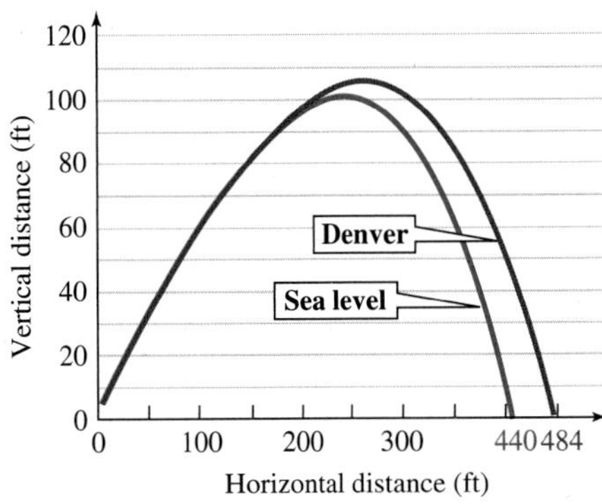

Source: Los Angeles Times, September 16, 1996

75. EARTH MOVING The illustration below shows the typical soil volume change during earth moving. (One cubic yard of soil fits in a cube that is 1 yard long, 1 yard wide, and 1 yard high.)

a. Find the percent of increase in the soil volume as it goes through step 1 of the process.

b. Find the percent of decrease in the soil volume as it goes through step 2 of the process.

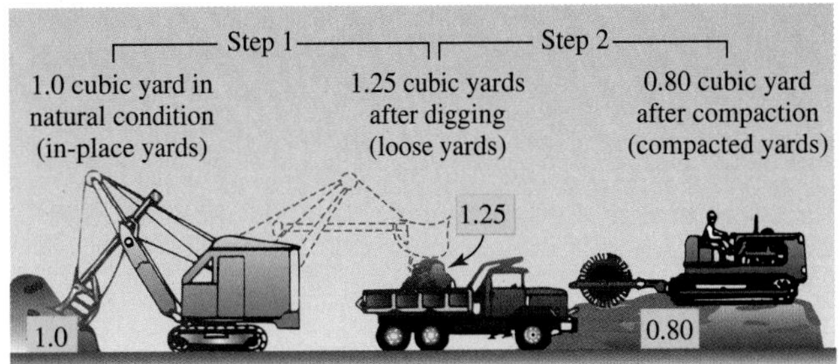

Source: U.S. Department of the Army

76. PARKING The management of a mall has decided to increase the parking area. The plans are shown in the next column. What will be the percent of increase in the parking area when the project is completed?

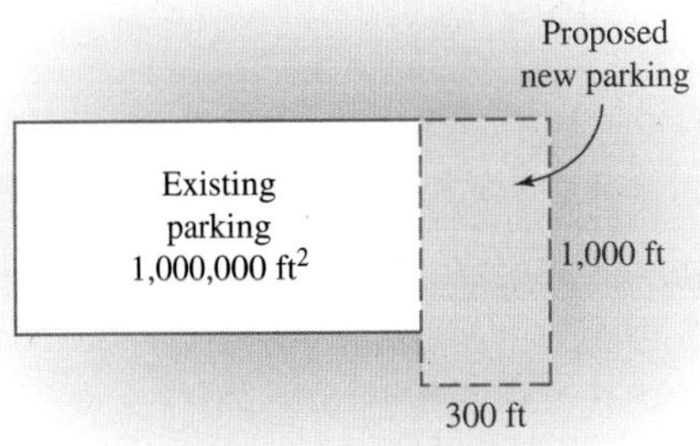

77. REAL ESTATE After selling a house for \$98,500, a real estate agent split the 6% commission with another agent. How much did each person receive?

78. COMMISSIONS A salesperson for a medical supplies company is paid a commission of 9% for orders less than $8,000. For orders exceeding $8,000, she receives an additional 2% in commission on the total amount. What is her commission on a sale of $14,600?

79. SPORTS AGENTS A sports agent charges her clients a fee to represent them during contract negotiations. The fee is based on a percent of the contract amount. If the agent earned $37,500 when her client signed a $2,500,000 professional football contract, what rate did she charge for her services?

80. ART GALLERIES An art gallery displays paintings for artists and receives a commission from the artist when a painting is sold. What is the commission rate if a gallery received $135.30 when a painting was sold for $820?

81. WHOLE LIFE INSURANCE For the first 12 months, insurance agents earn a very large commission on the monthly premium of any whole life policy that they sell. After that, the commission rate is lowered significantly. Suppose on a new policy with monthly premiums of $160, an agent is paid monthly commissions of $144. Find the commission rate.

82. TERM INSURANCE For the first 12 months, insurance agents earn a large commission on the monthly premium of any term life policy that they sell. After that, the commission rate is lowered significantly. Suppose on a new policy with monthly premiums of $180, an agent is paid monthly commissions of $81. Find the commission rate.

83. CONCERT PARKING A concert promoter gets a commission of $33\frac{1}{3}\%$ of the revenue an arena receives from parking the night of the performance. How much can the promoter make if 6,000 cars are expected and parking costs $6 a car?

84. PARTIES A homemaker invited her neighbors to a kitchenware party to show off cookware and utensils. As party hostess, she received 12% of the total sales. How much was purchased if she received $41.76 for hosting the party?

85. WATCH SALE Refer to the advertisement below.

a. Find the amount of the discount on the watch.

b. Find the sale price of the watch.

SALE
WATCHES
Regularly $39.95
Now 20% OFF

86. SCOOTER SALE Refer to the advertisement below.

a. Find the amount of the discount on the scooter.

b. Find the sale price of the scooter.

87. SEGWAYS Find the discount rate on a Segway PT shown in the advertisement. Round to the nearest one percent.

88. FAX MACHINES An HP 3180 fax machine, regularly priced at $160, is on sale for $116. What is the discount rate?

89. DISC PLAYERS What are the sale price and the discount rate for a Blu-ray disc player that regularly sells for $399.97 and is being discounted $50? Round to the nearest one percent.

90. CAMCORDER SALE What are the sale price and the discount rate for a full HD camcorder that regularly sells for $559.97 and is being discounted $80? Round to the nearest one percent.

91. REBATES Find the discount rate and the new price for a case of motor oil if a shopper receives the manufacturer's rebate mentioned in the advertisement. Round to the nearest one percent.

92. DOUBLE COUPONS Find the discount, the discount rate, and the reduced price for a box of cereal that normally sells for $3.29 if a shopper presents the coupon at a store that doubles the value of the coupon.

93. TV SHOPPING Determine the Home Shopping Network (HSN) price of the ring described in the illustration if it sells it for 55% off of the retail price. Ignore shipping and handling costs.

Item 169-117
2.75 lb ctw
10K Blue Topaz Ring
6, 7, 8, 9, 10
Retail value $170
HSN Price
$??.??
S&H $5.95

94. INFOMERCIALS The host of a TV infomercial says that the suggested retail price of a rotisserie grill is $249.95 and that it is now offered "for just 4 easy payments of only $39.95." What is the discount, and what is the discount rate?

95. RING SALE What does a ring regularly sell for if it has been discounted 20% and is on sale for $149.99? (*Hint:* The ring is selling for 80% of its regular price.)

96. BLINDS SALE What do vinyl blinds regularly sell for if they have been discounted 55% and are on sale for $49.50? (*Hint:* The blinds are selling for 45% of their regular price.)

WRITING

97. Explain the difference between a sales tax and a sales tax rate.

98. List the pros and cons of working on commission.

99. Suppose the price of an item increases $25 from $75 to $100. Explain why the following percent sentence *cannot* be used to find the percent of increase in the price of the item.

25 is what percent of 100?

100. Explain how to find the sale price of an item if you know the regular price and the discount rate.

MODULE 3 TEST

1. Fill in the blanks.

a. A ______ is the quotient of two numbers or the quotient of two quantities that have the same units.

b. A ______ is the quotient of two quantities that have different units.

c. A __________ is a statement that two ratios (or rates) are equal.

d. The ______ products for the proportion $\frac{3}{8} = \frac{6}{16}$ are $3 \cdot 16$ and $8 \cdot 6$.

e. *Deci* means _______, *centi* means ___________, and *milli* means ___________.

f. The meter, the gram, and the liter are basic units of measurement in the ______ system.

g. In the American system, temperatures are measured in degrees __________. In the metric system, temperatures are measured in degrees ________.

h. _______ means parts per one hundred.

i. In the percent sentence "5 is 25% of 20," 5 is the ________, 25% is the percent, and 20 is the _____.

j. When we use percent to describe how a quantity has increased compared to its original value, we are finding the percent of ________.

2. PIANOS A piano keyboard is made up of a total of eighty-eight keys, as shown below. What is the ratio of the number of black keys to white keys?

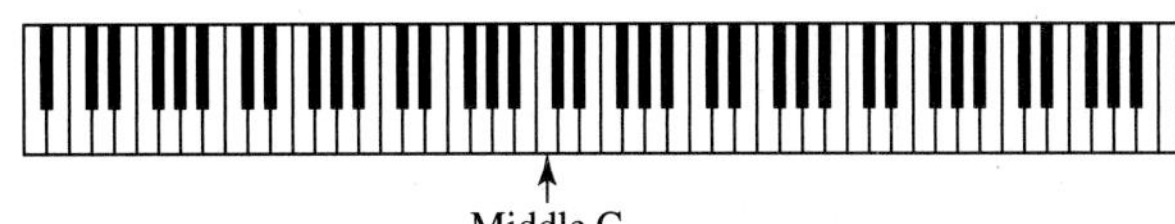

Write each ratio as a fraction in simplest form.

3. 6 feet to 8 feet

4. 8 ounces to 3 pounds

5. 0.26 : 0.65

6. $3\frac{1}{3}$ to $3\frac{8}{9}$

7. ASPECT RATIO The *aspect ratio* of an image describes the relationship between its width and height. Traditional TV programming has an aspect ratio of 4:3 while HDTV programming has an aspect ratio of 16:9. Use that information to label the measure of the width and height of each screen below so that it displays the proper ratio. Use the measures defined in the given ratios.

8. AIR JORDAN Michael Jordan's free throw statistics are shown below. What is the ratio of free throws *missed* to free throws attempted?
Michael Jordan- NBA Career

Free throws made: 7,327 Free throws attempted: 8,772

9. Write the rate 54 feet in 36 seconds as a fraction in simplest form.

10. COMPARISON SHOPPING A 2-pound can of coffee sells for \$3.38, and a 5-pound can of the same brand of coffee sells for \$8.50. Which is the better buy?

11. UTILITY COSTS A household used 675 kilowatt-hours of electricity during a 30-day month. Find the rate of electric usage in kilowatt-hours per day.

12. Write the following statement as a proportion: 15 billboards to 50 miles as 3 billboards to 10 miles.

13. Determine whether each proportion is true.

a. $\frac{25}{33} = \frac{2}{3}$ **b.** $\frac{2.2}{3.5} = \frac{1.76}{2.8}$

14. Are the numbers 7, 15 and 35, 75 proportional?

Solve each proportion.

15. $\frac{x}{3} = \frac{35}{7}$

16. $\frac{15.3}{x} = \frac{3}{12.4}$

17. $\frac{2\frac{2}{9}}{\frac{4}{3}} = \frac{x}{1\frac{1}{2}}$

18. $\frac{25}{\frac{1}{10}} = \frac{50}{x}$

19. SHOPPING If 13 ounces of tea costs \$2.79, how much would you expect to pay for 16 ounces of tea?

20. BAKING A recipe calls for $1\frac{2}{3}$ cup of sugar and 5 cups of flour. How much sugar should be used with 6 cups of flour?

21. WEIGHT LOSS Phil decided he needed to lose a few pounds. He saw an advertisement for an exercise program that claimed a person could safely lose $3\frac{1}{2}$ pounds every 3 weeks. If he wants to lose 14 pounds, how many days would it take him to do that on the exercise program?

22. METALURGY An *alloy* (mixture) consisting of copper, zinc, and tin in the ratio 2:3:5, respectively, is to be produced at a metallurgy plan. If 75 kilograms of alloy is needed, find the amount of each metal needed to make the mixture.

23. DENTISTRY The diagram below was displayed in a dentist's office. According to the diagram, if the dentist has 340 adult patients, how many will develop gum disease?

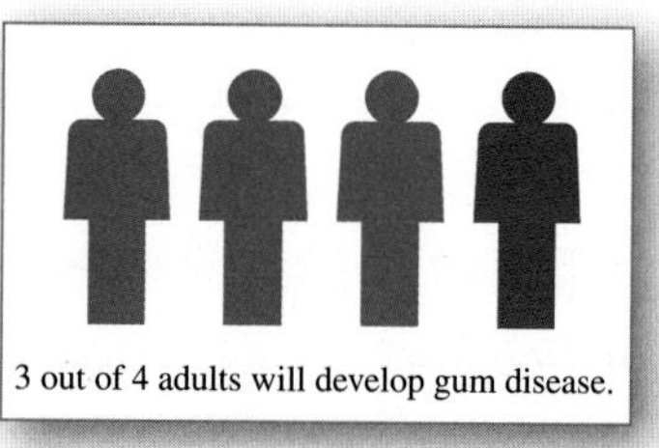

24. TV TOWERS A television tower casts a shadow 114 feet long at the same time that a 6-foot-tall television reporter casts a shadow of 4 feet. Find the height of the tower.

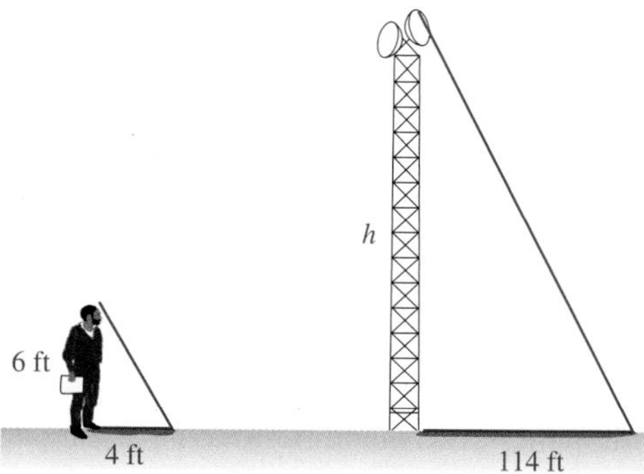

25. SHADOWS John and Antonio stood side-by-side one sunny summer day. John cast a shadow $7\frac{1}{2}$ feet long on the ground and Antonio cast a shadow 8 feet 3 inches long. If John is 5 feet 10 inches tall, how tall is Antonio?

26. MINIATURES A scale is a ratio (or rate) that compares the size of a model, drawing, or map with the size of an actual object. The scale indicates that 1 inch on the model carousel is equivalent to 160 inches on the actual carousel. How wide should the model be if the actual carousel is 35 feet wide?

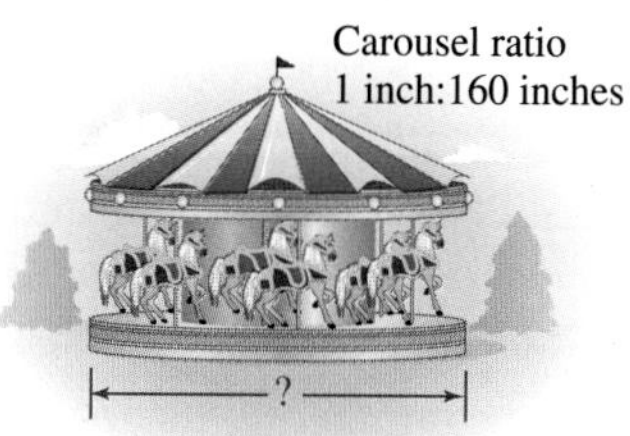

27. a. Refer to the ruler below. Each inch is divided into how many equal parts?

b. Determine which measurements the arrows point to on the ruler.

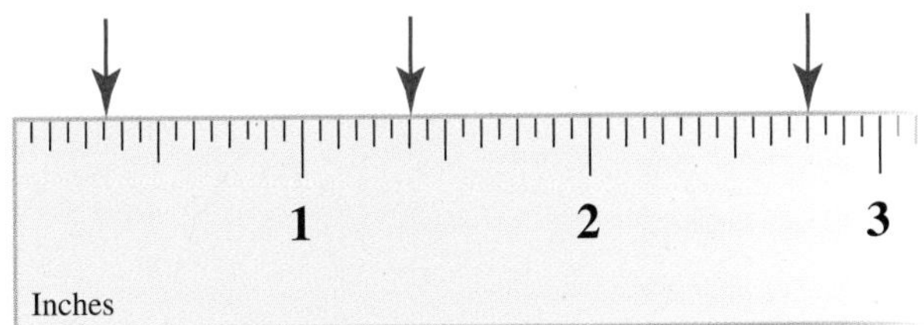

28. MILEAGE Refer to the data below that gives the number of highway miles that can be driven on one tank of gasoline.

2012 Toyota Corolla	**2012 Chevrolet Cruze**
448.8 highway miles	592.8 highway miles
Fuel tank: 13.2 gal	Fuel tank: 15.6 gal

a. Calculate the fuel efficiency for each car.

b. Which car has the better highway fuel efficiency?

29. Convert 180 inches to feet.

30. TOOLS If a 25-foot tape measure is completely extended, how many yards does it stretch? Write your answer as a mixed number.

31. Convert $10\frac{3}{4}$ pounds to ounces.

32. AUTOMOBILES A car weighs 1.6 tons. Find its weight in pounds.

33. CONTAINERS How many fluid ounces are in a 1-gallon carton of milk?

34. LITERATURE An excellent work of early science fiction is the book *Around the World in 80 Days* by Jules Verne (1828–1905). Convert 80 days to minutes.

35. a. A quart and a liter of fruit punch are shown below. Which is the 1-liter carton: The one on the left side or the right side?

b. The figures in the next column show the relative lengths of a yardstick and a meterstick. Which one represents the meterstick: the longer one or the shorter one?

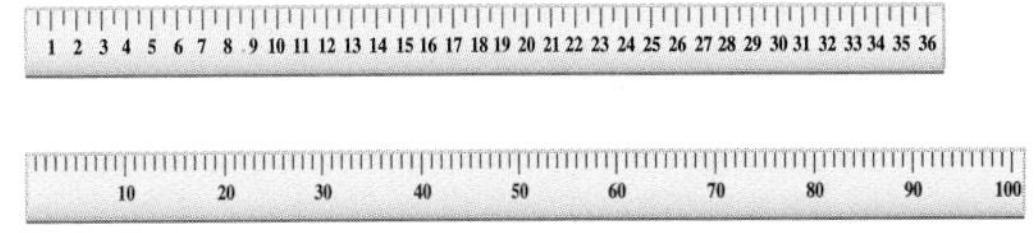

c. One ounce and one gram weights are placed on a balance, as shown below. On which side is the gram: the left side or the right side?

36. Determine which measurements the arrows point to on the metric ruler shown below.

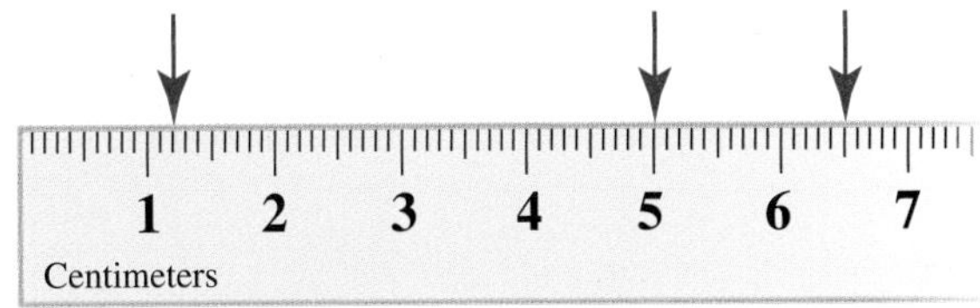

37. SPEED SKATING American Bonnie Blair won gold medals in the women's 500-meter speed skating competitions at the 1988, 1992, and 1994 Winter Olympic Games. Convert the race length to kilometers.

38. How many centimeters are in 5 meters?

39. Convert 8,000 centigrams to kilograms.

40. Convert 70 liters to milliliters.

41. PRESCRIPTIONS A bottle contains 50 tablets, each containing 150 mg of medicine. How many grams of medicine does the bottle contain?

42. TRACK Which is the longer distance: a 100-yard race or an 80-meter race?

43. BODY WEIGHT Which person is heavier: Jim, who weighs 160 pounds, or Ricardo, who weighs 71 kilograms?

44. MIXING CONCRETE Suppose you are mixing some concrete for a home improvement project and the directions call for adding 5 gallons of water. If all you have that can hold water is an empty two-liter soda bottle, how many times will you have to fill it to make the concrete mixture?

45. Convert 810 milliliters to quarts. Round to the nearest tenth.

46. Convert 16.5 inches to centimeters. Round to the nearest centimeter.

47. COOKING MEAT The USDA recommends that turkey be cooked to a temperature of 83°C. Change this to degrees Fahrenheit. To be safe, *round up* to the next degree. (*Hint:* $F = \frac{9}{5}C + 32$.)

48. a. Express the amount of the figure that is shaded as a percent, as a fraction, and as a decimal.

b. What percent of the figure is not shaded?

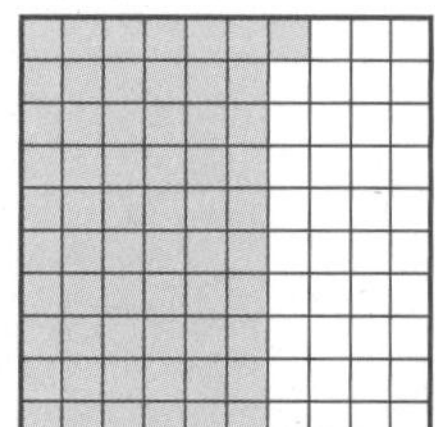

49. In the illustration below, each set of 100 square regions represents 100%. Express as a percent the amount of the figure that is shaded. Then express that percent as a fraction and as a decimal.

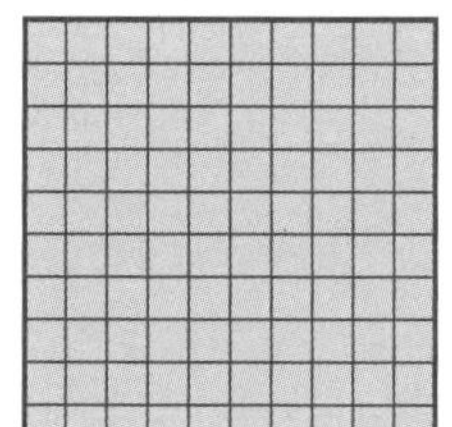

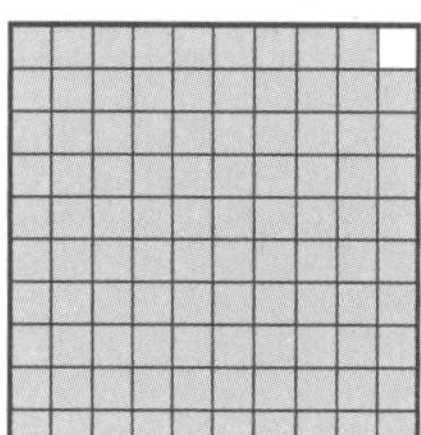

50. a. Shade 87.5% of the figure shown below.

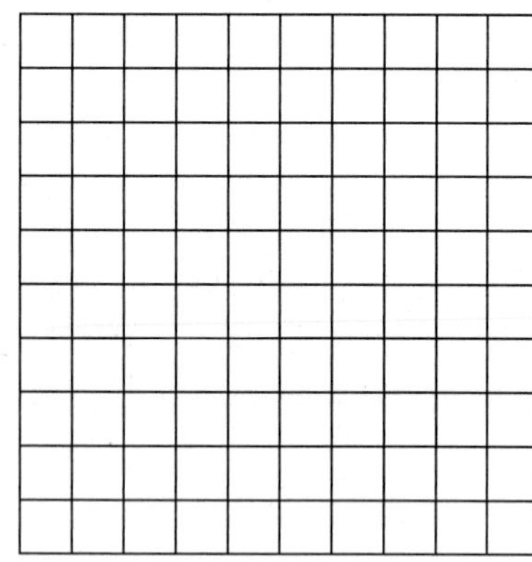

b. Express the shaded portion of the entire figure as a decimal.

c. Fill in the blanks to complete the expanded notation: $0.875 = \frac{8}{\quad} + \frac{7}{\quad} + \frac{5}{\quad}$

d. For your answer to part a, what shaded portion represents $\frac{8}{10}$? What shaded portion represents $\frac{7}{100}$? What shaded portion represents $\frac{5}{1{,}000}$?

51. a. Shade $\frac{1}{6}$ of the figure shown below.

b. What percent of the figure did you shade? Express your answer using a mixed number.

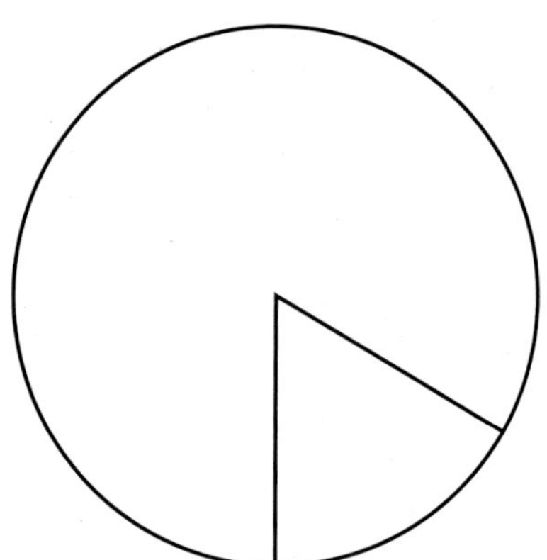

52. Write each percent as a decimal.

a. 67% **b.** 12.3% **c.** $9\frac{3}{4}\%$

53. Write each percent as a decimal.

a. 0.06% **b.** 210% **c.** 55.375%

54. Write each fraction as a percent.

a. $\frac{1}{4}$ **b.** $\frac{5}{8}$ **c.** $\frac{28}{25}$

55. Write each decimal as a percent.

a. 0.19 **b.** 3.47 **c.** 0.005

56. Write each decimal or whole number as a percent.

a. 0.667 **b.** 2 **c.** 0.9

57. Write each percent as a fraction. Simplify, if possible.

a. 55% **b.** 0.01% **c.** 125%

58. Write each percent as a fraction. Simplify, if possible.

a. $6\frac{2}{3}\%$ **b.** 37.5% **c.** 8%

59. Write each fraction as a percent. Give the exact answer and an approximation to the nearest tenth of a percent.

a. $\frac{1}{30}$ **b.** $\frac{16}{9}$

60. 65 is what percent of 1,000?

61. What percent of 14 is 35?

62. FUGITIVES As of May 16, 2012, exactly 466 of the 496 fugitives who have appeared on the FBI's Ten Most Wanted list have been captured or located. What percent is this? Round to the nearest one percent. (*Source:* www.fbi.gov/wanted)

63. SWIMMING WORKOUTS A swimmer was able to complete 18 laps before a shoulder injury forced him to stop. This was only 20% of a typical workout. How many laps does he normally complete during a workout?

64. COLLEGE EMPLOYEES The 700 employees at a community college fall into three major categories, as shown in the circle graph. How many employees are in administration?

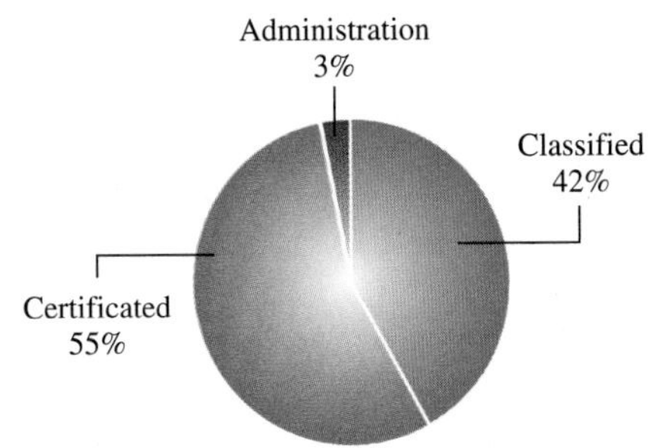

65. What number is 224% of 60?

66. 2.6 is $33\frac{1}{3}$% of what number?

67. TIPPING Find the amount of a 15% tip on a lunch costing $28.40.

68. CAR SHOWS 24% of 63,400 people that attended a five-day car show were female. Find the number of females that attended the car show.

69. SHRINKAGE See the following label from a new pair of jeans. The measurements are in inches. (*Inseam* is a measure of the length of the jeans.)

WAIST INSEAM
33 34
Expect shrinkage of approximately
3%
in length after the jeans are washed.

a. How much length will be lost due to shrinkage?

b. What will be the length of the jeans after being washed?

70. TOTAL COST Find the total cost of a $25.50 purchase if the sales tax rate is 2.9%.

71. SALES TAX The purchase price for a watch is $90. If the sales tax is $2.70, what is the sales tax rate?

72. POPULATION INCREASES After a new freeway was completed, the population of a city it passed through increased from 2,800 to 3,444 in two years. Find the percent of increase.

73. INSURANCE An automobile insurance salesperson receives a 4% commission on the annual premium of any policy she sells. Find her commission on a policy if the annual premium is $898.

74. TELEMARKETING A telemarketer earned a commission of $528 on $4,800 worth of new business that she obtained over the telephone. Find her rate of commission.

75. COST-OF-LIVING A teacher earning $40,000 just received a cost-of-living increase of 3.6%. What is the teacher's new salary?

76. AUTO CARE Refer to the advertisement below. Find the discount, the sale price, and the discount rate on the car waxing kit.

77. TOWEL SALES Find the amount of the discount on a beach towel if it regularly sells for $20, but is on sale for 33% off. Then find the sale price of the towel.

78. BRAKE INSPECTIONS Of the 1,920 trucks inspected at a safety checkpoint, 5% had problems with their brakes. Estimate the number of trucks that had brake problems?

79. IMPROVING HORSEPOWER The following graph shows how the installation of a special computer chip increases the horsepower of a truck. Find the percent of increase in horsepower for the engine running at 4,000 revolutions per minute (rpm) and round to the nearest tenth of one percent.

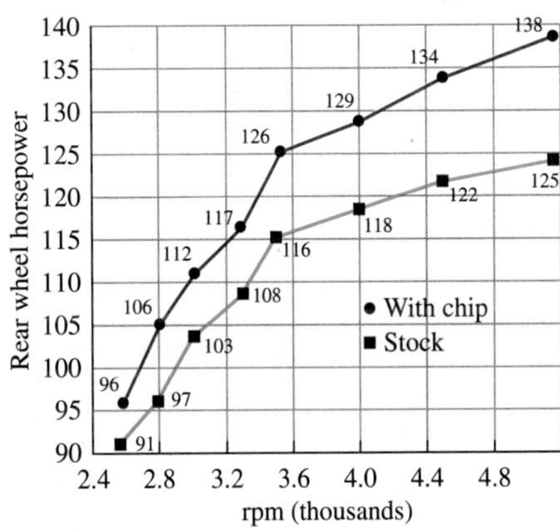

80. COMPARISON SHOPPING You want to purchase two pairs of shoes that sell for $36 each. Which offer below is the better deal?

- Offer 1: Buy one pair at the full price- Get the second pair for $66\frac{2}{3}$ % off!
- Offer 2: Buy two pairs- Get 40% off of each pair!

Module 3 Answers

Applications Introduction: Mathematical Comparisons Section 3.1 (Page 5)

1. a. $\frac{17}{3}$; 17 to 3; 17:3 **b.** $\frac{3}{20}$; 3 to 20; 3:20 **c.** $\frac{17}{20}$; 17 to 20; 17:20 **2. a.** iii. $\frac{43}{39} = \frac{86}{78}$ **b.** iv. $\frac{5}{132} = \frac{25}{660}$ **c.** i. $\frac{16}{9} = \frac{64}{36}$ **d.** v. $\frac{15}{1} = \frac{450}{30}$ **e.** vi. $\frac{5}{6} = \frac{125}{150}$ **f.** ii. $\frac{21}{49} = \frac{315}{735}$ **3.** $\frac{85}{100}$

4. a.

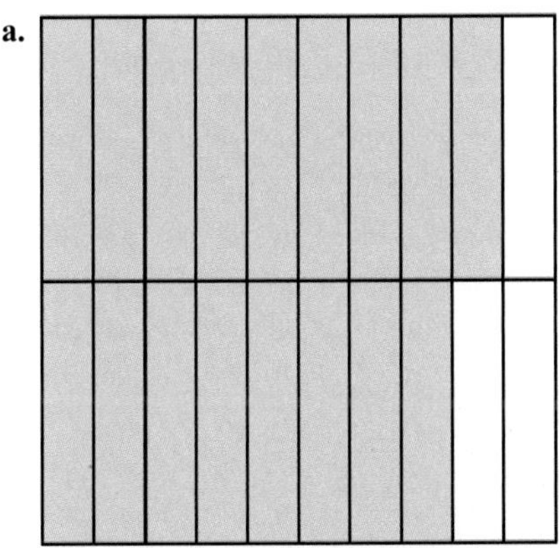

b.

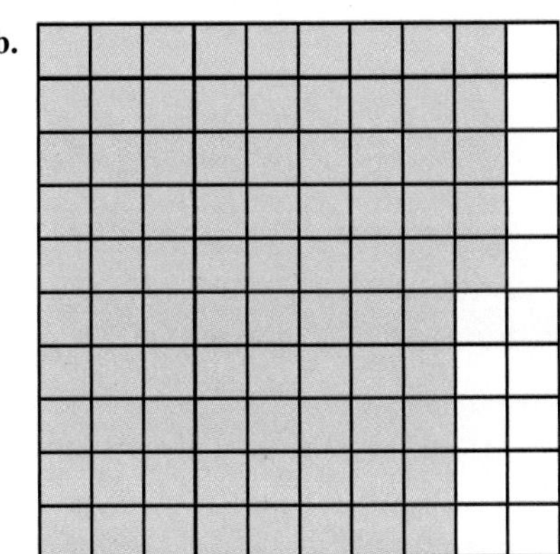

c. The same amount of the figure is shaded.

d. 15%; the percent of the U.S. population that is left-handed

Are You Ready? Section 3.1 (Page 8)

1. $\frac{7}{9}$ **2.** 209 **3.** 4.75 **4.** $1\frac{2}{3}$

Study Set Section 3.1 (Page 17)

1. ratio **3.** unit **5.** 3 **7.** 10 **9.** $\frac{11 \text{ minutes}}{60 \text{ minutes}} = \frac{11}{60}$ **11. a.** $\frac{13}{9}$, 13 to 9, 13:9 **b.** $\frac{6}{5}$ **13.** $\frac{5}{8}$ **15.** $\frac{11}{16}$ **17.** $\frac{5}{3}$ **19.** $\frac{7}{4}$ **21.** $\frac{2}{3}$ **23.** $\frac{1}{2}$ **25.** $\frac{1}{3}$ **27.** $\frac{3}{4}$ **29.** $\frac{1}{3}$ **31.** $\frac{13}{3}$ **33.** $\frac{19}{39}$ **35.** $\frac{2}{7}$ **37.** $\frac{1}{2}$ **39.** $\frac{6}{1}$ **41.** $\frac{1}{5}$ **43.** $\frac{3}{7}$ **45.** $\frac{3}{4}$ **47.** $\frac{7}{12}$ **49.** $\frac{32 \text{ ft}}{3 \text{ sec}}$ **51.** $\frac{15 \text{ days}}{4 \text{ gal}}$ **53.** $\frac{21 \text{ made}}{25 \text{ attempts}}$ **55.** $\frac{3 \text{ beats}}{2 \text{ measures}}$ **57.** 12 revolutions per min **59.** $5,000 per year **61.** 1.5 errors per hr **63.** 320.6 people per square mi **65.** $4 per min **67.** $68 per person **69.** 1.2 cents per ounce **71.** $0.07 per ft **73.** $\frac{3}{2}$ **75. a.** 6:4:5 **b.** 5:6:4 **77. a.** $\frac{2}{3}$ **b.** $\frac{3}{2}$ **79.** $\frac{1}{55}$ **81.** $\frac{3}{1}$ **83. a.** 462 **b.** $\frac{11}{12}$; 11 to 12; 11:12 **85. a.** $1,800 **b.** $\frac{4}{9}$ **c.** $\frac{1}{3}$ **d.** $\frac{1}{18}$ **87.** $\frac{1}{1}$; 1 to 1; 1:1 **89.** $\frac{1}{20}$ **91.** $\frac{30 \text{ compressions}}{1 \text{ breaths}}$ **93.** $\frac{329 \text{ complaints}}{100{,}000 \text{ passengers}}$ **95. a.** 108,000 **b.** 24 browsers per buyer **97.** 7¢ per oz **99.** 1.25¢ per min **101.** $4.45 per lb **103.** 440 gal per min. **105. a.** 325 mi **b.** 65 mph **107.** the 6-oz can **109.** the 50 tablet boxes **111.** the truck **113.** the second car **115.** Four 4-oz cartons

Are You Ready? Section 3.2 (Page 22)

1. $\frac{2}{5}$ **2.** 10 **3.** 5.5692 **4.** 3.57

Study Set Section 3.2 (Page 33)

1. proportion **3.** cross **5.** variable **7.** isolated **9.** true, false **11.** 9, 90, 45, 90

13. Teacher's aides → 12 / Children → 100 = 3 ← Teacher's aides / 25 ← Children

$$\frac{12}{100} = \frac{3}{25}$$

15. $3 \cdot x$, 18, 3, 3, 6, 6 **17.** $\frac{20}{30} = \frac{2}{3}$ **19.** $\frac{400 \text{ sheets}}{100 \text{ beds}} = \frac{4 \text{ sheets}}{1 \text{ bed}}$ **21.** false **23.** true **25.** true **27.** false **29.** false **31.** true **33.** true **35.** false **37.** yes **39.** no **41.** 6 **43.** 4 **45.** 0.3 **47.** 2.2 **49.** $3\frac{1}{2}$ **51.** $\frac{7}{8}$ **53.** 3,500 **55.** $\frac{1}{2}$ **57.** 3600 **59.** 1 **61.** 2 **63.** $8\frac{1}{5}$ **65.** 180 **67.** 18 **69.** 3.1 **71.** $\frac{1}{6}$ **73.** $\frac{8}{3} = \frac{40}{15}$, $\frac{3}{15} = \frac{8}{40}$, $\frac{40}{8} = \frac{15}{3}$ **75.** no **77.**.yes, $\frac{40}{60} = \frac{60}{90}$ **79.** $218.75 **81.** $77.32 **83.** yes **85.** 24 **87.** 975 **89.** 91 ft **91.** Eye: 49.9 in.; seat: 17.6 in.; elbow: 27.8 in. **93.** 140 **95.** About 2 gal **97.** 10 ft **99.** 720 in.; 60 ft **101.** 2.625 in. = $2\frac{5}{8}$ in. **103.** $4\frac{2}{7}$, which is about $4\frac{1}{4}$ **105.** 19 sec **107.** 31.25 in. = $31\frac{1}{4}$ in. **109.** $309

Are You Ready? Section 3.3 (Page 38)

1. yes **2.** 24 **3.** 120 **4. a.** 3 **b.** 3

Study Set Section 3.3 (Page 44)

1. Congruent **3.** congruent **5.** proportion **7.** vertex **9. a.** No, they are different sizes. **b.** Yes, they have the same shape. **11.** $\angle S \cong \angle F, \angle T \cong \angle G, \angle R \cong \angle E, \overline{TS} \cong \overline{GF}, \overline{TR} \cong \overline{GE}, \overline{RS} \cong \overline{EF}$

13. $\frac{AB}{DE} = \frac{BC}{EF}$ $\quad \frac{BC}{EF} = \frac{CA}{FD}$ $\quad \frac{CA}{FD} = \frac{AB}{DE}$

15. similar **17.** congruent **19.** is congruent to **21.** segment **23.** angle **25.** triangle **27.** x, 288, 18, 18 **29. a.** $\angle B \cong \angle M, \angle C \cong \angle N, \angle D \cong \angle O, \overline{BC} \cong \overline{MN}, \overline{CD} \cong \overline{NO}, \overline{BD} \cong \overline{MO}$ **b.** 72° **c.** 10 ft **d.** 9 ft

31. a. $\angle L \cong \angle H, \angle M \cong \angle J, \angle R \cong \angle E$

b. $\frac{LM}{HJ} = \frac{MR}{JE}$ $\quad \frac{MR}{JE} = \frac{LR}{HE}$ $\quad \frac{LM}{HJ} = \frac{LR}{HE}$

c. $\frac{LM}{HJ} = \frac{MR}{JE} = \frac{LR}{HE}$ **33.** yes **35.** yes **37.** 15 **39.** 8

41. 8, 35 **43.** 60, 38 **45.** 76 ft **47.** $\frac{3}{2}$ **49.** 36 ft **51.** 555 ft **53.** 1,056 ft **55.** 4 cm

Are You Ready? Section 3.4 (Page 48)

1. $\frac{3}{44}$ **2. a.** $\frac{5}{2}$ **b.** $1\frac{3}{4}$ **3.** 27 **4.** $4\frac{1}{2} = 4.5$ **5. a.** 416 **b.** 2.5 **6.** $\frac{5}{9}$

Study Set Section 3.4 (Page 58)

1. length **3.** unit **5.** capacity **7. a.** 1 **b.** 3 **c.** 36 **d.** 5,280 **9. a.** 8 **b.** 2 **c.** 1 **d.** 1 **11.** 1 **13. a.** oz **b.** lb **15. a.** $\frac{1 \text{ ton}}{2{,}000 \text{ lb}}$ **b.** $\frac{2 \text{ pt}}{1 \text{ qt}}$ **17. a.** iv **b.** i **c.** ii **d.** iii **19. a.** iii **b.** iv **c.** i **d.** ii **21. a.** pound **b.** ounce **c.** fluid ounce **23.** 36, in., 72 **25.** 2,000, 16, oz, 32,000 **27. a.** 8 **b.** $\frac{5}{8}$ in., $1\frac{1}{4}$ in., $2\frac{7}{8}$ in. **29. a.** 16 **b.** $\frac{9}{16}$ in., $1\frac{3}{4}$ in., $2\frac{3}{16}$ in. **31.** $2\frac{9}{16}$ in. **33.** $10\frac{7}{8}$ in. **35.** 12 ft **37.** 105 ft **39.** 42 in. **41.** 63 in. **43.** $\frac{21}{352}$ mi ≈ 0.06 mi. **45.** $\frac{7}{8}$ mi = 0.875 mi. **47.** $2\frac{3}{4}$ lb = 2.75 lb **49.** $4\frac{1}{2}$ lb = 4.5 lb **51.** 800 oz **53.** 1,392 oz **55.** 128 fl oz **57.** 336 fl oz **59.** $2\frac{3}{4}$ hr **61.** $5\frac{1}{2}$ hr **63.** 6 pt **65.** 5 days **67.** $4\frac{2}{3}$ ft **69.** 48 in. **71.** 2 gal **73.** 5 lb **75.** 4 hr **77.** 288 in. **79.** $2\frac{1}{2}$ yd = 2.5 yd **81.** 15 ft **83.** 24,800 lb **85.** $2\frac{1}{3}$ yd **87.** 3 mi **89.** 2,640 ft **91.** $3\frac{1}{2}$ tons = 3.5 tons **93.** 2 pt **95.** 38 ft **97.** 21 lb 5 oz **99.** 24 gal 1 qt 1 pt 1 cup 3 oz **101.** 48 pt **103.** 150 yd **105.** 2,880 in. **107.** 0.28 mi **109.** 469 mi **111.** 128 oz **113.** $4\frac{19}{20}$ tons = 4.95 tons **115.** 68 quart cans **117.** $71\frac{7}{8}$ gal = 71.875 gal **119.** 320 oz **121.** $6\frac{1}{8}$ days= 6.125 days

Are You Ready? Section 3.5 (Page 62)

1. 2,400 **2.** 786 **3.** 10,000 **4.** 35 **5.** 0.000032 **6. a.** 0.01 **b.** $\frac{1}{1{,}000}$

Study Set Section 3.5 (Page 72)

1. metric **3. a.** tens **b.** hundreds **c.** thousands **5.** unit, chart **7.** weight **9. a.** 1,000 **b.** 100 **c.** 1,000 **11. a.** 1,000 **b.** 10 **13. a.** $\frac{1 \text{ km}}{1{,}000 \text{ m}}$ **b.** $\frac{100 \text{ cg}}{1 \text{ g}}$ **c.** $\frac{1{,}000 \text{ milliliters}}{1 \text{ liter}}$ **15. a.** iii **b.** i **c.** ii **17. a.** ii **b.** iii **c.** i **19.** 1, 100, 0.2 **21.** 1,000; 1; mg; 200,000 **23.** 1 cm, 3 cm, 5 cm **25. a.** 10,1 millimeter b. 27 mm, 41 mm, 55 mm **27.** 156 mm **29.** 280 mm **31.** 3.8 m **33.** 1.2 m **35.** 8,700 mm **37.** 2,890 mm **39.** 0.000045 km **41.** 0.000003 km **43.** 1,930 g **45.** 4,531 g **47.** 6 g **49.** 3.5 g **51.** 3,000 mL **53.** 26,300 mL **55.** 0.5 L **57.** 2,000 g **59.** 0.74 mm **61.** 1,000,000 g **63.** 0.65823 kL **65.** 0.472 dm **67.** 10 **69.** 0.5 g **71.** 5.689 kg **73.** 4.532 m **75.** 0.0325 L **77.** 675,000 **79.** 0.0000077 **81.** 1.34 hm **83.** 6,578 dam **85. a.** 0.004 km **b.** 400 cm **87.** (answers may vary) **89. a.** 1,829 m **b.** 7.26 kg **c.** 85.5 L **91.** 10,000 cm^2 **93.** 0.5 km, 1 km, 1.5 km, 5 km, 10 km **95.** 2.65 hm **97.** 12 cm, 8 cm **99.** 0.00005 L **101.** 3 g **103.** 3,000 mL **105.** 4 **107.** 3 mL

Applications Introduction: American and Metric Units Review (page 77)

Across **6.** ounce **7.** minute **9.** quart **10.** weight **12.** dekagram **16.** milliliter **17.** day **18.** centimeter **19.** gram **21.** liter **22.** milligram **23.** hectometer **24.** deciliter

Down **1.** gallon **2.** length **3.** pint **4.** cup **5.** second **8.** capacity **11.** hour **13.** kilogram **14.** millimeter **15.** prefix for tenths **20.** kilometer **22.** meter

Are You Ready? Section 3.6 (Page 78)

1. 4,233 **2.** 22,680 **3.** 3.3 **4.** 32.2 **5.** 176 **6.** 10

Study Set Section 3.6 (Page 84)

1. Fahrenheit **3. a.** meter **b.** meter **c.** inch **d.** mile **5. a.** liter **b.** liter **c.** gallon **7. a.** $\frac{0.03 \text{ m}}{1 \text{ ft}}$ **b.** $\frac{0.45 \text{ kg}}{1 \text{ lb}}$ **c.** $\frac{3.79 \text{ L}}{1 \text{ gal}}$ **9.** 0.30 m; m **11.** 0.035; 1,000; oz **13.** 10 in. **15.** 34 in. **17.** 2,520 m **19.** 7,534.5 m **21.** 9,072 g **23.** 34,020 g **25.** 14.3 lb **27.** 660 lb **29.** 0.7 qt **31.** 1.3 qt **33.** 48.9°C **35.** 1.7°C **37.** 167°F **39.** 50°F **41.** 11,340 g **43.** 122°F **45.** 712.5 mL **47.** 17.6 oz **49.** 147.6 in. **51.** 0.1 L **53.** 39,283 ft **55.** 1.0 kg **57.** 14°F **59.** 0.6 oz **61.** 243.4 fl oz **63.** 91.4 cm **65.** 0.5 qt **67.** 10°C **69.** 127 m **71.** –20.6°C **73.** < **75.** > **77.** > **79.** < **81.** 5 mi **83.** 70 mph **85.** 1.9 km **87.** 1.9 cm **89.** 411 lb, 770 lb **91. a.** 226.8 g **b.** 0.24 L **93.** no **95.** 36°C to 38°C **97.** 28°C **99.** –5°C and 0°C **101.** the 3 quarts

Are You Ready? Section 3.7 (Page 87)

1. $\frac{39}{50}$ **2.** 1 **3.** $\frac{1}{3}$ **4. a.** 22 **b.** 0.3286 **5. a.** true **b.** true **6. a.** 0.6 **b.** $0.8\overline{3}$

Study Set Section 3.7 (Page 97)

1. Percent **3.** 100, simplify **5.** right **7.** percent **9.** 84%, 16% **11.** 107% **13.** 99% **15. a.** 15% **b.** 85% **17.** $\frac{17}{100}$ **19.** $\frac{91}{100}$ **21.** $\frac{1}{25}$ **23.** $\frac{3}{5}$ **25.** $\frac{19}{1{,}000}$ **27.** $\frac{547}{1{,}000}$ **29.** $\frac{1}{8}$ **31.** $\frac{17}{250}$ **33.** $\frac{1}{75}$ **35.** $\frac{17}{120}$ **37.** $\frac{13}{10}$ **39.** $\frac{11}{5}$ **41.** $\frac{7}{2{,}000}$ **43.** $\frac{1}{400}$ **45.** 0.16 **47.** 0.81 **49.** 0.3412 **51.** 0.50033 **53.** 0.0699 **55.** 0.013 **57.** 0.0725 **59.** 0.185 **61.** 4.6 **63.** 3.16 **65.** 0.005 **67.** 0.0003 **69.** 36.2% **71.** 98% **73.** 171% **75.** 400% **77.** 40% **79.** 16% **81.** 62.5% **83.** 43.75% **85.** 225% **87.** 105% **89.** $16\frac{2}{3}\% \approx 16.7\%$ **91.** $166\frac{2}{3}\% \approx 166.7\%$

93. a.

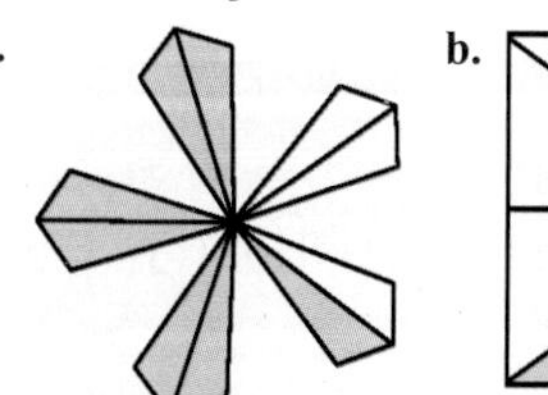

b.

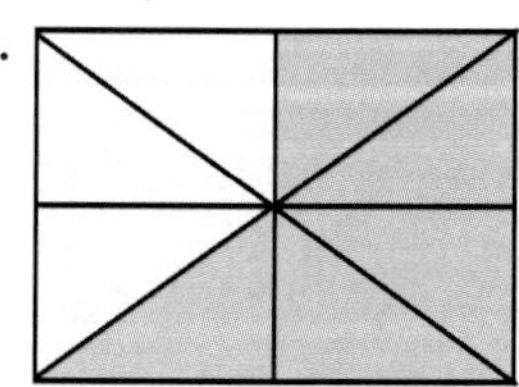

95. $\frac{6}{18} = \frac{1}{3}$, $0.\overline{3}$, $33\frac{1}{3}\%$

	Fraction	Decimal	Percent
97.	$\frac{157}{5,000}$	0.0314	3.14%
99.	$\frac{51}{125}$	0.408	40.8%
101.	$\frac{21}{400}$	0.0525	$5\frac{1}{4}\%$
103.	$\frac{7}{3}$	2.33	$233\frac{1}{3}\% \approx 233.3\%$

105. 91% **107. a.** 12% **b.** 24% **c.** 4% (Alaska, Hawaii) **109. a.** 0.0775 **b.** 0.05 **c.** 0.1425 **111.** torso: 27.5%

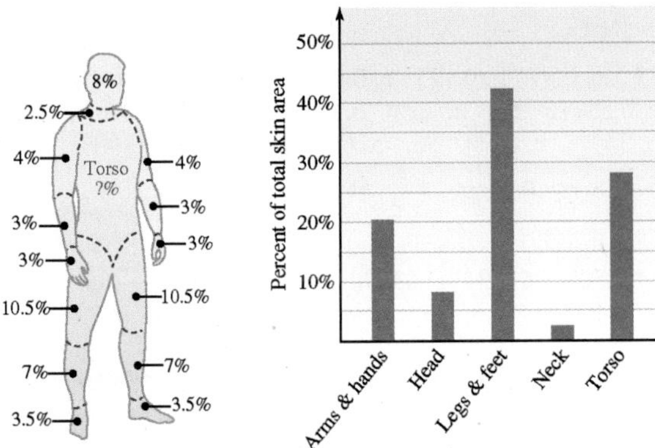

113. a. $\frac{5}{64}$ **b.** 0.078125 **c.** 7.8125% **115.** $33\frac{1}{3}\%, \frac{1}{3}, 0.\overline{3}$

117. a. $\frac{13}{15}$ **b.** $86\frac{2}{3}\% \approx 86.7\%$ **119. a.** $\frac{1}{4}\%$ **b.** $\frac{1}{400}$ **c.** 0.0025 **121.** 0.27%

Applications Introduction: Percent on the Internet Section 3.8 (Page 102)

1. \$14.05 **2.** \$12.40 **3.** \$10.75
4. $F = 0.50 + 10\% \cdot 50 + 8\% \cdot 950 + 0.02(P - 1,000)$
5. \$93.50

Are You Ready? Section 3.8 (Page 103)

1. 25.28 **2.** 0.95 **3. a.** 0.75 **b.** 1.25 **4.** 94.5 **5.** 420 **6.** $\frac{100}{3}$

Study Set Section 3.8 (Page 120)

1. sentence, equation **3.** solved **5.** part, whole **7.** cross **9.** Amount, base, percent, whole **11.** 100% **13. a.** 0.12 **b.** 0.056 **c.** 1.25 **d.** 0.0025 **15. a.** $x = 7\% \cdot 16$; $\frac{x}{16} = \frac{7}{100}$ **b.** $125 = x \cdot 800$; $\frac{125}{800} = \frac{x}{100}$ **c.** $1 = 94\% \cdot x$; $\frac{1}{x} = \frac{94}{100}$ **17. a.** $5.4\% \cdot 99 = x$; $\frac{x}{99} = \frac{5.4}{100}$ **b.** $75.1\% \cdot x = 15$; $\frac{15}{x} = \frac{75.1}{100}$ **c.** $x \cdot 33.8 = 3.8$; $\frac{3.8}{33.8} = \frac{x}{100}$ **19.** 68 **21.** 132 **23.** 17.696 **25.** 24.36 **27.** 25% **29.** 85% **31.** 62.5% **33.** 43.75% **35.** 110% **37.** 350% **39.** 30 **41.** 150 **43.** 57.6 **45.** 72.6 **47.** 1.25% **49.** 65 **51.** 99 **53.** 90 **55.** 80% **57.** 0.096 **59.** 44 **61.** 2,500% **63.** 107.1 **65.** 60 **67.** 31.25% **69.** 43.5 **71.** 150%

73. (answers may vary)
a. What number is 32% percent of 300? **b.** 25.8 is what percent of 77.4? **c.** 18 is 81.5% of what number?
75. 12K bytes = 12,000 bytes **77. a.** \$20.75 **b.** \$4.15 **79.** 2.7 in. **81.** yes **83.** 5% **85.** 120 **87.** $4\frac{1}{2}$ in. **89.** \$1,245.6 billion **91.** 60%, 40% **93.** \$6,164.75 **95.** 19% **97.** 87.5% **99.** 24 oz **101.** 30, 12 **103.** 40,000%

105.

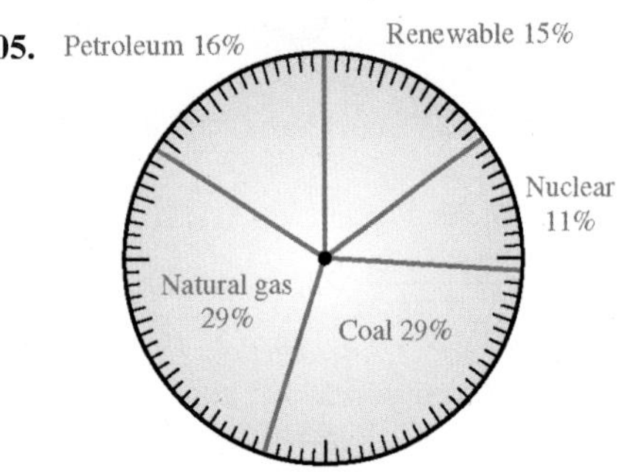

107. 25% , 26%, 6%, 6%, 37%

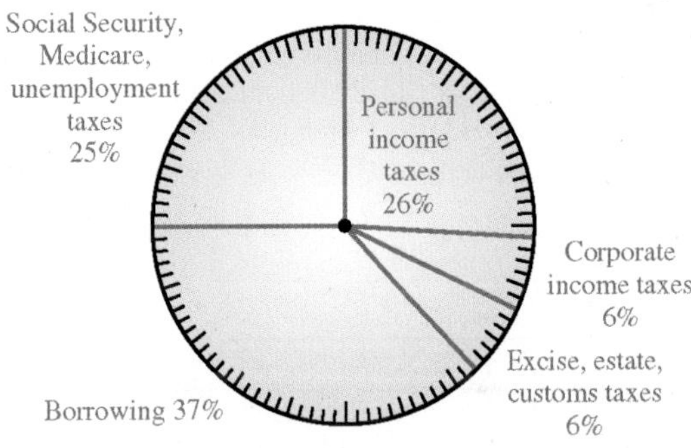

Are You Ready? Section 3.9 (Page 126)

1. a. 0.37 **b.** 0.084 **2.** 0.046 **3.** 72 **4.** 51.95
5. an increase of 146 stores **6.** a decrease of 40,000,000 tickets

Study Set Section 3.9 (Page 137)

1. commission **3. a.** increase **b.** original **5.** purchase price **7.** sales **9. a.** \$64.07 **b.** \$135.00 **11.** subtract, original **13.** \$3.71 **15.** \$4.20 **17.** \$70.83 **19.** \$64.03 **21.** 5.2% **23.** 15.3% **25.** \$11.40 **27.** \$168 **29.** 2% **31.** 4% **33.** 10% **35.** 15% **37.** 20% **39.** 10% **41.** \$29.70, \$60.30 **43.** \$8.70, \$49.30 **45.** 19% **47.** 14% **49. a.** 100% **b.** 200%
51. No; defensive back: 20% increase, lineman: $13.\overline{3}\%$ increase
53. \$68.60 **55.** \$47.34, \$2.84, \$50.18 **57.** 8% **59.** 0.25% **61.** \$150 **63.** 8%, 3.75%, 1.2%, 6.2% **65.** 5% **67.** 31% **69.** 152% **71.** 36% **73.** 12.5% **75. a.** 25% **b.** 36% **77.** \$2,955 **79.** 1.5% **81.** 90% **83.** \$12,000 **85. a.** \$7.99 **b.** \$31.96 **87.** 6% **89.** \$349.97, 13% **91.** 23%, \$11.88 **93.** \$76.50 **95.** \$187.49

Module 3 Test (Page 143)

1. a. ratio **b.** rate **c.** proportion **d.** cross **e.** tenths, hundredths, thousandths **f.** metric **g.** Fahrenheit, Celsius

h. Percent **i.** amount, base **j.** increase **2.** $\frac{9}{13}$, 9:13, 9 to 13
3. $\frac{3}{4}$ **4.** $\frac{1}{6}$ **5.** $\frac{2}{5}$ **6.** $\frac{6}{7}$
7.

8. $\frac{1{,}445}{8{,}772}$ **9.** $\frac{3 \text{ feet}}{2 \text{ seconds}}$ **10.** the 2-pound can **11.** 22.5 kwh per day **12.** $\frac{15 \text{ billboards}}{50 \text{ miles}} = \frac{3 \text{ billboards}}{10 \text{ miles}}$ **13. a.** no **b.** yes
14. yes **15.** 15 **16.** 63.24 **17.** $2\frac{1}{2}$ **18.** 0.2 **19.** $3.43
20. 2 c **21.** 84 days **22.** copper: 15 kg,; zinc: 22.5 kg; tin: 37.5 kg **23.** 255 **24.** 171 ft **25.** 6 feet 5 inches
26. 2.625 in. or $2\frac{5}{8}$ in. **27. a.** 16 **b.** $\frac{5}{16}$ in., $1\frac{3}{8}$ in., $2\frac{3}{4}$ in.
28. a. Corolla: 34 mpg; Cruze: 38 mpg **b.** Cruze **29.** 15 ft
30. $8\frac{1}{3}$ yd **31.** 172 oz **32.** 3,200 lb **33.** 128 fl oz
34. 115,200 min **35. a.** the one on the left **b.** the longer one **c.** the right side **36.** 12 mm, 5 cm, 65 mm **37.** 0.5 km
38. 500 cm **39.** 0.08 kg **40.** 70,000 mL **41.** 7.5 g
42. the 100-yd race **43.** Jim **44.** 5 gal ≈ 19L; You would have to fill the soda bottle $9\frac{1}{2}$ times. **45.** 0.9 qt **46.** 42 cm
47. 182°F **48. a.** 61%, $\frac{61}{100}$, 0.61 **b.** 39%
49. 199%, $\frac{199}{100}$, 1.99
50. a.

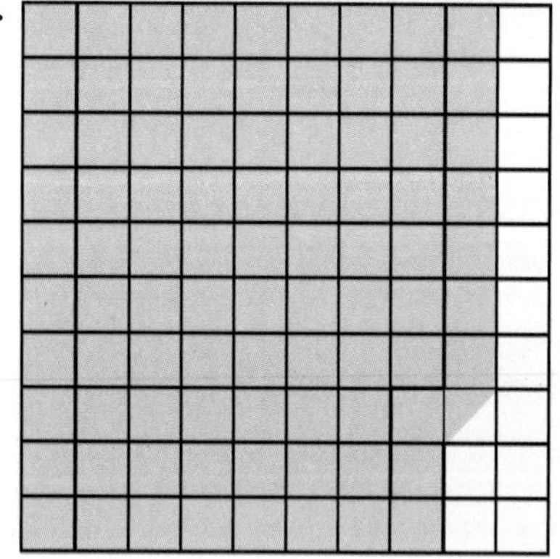

b. 0.875 **c.** 10; 100; 1,000 **d.** 8 rows of ten small squares; 7 small squares; one-half of one small square: $\frac{5}{1{,}000} = \frac{1}{200}$

51. a.

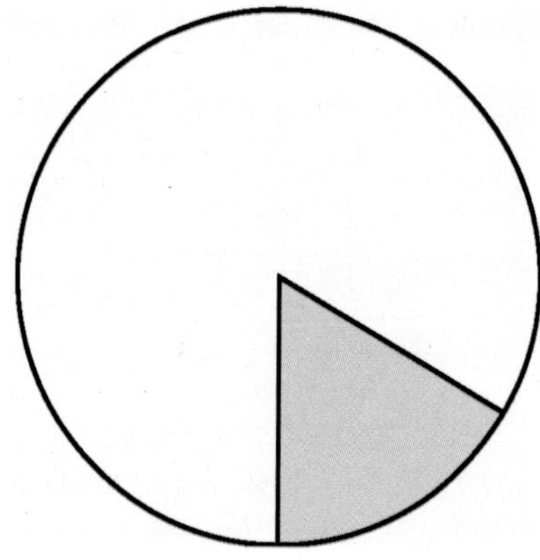

b. $16\frac{2}{3}$ %

52. a. 0.67 **b.** 0.123 **c.** 0.0975 **53. a.** 0.0006 **b.** 2.1 **c.** 0.55375 **54. a.** 25% **b.** 62.5% **c.** 112% **55. a.** 19% **b.** 347% **c.** 0.5% **56. a.** 66.7% **b.** 200% **c.** 90%
57. a. $\frac{11}{20}$ **b.** $\frac{1}{10{,}000}$ **c.** $\frac{5}{4}$ **58. a.** $\frac{1}{15}$ **b.** $\frac{3}{8}$ **c.** $\frac{2}{25}$
59. a. $3\frac{1}{3}\% \approx 3.3\%$ **b.** $177\frac{7}{9}\% \approx 177.8\%$ **60.** 6.5%
61. 250% **62.** 94% **63.** 90 **64.** 21 **65.** 134.4 **66.** 7.8
67. $4.26 **68.** 15,216 females **69. a.** 1.02 in. **b.** 32.98 in.
70. $26.24 **71.** 3% **72.** 23% **73.** $35.92
74. 11% **75.** $41,440 **76.** $9, $66, 12% **77.** $6.60, $13.40 **78.** 100 **79.** 9.3% **80.** Offer 1: $48 for two pairs of shoes; Offer 2 is better: $43.20 for two pairs of shoes